# American Medical Association

Physicians dedicated to the health of America

D1312297

# Physician Marketplace Statistics 1995

Profiles for Detailed Specialties,
Selected States and
Practice Arrangements

Edited by
Martin L. Gonzalez

Center for Health Policy Research

Additional copies may be ordered from:

Order Department OP 193195
American Medical Association
*For order information*
*call toll free 800 621-8335*

ISBN 0-89970-736-X

BP63: 95-645: 1.2M: 1/96

# Foreword

Changes are occurring rapidly in the physician services market, perhaps none as important as the shift in physician employment status. In 1992, over 67% of all nonfederal patient care physicians were self-employed, 27% were employees, and the remainder were independent contractors. In 1995, only 54.6% of physicians are self-employed and the percentage of employees has increased to 39.0 %. *Physician Marketplace Statistics* provides a means to assess the impact of changes in employment status and other factors that affect physician practices.

The data published in *Physician Marketplace Statistics 1995* are derived primarily from the American Medical Association's (AMA's) Socioeconomic Monitoring System (SMS) survey of nonfederal patient care physicians. In 1995, a survey of physicians employed by the federal government was also conducted. Patterned after the SMS survey of nonfederal physicians, the federal survey was used to obtain information on the practice patterns of physicians employed by the Department of Veterans Affairs or the Department of Defense. Data, from both surveys, reported in this volume are primarily for 1995. However, data on income, weeks worked, and expenses are for 1994.

The tables and charts that comprise the main body of *Physician Marketplace Statistics 1995* are presented in 12 sections. Ten of the sections report information on nonfederal physicians only. One section, "Selected Statistics for Federal Physicians" reports information on federal physicians only and contains a summary of the federal survey questionnaire. The last section presents information derived from the combination of the results from both the federal and nonfederal surveys. An overview section brings together key statistics on nonfederal physicians that are published in this volume and presents them in seven charts. The appendices include a discussion of the methodologies for both the nonfederal and federal surveys, the procedures used to compute and weight the statistics, and definitions of the physician classifications and characteristics used in this volume.

In addition to the tables that present information for federal physicians and federal and nonfederal physicians combined, several other new tables are included in *Physician Marketplace Statistics 1995*. New tables include the percentage of a physician's time spent in primary care activities, the percentage of a physician's revenue derived from inpatient and outpatient hospital care and the distribution of employee nonfederal physicians by type of employer.

Overall, there are 136 tables and 43 figures published in *Physician Marketplace Statistics 1995*. Most of the tables present information for up to 21 specialty classifications of physicians. The enhanced specialty detail breaks out internal medicine, surgical, and other subspecialties. Geographic detail in this volume is presented in 18 areas, including the ten individual states with the highest population. Most of the tables have breakouts by employment status and the nonfederal tables also break out five groupings of self-employed physicians by practice size. Because of a limited sample size, only national level information on federal physicians is reported. However, tables showing the results from both surveys have the standard breakouts.

A program of the magnitude of the Socioeconomic Monitoring System (SMS) requires major commitment and substantial effort from many individuals. I would like to express my gratitude to all who have contributed to SMS and this edition of *Physician Marketplace Statistics*.

James F. Rodgers, Ph.D
Director
Center for Health Policy Research

# Table of Contents

# List of Figures

**Selected Medicare Statistics for Nonfederal Physicians**

**Fees for Selected Nonfederal Physician Visits and Procedures**

**Professional Expenses of Self-Employed Nonfederal Physicians**

**Compensation of Nonfederal Physicians**

# List of Tables

## Weeks and Hours of Practice for Nonfederal Physicians

## Physician Service and Hospital Utilization for Nonfederal Physicians

**Selected Medicare Statistics for Nonfederal Physicians**

**Fees for Selected Nonfederal Physician Visits and Procedures**

**Professional Expenses of Self-Employed Nonfederal Physicians**

## Compensation of Nonfederal Physicians

## Distribution of Nonfederal Physician Revenue by Source of Payer

## Special Topics on the Nonfederal Physician Marketplace

## Nonfederal Physicians and Nonphysician Employees in Medical Practices

## Selected Statistics for Federal Physicians

## Selected Statistics for Federal and Nonfederal Physicians

**Appendix B: Weighting and Computation Methodology**

**Appendix C: Definitions of Physician Characteristics, Questionnaire Summary, and Computations**

## Introduction: How to Use and Interpret *Physician Marketplace Statistics*

*Physician Marketplace Statistics* and its companion volume, *Socioeconomic Characteristics of Medical Practice*, are published by the American Medical Association (AMA) as basic references on the results and methodology of the Socioeconomic Monitoring System surveys. The data published in the 1995 edition of *Physician Marketplace Statistics* are derived primarily from the SMS survey of nonfederal patient care physicians (excluding residents). SMS is the AMA's major survey program that provides detailed and timely information on socioeconomic aspects of medical practice. The SMS surveys regularly collect physician-level data on a broad range of characteristics including weeks and hours of practice, utilization patterns, fees, practice expenses, and physician earnings.

In 1995 a survey of physicians employed by the federal government was conducted in addition to the annual SMS survey of nonfederal physicians. Patterned after the SMS survey of nonfederal physicians, the federal survey was used to obtain information on the practice patterns of physicians employed by the Department of Veterans Affairs or the Department of Defense. Data obtained from the respondents included information on:

- Weeks and hours of practice;

- Physician service and hospital utilization; and

- Net income, time spent in primary care activities, appointment delays and waiting times.

The federal survey yielded responses from 119 physicians for a response rate of 55.6%. The SMS nonfederal survey yielded responses from 4,026 physicians for a response rate of 58.8%. Data obtained from both surveys are primarily for 1995. However, income and weeks worked data are for 1994. Expense data, obtained only from nonfederal physicians, are also for 1994.

The tables and charts that comprise the main body of the 1995 edition of *Physician Marketplace Statistics* are presented in 12 sections. Ten of the sections report information on nonfederal physicians only. One section, "Selected Statistics for Federal Physicians" reports information on federal physicians only. The last section presents information derived from the combination of the results from the federal and nonfederal surveys. The section headings are as follows:

- Overview of the Nonfederal Physician Marketplace;

- Weeks and Hours of Practice for Nonfederal Physicians;

- Physician Service and Hospital Utilization for Nonfederal Physicians;

- Selected Medicare Statistics for Nonfederal Physicians;

- Fees for Selected Nonfederal Physician Visits and Procedures;

- Professional Expenses of Self-Employed Nonfederal Physicians;

- Compensation of Nonfederal Physicians;

- Distribution of Nonfederal Physician Revenue by Source of Payer;

- Special Topics on the Nonfederal Physician Marketplace;

- Nonfederal Physicians and Nonphysician Employees in Medical Practices;

- Selected Statistics for Federal Physicians; and

- Selected Statistics for Federal and Nonfederal Physicians;

The overview section brings together key statistics on nonfederal physicians that are published in this volume and presents them in seven charts. Each of the remaining sections are introduced by a discussion of the definitions of characteristics reflected in the tables, a summary of survey questions from which information in the tables is derived and several charts highlighting the major variations in the characteristics of most interest. The survey used to obtain information on federal physicians is summarized at the beginning of the section "Selected Statistics for Federal Physicians." The appendices include a discussion of the methodologies for both the nonfederal and federal surveys, the procedures used to compute and weight the statistics, and definitions of the physician classifications and characteristics used in this volume.

Overall, there are 136 tables and 43 figures published in *Physician Marketplace Statistics 1995*, including several new tables. The section "Special Topics on the Nonfederal Physician Marketplace" includes tables showing the percentage of a physician's time spent in primary care activities. New tables showing the percentage of a physician's revenue derived from inpatient and outpatient hospital care are also included in this section. The section "Nonfederal Physicians and Nonphysician Employees in Medical Practices" includes tables showing the distribution of physicians by employment status and size of practice. This section also includes a table showing the distribution of employee physicians by type of employer.

Most of the tables present information for up to 21 specialty classifications of physicians. The enhanced specialty detail breaks out internal medicine, surgical, and other subspecialties. Geographic detail in this volume is presented in 18 areas, including ten individual states. The states are the ten largest in terms of both civilian and physician population. Publishing state level figures based on adequate sample size was the only factor that was considered when choosing the ten states. State level data are presented in all tables except those that present physician net income and total practice revenue. Because of wide variation in the earnings of physicians, imprecision caused by small samples is magnified. In an effort to ensure precision, census division is the most detailed breakout presented in these tables. Most of the tables have breakouts by employment status and the nonfederal tables also break out five groupings of self-employed physicians by practice size. Because of a limited sample size, only national level information on federal physicians is reported. However, tables showing the results from both surveys have the standard breakouts.

Forty-four tables present selected information on nonfederal physicians for a single specialty broken out by census division and practice arrangement. Information on total visit hours, total visits, fees for new and established patient office visits, income, and expenses are presented in these tables.

All of the tables in this volume present an array of statistics on each practice characteristic. In addition to the mean and standard error of the mean, STATS reports the number of responses, the 25th percentile, the median or 50th percentile, and the 75th percentile values for each characteristic. The purpose of including these statistics is to make it possible to more fully assess variations in practice characteristics and to consider more fully the reliability of inferences that might be drawn from the survey results. A discussion of each statistic is presented below.

## How to Interpret Physician Marketplace Statistics

The information in this volume is intended for use by a variety of individuals who come into contact with medical practice issues from different perspectives. For example, physicians might use this information in assessing the likely impact of such practice changes as relocating or joining a group practice on their earnings, patient volume, and practice costs. Medical practice consultants may use this information to improve their ability to assess their client's performance and suggest areas for improvement. Hospital administrators may find the volume useful in determining appropriate compensation levels and hours for their medical staff.

A statistic is simply a summary measure based on survey results to describe an attribute of the distribution of a characteristic across a given population.

Since the information in this volume has numerous applications, a range of statistics is provided for each characteristic so that individual users can decide the most apt manner in which to interpret the information from the SMS surveys for their circumstances. For some purposes, it may be more appropriate to focus on one statistic rather than another.

It must also be kept in mind that the statistics presented are only estimates of population characteristics derived from surveying a sample of physicians.

This may cause characteristics of the full physician population to differ from information from SMS survey results. For this reason, the results include measures that should be considered carefully in judging what degree of confidence to attribute to inferences drawn from the SMS results. The statistics presented for each characteristic and a brief discussion of how each may be used follows.

### Number of Respondents

This indicates the number of survey respondents within a specified group who reported information in the survey which was used in computing statistics for the group on a given characteristic. Larger numbers of respondents cause the estimates of characteristics of the population reflected in the statistics to be more reliable.

Since fewer observations are available for less aggregated groups, the results for these groups will always be less accurate than for more aggregated groups.

For example, statistics for the state of Ohio will be less accurate than those for the entire East North Central Census Division (of which Ohio is a part) because the number of respondents is greater for the entire Census Division than for Ohio. Similarly, results for all physicians are more reliable than those for any individual geographic area or specialty.

In reporting results in this volume, statistics are not given for characteristics in groups in which there are fewer than twenty-five respondents because of concern that the sample size is insufficient for making any inferences with reasonable accuracy. In these instances and other "borderline" cases, statistics for more aggregated groups should be considered.

### Mean (or Average)

The sample mean is an estimate of the average value of a characteristic for a given population. The mean is often referred to as a measure of "central tendency" for a characteristic because it tends to be located in the middle of the distribution of all possible values for the characteristic. However, it may neither be the most common nor a typical value. For example, for many physician characteristics a large share of physicians are concentrated in a range of lower possible values for the characteristic while a small share of physicians have extremely high values. An example of this type of characteristic is physician net income after expenses before taxes. For such characteristics, the mean will exceed the

most common value and the values more representative of the experience of most typical physicians. In these instances, the median (as discussed below) may be a more appropriate measure to use for making some types of inferences.

If information were available on the characteristic from the entire population of physicians in a group, the mean would be computed as the sum of the values of the characteristic across the group divided by the number of physicians in that group. This approach would also be followed using sample information to obtain an estimate of the mean if the sample were perfectly representative of the entire group. However, an examination of SMS survey results indicates that, although the initial samples are representative of the underlying physician population, some physician groups are under-represented and others overrepresented among physicians from the initial sample who complete the survey. To alleviate potential biases that might arise from this result, the estimates of the mean reported in this volume are weighted averages of survey responses. The weights give greater importance to information reported by groups of physicians who are underrepresented in the final survey sample in calculating the mean so that it is a more accurate estimate of the population mean. A further discussion of the weighting procedure and computation methods appears in Appendix B.

### Standard Error of the Mean

The standard error is used in assessing the reliability of the estimate of the mean based on sample information in drawing conclusions about the mean of a characteristic for the underlying population. Larger standard errors indicate that the sample mean is subject to greater possible error as a representation of the mean for the entire population. Two factors directly affect the standard error. First, the standard error diminishes as the number of respondents increases. Second, the standard error will tend to be greater for characteristics with a greater dispersion in the values in the population.

This is because greater dispersion increases the chance that a single unusual value will be reflected in the sample information (sometimes called an "outlier") which will have inordinate influence in the calculation of the mean. However, as the overall sample increases, the influence of any single response will diminish so that outlier problems that may introduce error into the estimates of the means will diminish.

A common use of standard errors estimates is in the construction of confidence intervals. Confidence intervals are used for making statements about the probability with which the mean for the population of a group falls within certain bounds. For a 95% confidence interval, the bounds are given by the mean estimate plus twice times the standard error and the mean estimate minus twice times the standard error. The mean for the population will fall within these bounds with a probability of 95%. For a 90% confidence interval, the bounds are given by the mean estimate plus and minus 1.64 times the standard error.

For example, the sample mean number of office visits per week per physician in 1995 was 73.7 and the standard error was 1.0. This indicates that there was a 90% probability that the population mean was between 72.1 and 75.3 and a 95% probability that the population mean was between 71.7 and 75.7.

### 25th Percentile

The 25th percentile is the value of the characteristic larger than that experienced by 25% of a specified group and exceeded by the remaining three-quarters of that group.

### Median (or 50th Percentile)

The 50th percentile is the value of the characteristic larger than experienced by half of the group, but smaller or equal to that experienced by the other half. This is a measure of central tendency often used as an alternative to the mean because it provides a better representation of the typical experience of individuals in the population group. It is also less subject to the influence of outliers than the mean.

### 75th Percentile

This is the value of the characteristic larger than that occurring for 75% of the group, but equal to or exceeding that for the other 25%.

Although the mean and median are more commonly employed statistics, the information on the 25th and 75th percentiles of each characteristic is included to emphasize how characteristics vary across groups within the physician population. In some instances, the information on 25th and 75th percentiles might be more typical of the experience of subgroups of physicians than either the mean or median. For example, in some states there may be wide disparities in the cost of living between major metropolitan areas and the rest of the state that might cause differences in such physician characteristics as fees, practice costs, and earnings. The typical experience of physicians in large metropolitan areas may be closer to the 75th percentile in such states, while rural physicians may have experiences more closely reflected by the 25th percentile.

Of course, other factors also contribute to variation in physician characteristics. The particular circumstances need to be considered carefully in each case when using the survey results in order to assess which statistics are most pertinent and what inferences are appropriate.

# Overview of the Nonfederal Physician Marketplace

Patient Visit Hours by Setting

Patient Visits by Setting

Practice Expenses by Expense Component

Practice Revenue by Revenue Component

Physician Revenue by Source of Payer

Employment Status of Nonfederal Physicians

Employers of Nonfederal Physicians

## Overview of the Nonfederal Physician Marketplace

*Physician Marketplace Statistics* is intended to provide a comprehensive set of information about physicians and their practices. In this section, selected graphics provide a brief overview of this information. The charts in this overview show the distribution of:

- Mean total patient visit hours per week by setting;

- Mean total visits per week by setting;

- Mean total expenses by expense component;

- Mean total practice revenues by revenue component;

- Nonfederal physician revenue by source of payer;

- Nonfederal physicians by employment status; and

- Employee nonfederal physicians by employer.

Information presented in these figures is from the 1995 Socioeconomic Monitoring System (SMS) survey of nonfederal physicians. The questions used to obtain this information are described at the beginning of the sections on nonfederal physicians that follow this overview.

Figure 1. **Distribution of Mean Total Patient Visit Hours per Week, for Nonfederal Physicians, by Setting, 1995**[a]

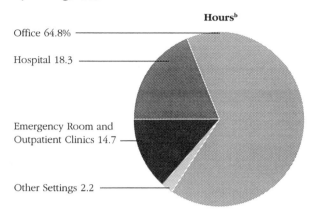

Hours[b]

Office 64.8%

Hospital 18.3

Emergency Room and Outpatient Clinics 14.7

Other Settings 2.2

a. Excludes radiologists, psychiatrists, anesthesiologists, and pathologists.
b. Based on responses from physicians who provided hours worked information for every component of total visit hours.

Figure 2. **Distribution of Mean Total Visits per Week, for Nonfederal Physicians, by Setting, 1995**[a]

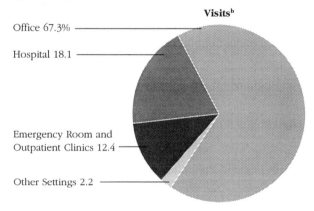

Visits[b]

Office 67.3%

Hospital 18.1

Emergency Room and Outpatient Clinics 12.4

Other Settings 2.2

a. Excludes radiologists, psychiatrists, anesthesiologists, and pathologists.
b. Based on responses from physicians who provided visit information for every component of total visits.

Figure 3. **Distribution of Mean Total Practice Revenue, by Revenue Component, for Self-Employed Nonfederal Physicians, 1994**

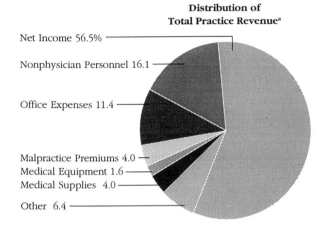

**Distribution of
Total Practice Revenue[a]**

Net Income 56.5%

Nonphysician Personnel 16.1

Office Expenses 11.4

Malpractice Premiums 4.0
Medical Equipment 1.6
Medical Supplies 4.0

Other 6.4

a. Based on responses from physicians who provided information on every component of total revenue.

Figure 4. **Distribution of Mean Total Professional Expenses, by Expense Component, for Self-Employed Nonfederal Physicians, 1994**

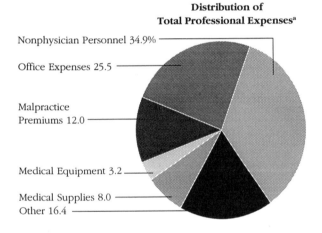

**Distribution of
Total Professional Expenses[a]**

Nonphysician Personnel 34.9%

Office Expenses 25.5

Malpractice
Premiums 12.0

Medical Equipment 3.2

Medical Supplies 8.0
Other 16.4

a. Based on responses from physicians who provided information on every component of total expenses.

Figure 5. **Distribution of Nonfederal Physician Revenue, by Source of Payer, 1995**[a]

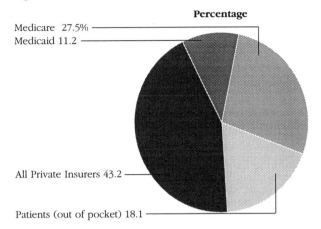

a. Based on responses from physicians who provided information on the percent of revenue derived from each payer.

Figure 6. **Distribution of Nonfederal Physicians by Employment Status, 1995**

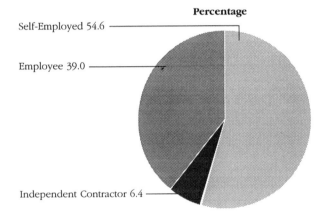

Figure 7. **Distribution of Employee Nonfederal Physicians, by Employer, 1995**

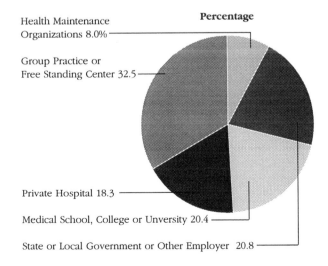

# Weeks and Hours of Practice for Nonfederal Physicians

Annual Weeks of Practice

Total Professional and Patient Care Hours

Hours in Selected Patient Care Activities

Specialty Specific Total Visit Hours,
by Census Division and Practice Arrangement

# Weeks and Hours of Practice for Nonfederal Physicians

The time spent in practice by physicians is measured in weeks per year and hours per week. Two measures of total hours in practice can be distinguished. Total professional hours combines hours in patient care with those in other professional activities, such as teaching, research, and administration. Hours in patient care activities excludes other professional hours.

For physicians in specialties other than radiology, psychiatry, anesthesiology, and pathology, patient care hours are primarily divided between time spent on patient visits and time in surgery. Time spent on patient visits is further subdivided into hours by visit setting. In each of the other specialties, a different breakdown of patient care hours is used to reflect the different nature of patient care activities in radiology, psychiatry, anesthesiology, and pathology.

Weeks of practice in 1994 in Table 1 was ascertained from responses to the following survey questions:

1. During 1994, how many weeks of medical practice did you miss because of illness, vacation, military service or professional conferences?

2. Altogether then, you missed [Number] weeks of practice and practiced [Number] weeks?

a. (If physician began practice in 1994). Excluding the [Number] of weeks of practice you missed in 1994 due to illness or vacation and the [Number] missed due to military service or professional conferences, for how many weeks did you practice in 1994?

Hours spent in various patient care activities (Tables 2-15) were ascertained from the following question:

3. During your most recent complete week of practice, how many hours did you spend:

*All specialties except radiology, psychiatry, anesthesiology, and pathology*

a. in the office or in freestanding primary care or urgent care centers seeing patients? Include time spent in all offices if the practice includes multiple offices. Freestanding or urgent care centers may be owned by a hospital or chain.

b. seeing patients in outpatient clinics or hospital emergency rooms?

c. on housecalls and with patients in nursing homes, convalescent homes or other extended care facilities?

d. in the operating, labor or delivery room, including waiting time before surgery?

e. making hospital rounds, including visits to newborn infants, but excluding hours spent on call when you are not actually working?

f. having telephone conversations with patients or their families, consulting with other physicians and providing other services to patients such as interpreting lab tests and x-rays?

*Radiology*

g. reading films, including time spent preparing reports on films read?

h. personally performing radiodiagnostic procedures?

i. personally providing radiotherapy to patients?

j. supervising technicians and paraprofessionals?

k. in consultation with other physicians?

*Psychiatry*

l. seeing individual patients in the office and in all other settings?

m. seeing nonfamily groups in the office and in all other settings? Nonfamily groups are sessions with unrelated individuals.

n. seeing family groups in the office and in all other settings? A family group consists of two or more people related by marriage, blood or adoption.

o. supervising psychiatric teams, consulting with other physicians, having telephone conversations with patients and their families, and providing other services to patients such as interpreting lab tests and EEG results?

*Anesthesiology*

p. personally anesthetizing patients, including waiting time before surgery?

q. supervising nurse anesthetists?

r. managing patients in intensive care units?

s. making pre-anesthesia visits, including histories and examinations as well as seeing patients on hospital rounds. Do not include time spent managing patients in intensive care units.

t. consulting with other physicians about their patients and providing any other services to patients,such as interpreting lab tests and x-rays?

*Pathology*

u. in consultations during surgery, including time spent interpreting frozen sections?

v. examining surgical specimens other than consultations during surgery?

w. doing autopsies, including time spent to complete the study and write the report?

x. personally performing nonsurgical laboratory procedures including time to write any reports?

y. supervising technicians and paraprofessionals?

If necessary, at any point in the course of eliciting responses to these questions, the interviewer may give the following clarification: "By complete week of practice, we mean the most recent week in which you worked your normal work schedule. We want to exclude weeks when you were sick or on vacation."

Following the questions on individual patient care activities, all physicians are asked:

4. During your most recent complete week of practice, how many hours did you spend in administrative and other professional activities not directly related to patient care? These activities include billing, handling claims, managing a practice or clinic, medical staff functions, supervising residents and interns, teaching, lecturing, professional reading and writing, and research.

If the physician responded to all applicable parts of Question 3 and to Question 4, total professional hours in Table 2 was calculated from the sum of responses to these questions. For physicians not responding to all applicable parts of Question 3 or to Question 4, an attempt was still made to obtain information on total professional hours by asking the following question:

5. During your most recent complete week of practice, how many hours altogether did you spend working at medical and administrative activities?

Hours in patient care activities (Table 3) is based on the sum of responses to applicable parts of Question 3 for each specialty. Total patient visit hours, given in Tables 4 and 10-15, reflects the sum of response to parts a, b, c, and e of Question 3. Tables 5-8 are based, respectively, on parts a, b, d, and e of Question 3. Hours by activity among radiologists, psychiatrists, anesthesiologists, and pathologists reported in Table 9 reflects responses to various parts of Question 3 applicable to these specialists.

Figure 8. **Mean and Median Hours in Patient Care Activities per Week, for Nonfederal Physicians, for Selected Specialties, 1995**

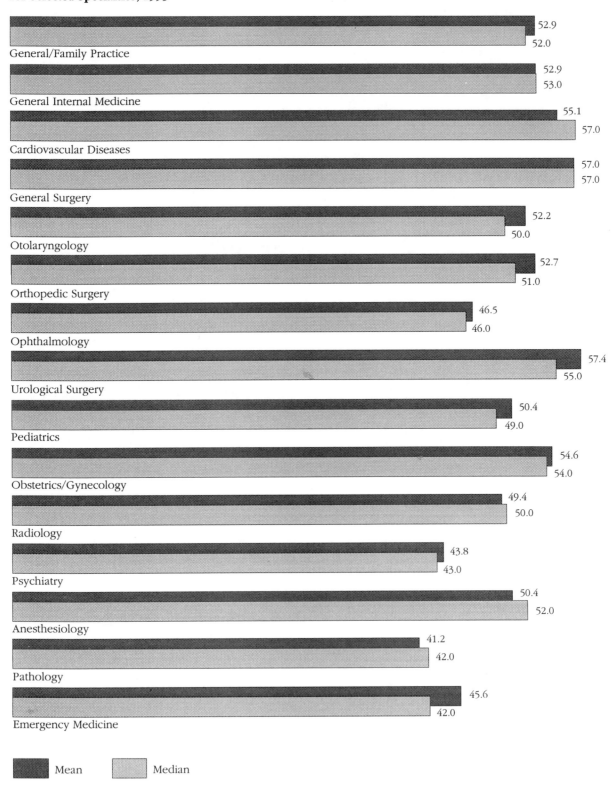

General/Family Practice — 52.9 / 52.0

General Internal Medicine — 52.9 / 53.0

Cardiovascular Diseases — 55.1 / 57.0

General Surgery — 57.0 / 57.0

Otolaryngology — 52.2 / 50.0

Orthopedic Surgery — 52.7 / 51.0

Ophthalmology — 46.5 / 46.0

Urological Surgery — 57.4 / 55.0

Pediatrics — 50.4 / 49.0

Obstetrics/Gynecology — 54.6 / 54.0

Radiology — 49.4 / 50.0

Psychiatry — 43.8 / 43.0

Anesthesiology — 50.4 / 52.0

Pathology — 41.2 / 42.0

Emergency Medicine — 45.6 / 42.0

■ Mean   ▢ Median

Figure 9. **Mean and Median Hours in Patient Care Activities per Week, for Nonfederal Physicians, for Selected States, 1995**

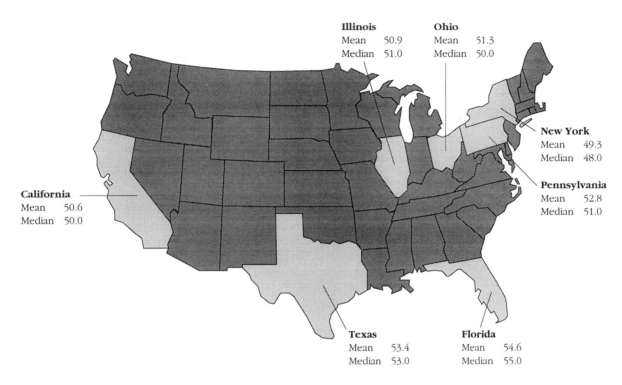

**Illinois**
Mean      50.9
Median   51.0

**Ohio**
Mean      51.3
Median   50.0

**New York**
Mean      49.3
Median   48.0

**Pennsylvania**
Mean      52.8
Median   51.0

**California**
Mean      50.6
Median   50.0

**Texas**
Mean      53.4
Median   53.0

**Florida**
Mean      54.6
Median   55.0

Figure 10. **Mean and Median Hours in Patient Care Activities per Week per Self-Employed Nonfederal Physician, by Size of Practice, 1995**

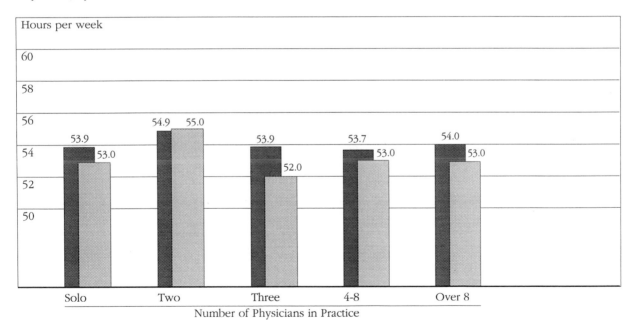

Hours per week

| Number of Physicians in Practice | Mean | Median |
| --- | --- | --- |
| Solo | 53.9 | 53.0 |
| Two | 54.9 | 55.0 |
| Three | 53.9 | 52.0 |
| 4-8 | 53.7 | 53.0 |
| Over 8 | 54.0 | 53.0 |

■ Mean      □ Median

## Table 1. **Weeks of Practice for Nonfederal Physicians, 1994**

| | Number of Responses | Mean | Standard Error | 25th Percentile | Median | 75th Percentile |
|---|---|---|---|---|---|---|
| All Physicians | 3897 | 47.2 | 0.1 | 46.0 | 48.0 | 49.0 |
| *Specialty* | | | | | | |
| General/Family Practice | 500 | 47.3 | 0.3 | 47.0 | 48.0 | 50.0 |
| Internal Medicine | 747 | 47.7 | 0.2 | 47.0 | 48.0 | 49.0 |
| · General Internal Medicine | 511 | 47.6 | 0.2 | 47.0 | 48.0 | 49.0 |
| · Cardiovascular Diseases | 97 | 47.1 | 0.4 | 46.0 | 48.0 | 49.0 |
| · Other | 139 | 48.1 | 0.2 | 47.0 | 48.0 | 50.0 |
| Surgery | 860 | 47.4 | 0.1 | 46.0 | 48.0 | 49.0 |
| · General Surgery | 211 | 47.5 | 0.3 | 46.0 | 48.0 | 50.0 |
| · Otolaryngology | 74 | 47.4 | 0.5 | 46.0 | 48.0 | 49.0 |
| · Orthopedic Surgery | 183 | 46.8 | 0.3 | 46.0 | 48.0 | 49.0 |
| · Ophthalmology | 182 | 47.6 | 0.2 | 46.0 | 48.0 | 49.0 |
| · Urological Surgery | 96 | 47.8 | 0.2 | 46.0 | 48.0 | 49.0 |
| · Other | 114 | 47.6 | 0.4 | 47.0 | 48.0 | 50.0 |
| Pediatrics | 301 | 47.7 | 0.2 | 47.0 | 48.0 | 50.0 |
| Obstetrics/Gynecology | 238 | 47.1 | 0.3 | 46.0 | 48.0 | 49.0 |
| Radiology | 272 | 44.2 | 0.3 | 43.0 | 45.0 | 47.0 |
| Psychiatry | 271 | 47.8 | 0.1 | 47.0 | 48.0 | 49.0 |
| Anesthesiology | 226 | 45.5 | 0.3 | 44.0 | 46.0 | 48.0 |
| Pathology | 118 | 47.2 | 0.3 | 46.0 | 48.0 | 49.0 |
| Other Specialty | 364 | 47.8 | 0.2 | 47.0 | 48.0 | 50.0 |
| · Emergency Medicine | 131 | 48.1 | 0.5 | 48.0 | 49.0 | 51.0 |
| · Other | 233 | 47.6 | 0.3 | 47.0 | 48.0 | 49.0 |
| *Geographic Area* | | | | | | |
| New England | 246 | 47.2 | 0.3 | 47.0 | 48.0 | 49.0 |
| · Massachusetts | 114 | 47.4 | 0.4 | 47.0 | 48.0 | 49.0 |
| · Other | 132 | 47.0 | 0.4 | 46.0 | 48.0 | 49.0 |
| Middle Atlantic | 616 | 46.8 | 0.2 | 46.0 | 48.0 | 49.0 |
| · New Jersey | 106 | 47.3 | 0.5 | 46.0 | 48.0 | 50.0 |
| · New York | 249 | 47.0 | 0.3 | 46.0 | 48.0 | 49.0 |
| · Pennsylvania | 261 | 46.3 | 0.4 | 46.0 | 48.0 | 49.0 |
| East North Central | 583 | 46.7 | 0.2 | 46.0 | 48.0 | 49.0 |
| · Illinois | 183 | 47.4 | 0.3 | 46.0 | 48.0 | 49.0 |
| · Michigan | 108 | 46.4 | 0.6 | 46.0 | 48.0 | 49.0 |
| · Ohio | 128 | 46.4 | 0.5 | 46.0 | 48.0 | 49.0 |
| · Other | 164 | 46.2 | 0.3 | 45.0 | 47.0 | 49.0 |
| West North Central | 286 | 46.8 | 0.3 | 46.0 | 48.0 | 49.0 |
| South Atlantic | 686 | 47.5 | 0.2 | 47.0 | 48.0 | 50.0 |
| · Florida | 194 | 47.8 | 0.2 | 46.0 | 48.0 | 50.0 |
| · Other | 492 | 47.4 | 0.2 | 47.0 | 48.0 | 49.0 |
| East South Central | 234 | 47.9 | 0.2 | 47.0 | 48.0 | 50.0 |
| West South Central | 362 | 48.1 | 0.2 | 48.0 | 49.0 | 50.0 |
| · Texas | 239 | 48.4 | 0.2 | 48.0 | 49.0 | 50.0 |
| · Other | 123 | 47.5 | 0.4 | 47.0 | 48.0 | 50.0 |
| Mountain | 227 | 46.9 | 0.4 | 46.0 | 48.0 | 50.0 |
| Pacific | 657 | 47.5 | 0.1 | 46.0 | 48.0 | 49.0 |
| · California | 460 | 47.8 | 0.1 | 46.0 | 48.0 | 50.0 |
| · Other | 197 | 46.7 | 0.3 | 46.0 | 47.0 | 49.0 |
| *Practice Arrangement* | | | | | | |
| Self-Employed | 2223 | 47.7 | 0.1 | 46.0 | 48.0 | 50.0 |
| · Solo Practice | 1001 | 48.4 | 0.1 | 48.0 | 49.0 | 50.0 |
| · Two Physician Practice | 262 | 47.8 | 0.2 | 47.0 | 48.0 | 50.0 |
| · Three Physician Practice | 205 | 47.6 | 0.2 | 47.0 | 48.0 | 49.0 |
| · 4-8 Physician Practice | 490 | 46.6 | 0.1 | 46.0 | 47.0 | 49.0 |
| · Over 8 Physician Practice | 263 | 46.4 | 0.2 | 44.0 | 47.0 | 49.0 |
| Employee | 1440 | 46.5 | 0.2 | 46.0 | 48.0 | 49.0 |
| Independent Contractor | 234 | 48.0 | 0.2 | 47.0 | 49.0 | 50.0 |

Source: 1995 Socioeconomic Monitoring System survey of nonfederal patient care physicians. See the beginning of this section, the introduction, and appendices for a discussion of the survey sample, definitions, and computation procedures. Statistics are not reported if the number of responses is less than 25.

## Table 2. **Hours in Professional Activities per Week, for Nonfederal Physicians, 1995**

| | Number of Responses | Mean | Standard Error | 25th Percentile | Median | 75th Percentile |
|---|---|---|---|---|---|---|
| All Physicians | 3964 | 56.7 | 0.3 | 46.0 | 55.0 | 66.0 |
| *Specialty* | | | | | | |
| General/Family Practice | 510 | 57.3 | 0.7 | 47.0 | 56.0 | 66.0 |
| Internal Medicine | 763 | 59.8 | 0.6 | 50.0 | 60.0 | 69.0 |
| · General Internal Medicine | 522 | 58.9 | 0.8 | 49.0 | 58.0 | 68.0 |
| · Cardiovascular Diseases | 101 | 60.6 | 1.9 | 51.0 | 62.0 | 70.0 |
| · Other | 140 | 62.6 | 1.4 | 54.0 | 61.0 | 72.0 |
| Surgery | 884 | 58.7 | 0.6 | 48.0 | 58.0 | 68.0 |
| · General Surgery | 218 | 62.5 | 1.3 | 52.0 | 62.0 | 71.0 |
| · Otolaryngology | 76 | 57.9 | 1.5 | 48.0 | 56.0 | 66.0 |
| · Orthopedic Surgery | 187 | 58.0 | 1.1 | 49.0 | 55.0 | 66.0 |
| · Ophthalmology | 187 | 52.1 | 0.9 | 43.0 | 51.0 | 61.0 |
| · Urological Surgery | 98 | 62.7 | 1.5 | 51.0 | 60.0 | 72.0 |
| · Other | 118 | 59.1 | 1.9 | 48.0 | 60.0 | 72.0 |
| Pediatrics | 306 | 56.5 | 0.9 | 45.0 | 55.0 | 65.0 |
| Obstetrics/Gynecology | 246 | 59.3 | 1.2 | 49.0 | 57.0 | 70.0 |
| Radiology | 270 | 52.2 | 0.9 | 45.0 | 52.0 | 60.0 |
| Psychiatry | 272 | 49.8 | 0.9 | 40.0 | 49.0 | 59.0 |
| Anesthesiology | 224 | 55.4 | 1.2 | 45.0 | 56.0 | 65.0 |
| Pathology | 120 | 47.1 | 1.2 | 41.0 | 49.0 | 56.0 |
| Other Specialty | 369 | 52.8 | 0.8 | 43.0 | 50.0 | 61.0 |
| · Emergency Medicine | 133 | 52.1 | 1.3 | 41.0 | 50.0 | 60.0 |
| · Other | 236 | 53.2 | 1.0 | 44.0 | 51.0 | 61.0 |
| *Geographic Area* | | | | | | |
| New England | 253 | 54.0 | 1.1 | 45.0 | 53.0 | 65.0 |
| · Massachusetts | 117 | 54.4 | 1.5 | 46.0 | 53.0 | 65.0 |
| · Other | 136 | 53.5 | 1.5 | 45.0 | 52.0 | 63.0 |
| Middle Atlantic | 626 | 55.5 | 0.7 | 45.0 | 55.0 | 66.0 |
| · New Jersey | 109 | 51.7 | 1.8 | 40.0 | 53.0 | 61.0 |
| · New York | 251 | 55.3 | 1.1 | 45.0 | 56.0 | 67.0 |
| · Pennsylvania | 266 | 57.8 | 0.9 | 48.0 | 57.0 | 67.0 |
| East North Central | 595 | 56.4 | 0.7 | 47.0 | 55.0 | 65.0 |
| · Illinois | 183 | 56.2 | 1.3 | 46.0 | 54.0 | 65.0 |
| · Michigan | 112 | 56.4 | 1.2 | 50.0 | 55.0 | 61.0 |
| · Ohio | 130 | 58.1 | 1.4 | 50.0 | 55.0 | 65.0 |
| · Other | 170 | 55.2 | 1.4 | 44.0 | 55.0 | 66.0 |
| West North Central | 289 | 58.5 | 1.0 | 48.0 | 56.0 | 66.0 |
| South Atlantic | 714 | 58.5 | 0.6 | 48.0 | 58.0 | 67.0 |
| · Florida | 200 | 59.5 | 1.3 | 49.0 | 60.0 | 67.0 |
| · Other | 514 | 58.1 | 0.7 | 48.0 | 57.0 | 67.0 |
| East South Central | 234 | 57.4 | 1.1 | 47.0 | 56.0 | 70.0 |
| West South Central | 363 | 58.9 | 0.8 | 49.0 | 57.0 | 66.0 |
| · Texas | 240 | 58.9 | 1.0 | 50.0 | 57.0 | 66.0 |
| · Other | 123 | 59.1 | 1.4 | 48.0 | 55.0 | 67.0 |
| Mountain | 229 | 56.1 | 1.0 | 46.0 | 55.0 | 64.0 |
| Pacific | 661 | 55.5 | 0.7 | 45.0 | 54.0 | 65.0 |
| · California | 461 | 56.5 | 0.8 | 45.0 | 54.0 | 67.0 |
| · Other | 200 | 52.6 | 1.0 | 43.0 | 52.0 | 60.0 |
| *Practice Arrangement* | | | | | | |
| Self-Employed | 2263 | 59.0 | 0.4 | 49.0 | 59.0 | 68.0 |
| · Solo Practice | 1015 | 59.3 | 0.6 | 48.0 | 59.0 | 70.0 |
| · Two Physician Practice | 270 | 60.3 | 1.0 | 48.0 | 59.0 | 72.0 |
| · Three Physician Practice | 211 | 58.7 | 1.1 | 49.0 | 57.0 | 66.0 |
| · 4-8 Physician Practice | 500 | 57.8 | 0.6 | 49.0 | 57.0 | 67.0 |
| · Over 8 Physician Practice | 265 | 58.7 | 0.9 | 50.0 | 59.0 | 65.0 |
| Employee | 1464 | 54.2 | 0.4 | 44.0 | 53.0 | 63.0 |
| Independent Contractor | 237 | 52.6 | 1.1 | 44.0 | 53.0 | 61.0 |

Source: 1995 Socioeconomic Monitoring System survey of nonfederal patient care physicians. See the beginning of this section, the introduction, and appendices for a discussion of the survey sample, definitions, and computation procedures. Statistics are not reported if the number of responses is less than 25.

Table 3. **Hours in Patient Care Activities per Week, for Nonfederal Physicians, 1995**

| | Number of Responses | Mean | Standard Error | 25th Percentile | Median | 75th Percentile |
|---|---|---|---|---|---|---|
| All Physicians | 3966 | 51.3 | 0.3 | 41.0 | 50.0 | 60.0 |
| *Specialty* | | | | | | |
| General/Family Practice | 510 | 52.9 | 0.7 | 43.0 | 52.0 | 61.0 |
| Internal Medicine | 763 | 53.9 | 0.6 | 43.0 | 54.0 | 63.0 |
| · General Internal Medicine | 522 | 52.9 | 0.8 | 42.0 | 53.0 | 62.0 |
| · Cardiovascular Diseases | 101 | 55.1 | 1.8 | 45.0 | 57.0 | 65.0 |
| · Other | 140 | 56.8 | 1.4 | 49.0 | 56.0 | 65.0 |
| Surgery | 884 | 53.2 | 0.5 | 43.0 | 52.0 | 62.0 |
| · General Surgery | 218 | 57.0 | 1.2 | 48.0 | 57.0 | 65.0 |
| · Otolaryngology | 76 | 52.2 | 1.3 | 44.0 | 50.0 | 60.0 |
| · Orthopedic Surgery | 187 | 52.7 | 1.0 | 42.0 | 51.0 | 61.0 |
| · Ophthalmology | 187 | 46.5 | 0.8 | 39.0 | 46.0 | 53.0 |
| · Urological Surgery | 98 | 57.4 | 1.5 | 47.0 | 55.0 | 67.0 |
| · Other | 118 | 53.1 | 1.7 | 44.0 | 56.0 | 65.0 |
| Pediatrics | 306 | 50.4 | 0.9 | 40.0 | 49.0 | 60.0 |
| Obstetrics/Gynecology | 246 | 54.6 | 1.1 | 44.0 | 54.0 | 65.0 |
| Radiology | 272 | 49.4 | 0.9 | 42.0 | 50.0 | 55.0 |
| Psychiatry | 273 | 43.8 | 0.9 | 34.0 | 43.0 | 52.0 |
| Anesthesiology | 224 | 50.4 | 1.2 | 40.0 | 52.0 | 60.0 |
| Pathology | 120 | 41.2 | 1.0 | 34.0 | 42.0 | 50.0 |
| Other Specialty | 368 | 46.0 | 0.8 | 37.0 | 45.0 | 53.0 |
| · Emergency Medicine | 133 | 45.6 | 1.3 | 36.0 | 42.0 | 53.0 |
| · Other | 235 | 46.3 | 0.9 | 37.0 | 46.0 | 54.0 |
| *Geographic Area* | | | | | | |
| New England | 253 | 47.2 | 1.1 | 36.0 | 48.0 | 58.0 |
| · Massachusetts | 117 | 46.9 | 1.4 | 36.0 | 48.0 | 55.0 |
| · Other | 136 | 47.6 | 1.6 | 37.0 | 48.0 | 59.0 |
| Middle Atlantic | 625 | 50.3 | 0.6 | 40.0 | 50.0 | 60.0 |
| · New Jersey | 109 | 47.8 | 1.6 | 38.0 | 48.0 | 58.0 |
| · New York | 250 | 49.3 | 1.1 | 38.0 | 48.0 | 60.0 |
| · Pennsylvania | 266 | 52.8 | 0.9 | 43.0 | 51.0 | 61.0 |
| East North Central | 597 | 50.9 | 0.7 | 41.0 | 50.0 | 60.0 |
| · Illinois | 183 | 50.9 | 1.3 | 40.0 | 51.0 | 61.0 |
| · Michigan | 113 | 50.4 | 1.2 | 41.0 | 50.0 | 58.0 |
| · Ohio | 130 | 51.3 | 1.4 | 42.0 | 50.0 | 60.0 |
| · Other | 171 | 51.1 | 1.3 | 40.0 | 52.0 | 61.0 |
| West North Central | 289 | 52.5 | 1.0 | 41.0 | 50.0 | 60.0 |
| South Atlantic | 714 | 53.3 | 0.6 | 43.0 | 52.0 | 62.0 |
| · Florida | 201 | 54.6 | 1.2 | 45.0 | 55.0 | 62.0 |
| · Other | 513 | 52.7 | 0.7 | 42.0 | 52.0 | 62.0 |
| East South Central | 233 | 53.2 | 1.0 | 43.0 | 52.0 | 64.0 |
| West South Central | 363 | 53.8 | 0.8 | 44.0 | 53.0 | 62.0 |
| · Texas | 240 | 53.4 | 1.0 | 44.0 | 53.0 | 60.0 |
| · Other | 123 | 54.7 | 1.4 | 44.0 | 52.0 | 62.0 |
| Mountain | 231 | 50.6 | 1.0 | 40.0 | 51.0 | 60.0 |
| Pacific | 661 | 49.8 | 0.6 | 40.0 | 49.0 | 59.0 |
| · California | 461 | 50.6 | 0.8 | 41.0 | 50.0 | 60.0 |
| · Other | 200 | 47.7 | 1.0 | 38.0 | 48.0 | 56.0 |
| *Practice Arrangement* | | | | | | |
| Self-Employed | 2264 | 54.0 | 0.3 | 44.0 | 53.0 | 63.0 |
| · Solo Practice | 1015 | 53.9 | 0.6 | 42.0 | 53.0 | 63.0 |
| · Two Physician Practice | 271 | 54.9 | 1.0 | 44.0 | 55.0 | 65.0 |
| · Three Physician Practice | 212 | 53.9 | 1.0 | 44.0 | 52.0 | 62.0 |
| · 4-8 Physician Practice | 501 | 53.7 | 0.6 | 45.0 | 53.0 | 62.0 |
| · Over 8 Physician Practice | 263 | 54.0 | 0.9 | 45.0 | 53.0 | 61.0 |
| Employee | 1465 | 47.8 | 0.4 | 38.0 | 47.0 | 57.0 |
| Independent Contractor | 237 | 48.7 | 1.1 | 40.0 | 50.0 | 60.0 |

Source: 1995 Socioeconomic Monitoring System survey of nonfederal patient care physicians. See the beginning of this section, the introduction, and appendices for a discussion of the survey sample, definitions, and computation procedures. Statistics are not reported if the number of responses is less than 25.

Table 4. **Total Patient Visit Hours per Week (excluding Physicians in Radiology, Psychiatry, Anesthesiology, and Pathology), for Nonfederal Physicians, 1995**

| | Number of Responses | Mean | Standard Error | 25th Percentile | Median | 75th Percentile |
|---|---|---|---|---|---|---|
| All Physicians | 3045 | 41.3 | 0.3 | 31.0 | 40.0 | 50.0 |
| *Specialty* | | | | | | |
| General/Family Practice | 506 | 46.9 | 0.6 | 39.0 | 46.0 | 55.0 |
| Internal Medicine | 756 | 45.0 | 0.6 | 35.0 | 45.0 | 55.0 |
| · General Internal Medicine | 517 | 46.0 | 0.7 | 36.0 | 46.0 | 55.0 |
| · Cardiovascular Diseases | 100 | 41.2 | 1.6 | 28.0 | 40.0 | 52.0 |
| · Other | 139 | 43.8 | 1.3 | 35.0 | 45.0 | 52.0 |
| Surgery | 872 | 33.9 | 0.4 | 25.0 | 33.0 | 40.0 |
| · General Surgery | 212 | 30.9 | 0.8 | 23.0 | 29.0 | 38.0 |
| · Otolaryngology | 76 | 35.0 | 1.2 | 26.0 | 34.0 | 41.0 |
| · Orthopedic Surgery | 183 | 33.9 | 0.8 | 26.0 | 33.0 | 40.0 |
| · Ophthalmology | 187 | 37.5 | 0.7 | 30.0 | 37.0 | 43.0 |
| · Urological Surgery | 98 | 38.4 | 1.4 | 29.0 | 35.0 | 48.0 |
| · Other | 116 | 30.4 | 1.2 | 20.0 | 28.0 | 38.0 |
| Pediatrics | 303 | 43.4 | 0.8 | 34.0 | 42.0 | 52.0 |
| Obstetrics/Gynecology | 243 | 36.6 | 0.8 | 30.0 | 36.0 | 44.0 |
| Other Specialty | 365 | 42.6 | 1.1 | 33.0 | 40.0 | 48.0 |
| · Emergency Medicine | 133 | 42.8 | 1.3 | 35.0 | 40.0 | 50.0 |
| · Other | 232 | 42.6 | 1.5 | 33.0 | 40.0 | 48.0 |
| *Geographic Area* | | | | | | |
| New England | 191 | 38.5 | 1.0 | 30.0 | 40.0 | 47.0 |
| · Massachusetts | 89 | 38.0 | 1.4 | 28.0 | 40.0 | 46.0 |
| · Other | 102 | 39.1 | 1.3 | 30.0 | 40.0 | 48.0 |
| Middle Atlantic | 473 | 40.1 | 0.7 | 30.0 | 40.0 | 50.0 |
| · New Jersey | 87 | 38.1 | 1.6 | 26.0 | 40.0 | 47.0 |
| · New York | 185 | 39.3 | 1.0 | 29.0 | 38.0 | 49.0 |
| · Pennsylvania | 201 | 42.2 | 1.0 | 34.0 | 40.0 | 51.0 |
| East North Central | 454 | 40.7 | 0.7 | 29.0 | 40.0 | 50.0 |
| · Illinois | 149 | 40.5 | 1.4 | 27.0 | 38.0 | 51.0 |
| · Michigan | 85 | 37.9 | 1.6 | 25.0 | 36.0 | 48.0 |
| · Ohio | 102 | 42.3 | 1.6 | 30.0 | 40.0 | 54.0 |
| · Other | 118 | 41.5 | 1.4 | 30.0 | 40.0 | 51.0 |
| West North Central | 230 | 41.5 | 1.0 | 31.0 | 40.0 | 50.0 |
| South Atlantic | 556 | 42.2 | 0.6 | 32.0 | 40.0 | 52.0 |
| · Florida | 155 | 42.1 | 1.3 | 30.0 | 40.0 | 52.0 |
| · Other | 401 | 42.3 | 0.7 | 33.0 | 40.0 | 50.0 |
| East South Central | 183 | 43.9 | 1.1 | 32.0 | 43.0 | 55.0 |
| West South Central | 279 | 43.7 | 0.8 | 35.0 | 42.0 | 52.0 |
| · Texas | 185 | 43.9 | 1.0 | 34.0 | 42.0 | 52.0 |
| · Other | 94 | 43.2 | 1.3 | 35.0 | 42.0 | 52.0 |
| Mountain | 181 | 40.9 | 1.0 | 32.0 | 40.0 | 50.0 |
| Pacific | 498 | 41.1 | 0.9 | 31.0 | 40.0 | 48.0 |
| · California | 347 | 40.6 | 0.7 | 33.0 | 40.0 | 50.0 |
| · Other | 151 | 42.6 | 2.2 | 30.0 | 40.0 | 45.0 |
| *Practice Arrangement* | | | | | | |
| Self-Employed | 1793 | 42.8 | 0.4 | 33.0 | 41.0 | 51.0 |
| · Solo Practice | 838 | 43.1 | 0.5 | 33.0 | 42.0 | 52.0 |
| · Two Physician Practice | 237 | 42.8 | 0.9 | 33.0 | 41.0 | 51.0 |
| · Three Physician Practice | 185 | 44.7 | 1.9 | 32.0 | 41.0 | 50.0 |
| · 4-8 Physician Practice | 385 | 41.0 | 0.6 | 32.0 | 40.0 | 49.0 |
| · Over 8 Physician Practice | 146 | 43.2 | 1.1 | 35.0 | 40.0 | 52.0 |
| Employee | 1106 | 38.8 | 0.4 | 30.0 | 38.0 | 47.0 |
| Independent Contractor | 146 | 43.5 | 1.4 | 34.0 | 41.0 | 53.0 |

Source: 1995 Socioeconomic Monitoring System survey of nonfederal patient care physicians. See the beginning of this section, the introduction, and appendices for a discussion of the survey sample, definitions, and computation procedures. Statistics are not reported if the number of responses is less than 25.

## Table 5. **Office Hours per Week, for Nonfederal Physicians (excluding Physicians in Radiology, Psychiatry, Anesthesiology, and Pathology), 1995**

| | Number of Responses | Mean | Standard Error | 25th Percentile | Median | 75th Percentile |
|---|---|---|---|---|---|---|
| All Physicians | 3072 | 26.5 | 0.3 | 16.0 | 30.0 | 36.0 |
| *Specialty* | | | | | | |
| General/Family Practice | 510 | 34.7 | 0.6 | 30.0 | 36.0 | 40.0 |
| Internal Medicine | 761 | 26.0 | 0.6 | 16.0 | 28.0 | 36.0 |
| · General Internal Medicine | 520 | 28.0 | 0.7 | 20.0 | 30.0 | 40.0 |
| · Cardiovascular Diseases | 101 | 19.0 | 1.2 | 10.0 | 20.0 | 25.0 |
| · Other | 140 | 22.8 | 1.1 | 15.0 | 20.0 | 30.0 |
| Surgery | 883 | 22.9 | 0.4 | 15.0 | 20.0 | 30.0 |
| · General Surgery | 217 | 14.8 | 0.6 | 9.0 | 14.0 | 20.0 |
| · Otolaryngology | 76 | 27.9 | 1.2 | 20.0 | 27.0 | 35.0 |
| · Orthopedic Surgery | 187 | 22.8 | 0.7 | 18.0 | 22.0 | 27.0 |
| · Ophthalmology | 187 | 34.4 | 0.7 | 30.0 | 35.0 | 40.0 |
| · Urological Surgery | 98 | 25.1 | 1.1 | 20.0 | 25.0 | 30.0 |
| · Other | 118 | 18.6 | 1.0 | 10.0 | 18.0 | 25.0 |
| Pediatrics | 305 | 31.2 | 0.9 | 22.0 | 35.0 | 40.0 |
| Obstetrics/Gynecology | 246 | 28.2 | 0.8 | 20.0 | 30.0 | 35.0 |
| Other Specialty | 367 | 19.1 | 1.0 | 0.0 | 16.0 | 35.0 |
| · Emergency Medicine | 133 | 4.4 | 1.1 | 0.0 | 0.0 | 0.0 |
| · Other | 234 | 27.0 | 1.2 | 15.0 | 30.0 | 40.0 |
| *Geographic Area* | | | | | | |
| New England | 192 | 24.7 | 1.1 | 12.0 | 25.0 | 35.0 |
| · Massachusetts | 89 | 23.6 | 1.6 | 14.0 | 25.0 | 35.0 |
| · Other | 103 | 25.7 | 1.6 | 12.0 | 25.0 | 36.0 |
| Middle Atlantic | 473 | 25.1 | 0.7 | 15.0 | 25.0 | 35.0 |
| · New Jersey | 87 | 25.8 | 1.7 | 20.0 | 28.0 | 35.0 |
| · New York | 185 | 23.6 | 1.2 | 14.0 | 25.0 | 35.0 |
| · Pennsylvania | 201 | 26.4 | 1.0 | 16.0 | 26.0 | 38.0 |
| East North Central | 461 | 25.5 | 0.7 | 15.0 | 27.0 | 36.0 |
| · Illinois | 151 | 23.9 | 1.3 | 12.0 | 25.0 | 35.0 |
| · Michigan | 86 | 25.4 | 1.7 | 16.0 | 25.0 | 35.0 |
| · Ohio | 103 | 26.8 | 1.4 | 18.0 | 30.0 | 40.0 |
| · Other | 121 | 26.7 | 1.2 | 18.0 | 30.0 | 40.0 |
| West North Central | 233 | 27.8 | 1.0 | 20.0 | 29.0 | 36.0 |
| South Atlantic | 562 | 26.4 | 0.7 | 16.0 | 28.0 | 39.0 |
| · Florida | 156 | 25.2 | 1.3 | 12.0 | 26.0 | 40.0 |
| · Other | 406 | 26.9 | 0.8 | 18.0 | 30.0 | 39.0 |
| East South Central | 186 | 26.4 | 1.1 | 16.0 | 30.0 | 36.0 |
| West South Central | 284 | 28.9 | 0.9 | 20.0 | 31.0 | 40.0 |
| · Texas | 187 | 29.3 | 1.1 | 20.0 | 32.0 | 40.0 |
| · Other | 97 | 28.1 | 1.4 | 20.0 | 30.0 | 40.0 |
| Mountain | 181 | 26.8 | 1.1 | 16.0 | 30.0 | 40.0 |
| Pacific | 500 | 27.3 | 0.7 | 18.0 | 30.0 | 36.0 |
| · California | 348 | 26.7 | 0.8 | 16.0 | 30.0 | 36.0 |
| · Other | 152 | 29.1 | 1.4 | 20.0 | 30.0 | 36.0 |
| *Practice Arrangement* | | | | | | |
| Self-Employed | 1810 | 29.4 | 0.3 | 20.0 | 30.0 | 40.0 |
| · Solo Practice | 848 | 30.5 | 0.5 | 20.0 | 30.0 | 40.0 |
| · Two Physician Practice | 237 | 30.5 | 0.8 | 20.0 | 30.0 | 40.0 |
| · Three Physician Practice | 188 | 29.6 | 1.1 | 20.0 | 29.0 | 36.0 |
| · 4-8 Physician Practice | 388 | 27.0 | 0.7 | 18.0 | 28.0 | 36.0 |
| · Over 8 Physician Practice | 147 | 25.7 | 1.2 | 16.0 | 28.0 | 38.0 |
| Employee | 1115 | 23.0 | 0.5 | 10.0 | 25.0 | 35.0 |
| Independent Contractor | 147 | 19.4 | 1.6 | 0.0 | 17.0 | 36.0 |

Source: 1995 Socioeconomic Monitoring System survey of nonfederal patient care physicians. See the beginning of this section, the introduction, and appendices for a discussion of the survey sample, definitions, and computation procedures. Statistics are not reported if the number of responses is less than 25.

## Table 6. **Hours on Hospital Rounds per Week, for Nonfederal Physicians (excluding Physicians in Radiology, Psychiatry, Anesthesiology, and Pathology), 1995**

| | Number of Responses | Mean | Standard Error | 25th Percentile | Median | 75th Percentile |
|---|---|---|---|---|---|---|
| All Physicians | 3052 | 7.7 | 0.2 | 0.0 | 5.0 | 10.0 |
| *Specialty* | | | | | | |
| General/Family Practice | 507 | 5.1 | 0.3 | 0.0 | 4.0 | 8.0 |
| Internal Medicine | 757 | 12.1 | 0.5 | 2.0 | 10.0 | 20.0 |
| · General Internal Medicine | 518 | 10.8 | 0.6 | 1.0 | 8.0 | 15.0 |
| · Cardiovascular Diseases | 100 | 17.2 | 1.3 | 9.0 | 15.0 | 25.0 |
| · Other | 139 | 13.8 | 1.2 | 5.0 | 10.0 | 20.0 |
| Surgery | 875 | 6.2 | 0.2 | 1.0 | 5.0 | 10.0 |
| · General Surgery | 214 | 10.6 | 0.5 | 5.0 | 10.0 | 15.0 |
| · Otolaryngology | 76 | 3.7 | 0.4 | 1.0 | 3.0 | 5.0 |
| · Orthopedic Surgery | 184 | 5.2 | 0.2 | 3.0 | 5.0 | 6.0 |
| · Ophthalmology | 187 | 0.7 | 0.1 | 0.0 | 0.0 | 1.0 |
| · Urological Surgery | 98 | 7.5 | 0.5 | 4.0 | 5.0 | 10.0 |
| · Other | 116 | 7.4 | 0.7 | 2.0 | 6.0 | 10.0 |
| Pediatrics | 303 | 8.7 | 0.6 | 2.0 | 5.0 | 10.0 |
| Obstetrics/Gynecology | 243 | 4.7 | 0.2 | 2.0 | 5.0 | 6.0 |
| Other Specialty | 367 | 4.8 | 0.5 | 0.0 | 0.0 | 5.0 |
| · Emergency Medicine | 133 | 0.2 | 0.1 | 0.0 | 0.0 | 0.0 |
| · Other | 234 | 7.2 | 0.8 | 0.0 | 2.0 | 10.0 |
| *Geographic Area* | | | | | | |
| New England | 191 | 6.0 | 0.6 | 0.0 | 5.0 | 9.0 |
| · Massachusetts | 89· | 5.7 | 0.8 | 0.0 | 5.0 | 10.0 |
| · Other | 102 | 6.2 | 0.8 | 0.0 | 4.0 | 8.0 |
| Middle Atlantic | 473 | 8.7 | 0.5 | 0.0 | 5.0 | 12.0 |
| · New Jersey | 87 | 6.9 | 1.0 | 0.0 | 5.0 | 10.0 |
| · New York | 185 | 7.6 | 0.8 | 0.0 | 4.0 | 10.0 |
| · Pennsylvania | 201 | 10.8 | 0.8 | 2.0 | 8.0 | 15.0 |
| East North Central | 454 | 8.4 | 0.4 | 1.0 | 5.0 | 12.0 |
| · Illinois | 149 | 8.7 | 0.7 | 2.0 | 6.0 | 15.0 |
| · Michigan | 85 | 6.5 | 0.9 | 0.0 | 4.0 | 10.0 |
| · Ohio | 102 | 10.0 | 1.1 | 1.0 | 7.0 | 15.0 |
| · Other | 118 | 7.9 | 0.9 | 1.0 | 5.0 | 10.0 |
| West North Central | 231 | 7.0 | 0.5 | 1.0 | 5.0 | 10.0 |
| South Atlantic | 559 | 8.3 | 0.5 | 0.0 | 5.0 | 10.0 |
| · Florida | 156 | 9.8 | 1.0 | 0.0 | 5.0 | 15.0 |
| · Other | 403 | 7.7 | 0.5 | 0.0 | 5.0 | 10.0 |
| East South Central | 184 | 9.4 | 0.8 | 1.0 | 6.0 | 15.0 |
| West South Central | 280 | 7.2 | 0.5 | 0.0 | 5.0 | 10.0 |
| · Texas | 185 | 6.5 | 0.6 | 0.0 | 5.0 | 10.0 |
| · Other | 95 | 8.6 | 1.0 | 1.0 | 6.0 | 10.0 |
| Mountain | 181 | 6.5 | 0.6 | 0.0 | 4.0 | 10.0 |
| Pacific | 499 | 6.6 | 0.4 | 0.0 | 4.0 | 10.0 |
| · California | 348 | 6.8 | 0.5 | 0.0 | 4.0 | 10.0 |
| · Other | 151 | 6.1 | 0.6 | 0.0 | 4.0 | 7.0 |
| *Practice Arrangement* | | | | | | |
| Self-Employed | 1797 | 8.2 | 0.2 | 2.0 | 5.0 | 10.0 |
| · Solo Practice | 840 | 7.6 | 0.3 | 1.0 | 5.0 | 10.0 |
| · Two Physician Practice | 237 | 7.6 | 0.5 | 2.0 | 5.0 | 10.0 |
| · Three Physician Practice | 186 | 9.9 | 0.7 | 3.0 | 6.0 | 15.0 |
| · 4-8 Physician Practice | 385 | 9.4 | 0.5 | 3.0 | 6.0 | 10.0 |
| · Over 8 Physician Practice | 147 | 7.8 | 0.8 | 0.0 | 5.0 | 10.0 |
| Employee | 1109 | 7.5 | 0.3 | 0.0 | 5.0 | 10.0 |
| Independent Contractor | 146 | 4.1 | 0.8 | 0.0 | 0.0 | 5.0 |

Source: 1995 Socioeconomic Monitoring System survey of nonfederal patient care physicians. See the beginning of this section, the introduction, and appendices for a discussion of the survey sample, definitions, and computation procedures. Statistics are not reported if the number of responses is less than 25.

Table 7. **Hours in Outpatient Clinics and Emergency Rooms per Week, for Nonfederal Physicians (excluding Physicians in Radiology, Psychiatry, Anesthesiology, and Pathology), 1995**

| | Number of Responses | Mean | Standard Error | 25th Percentile | Median | 75th Percentile |
|---|---|---|---|---|---|---|
| All Physicians | 3059 | 6.1 | 0.2 | 0.0 | 1.0 | 5.0 |
| *Specialty* | | | | | | |
| General/Family Practice | 508 | 4.8 | 0.5 | 0.0 | 0.0 | 3.0 |
| Internal Medicine | 760 | 5.5 | 0.4 | 0.0 | 2.0 | 6.0 |
| · General Internal Medicine | 519 | 5.2 | 0.5 | 0.0 | 1.0 | 5.0 |
| · Cardiovascular Diseases | 101 | 4.7 | 0.6 | 1.0 | 3.0 | 5.0 |
| · Other | 140 | 7.0 | 1.1 | 0.0 | 2.0 | 10.0 |
| Surgery | 876 | 4.1 | 0.2 | 0.0 | 2.0 | 5.0 |
| · General Surgery | 213 | 5.0 | 0.4 | 1.0 | 3.0 | 6.0 |
| · Otolaryngology | 76 | 3.2 | 0.4 | 0.0 | 2.0 | 4.0 |
| · Orthopedic Surgery | 184 | 5.1 | 0.4 | 1.0 | 4.0 | 8.0 |
| · Ophthalmology | 187 | 1.9 | 0.3 | 0.0 | 0.0 | 1.0 |
| · Urological Surgery | 98 | 5.5 | 0.9 | 0.0 | 1.0 | 5.0 |
| · Other | 118 | 3.8 | 0.5 | 0.0 | 2.0 | 5.0 |
| Pediatrics | 304 | 3.2 | 0.4 | 0.0 | 0.0 | 4.0 |
| Obstetrics/Gynecology | 245 | 3.6 | 0.4 | 0.0 | 1.0 | 4.0 |
| Other Specialty | 366 | 18.1 | 1.1 | 0.0 | 5.0 | 36.0 |
| · Emergency Medicine | 133 | 38.1 | 1.4 | 30.0 | 40.0 | 45.0 |
| · Other | 233 | 7.3 | 0.9 | 0.0 | 0.0 | 6.0 |
| *Geographic Area* | | | | | | |
| New England | 192 | 6.1 | 0.9 | 0.0 | 2.0 | 5.0 |
| · Massachusetts | 89 | 6.3 | 1.3 | 0.0 | 2.0 | 5.0 |
| · Other | 103 | 6.0 | 1.1 | 0.0 | 1.0 | 6.0 |
| Middle Atlantic | 474 | 5.1 | 0.4 | 0.0 | 1.0 | 5.0 |
| · New Jersey | 87 | 4.9 | 1.0 | 0.0 | 1.0 | 5.0 |
| · New York | 185 | 6.3 | 0.9 | 0.0 | 2.0 | 8.0 |
| · Pennsylvania | 202 | 3.8 | 0.5 | 0.0 | 1.0 | 5.0 |
| East North Central | 457 | 5.7 | 0.6 | 0.0 | 1.0 | 5.0 |
| · Illinois | 150 | 6.6 | 1.3 | 0.0 | 1.0 | 5.0 |
| · Michigan | 85 | 5.6 | 1.2 | 0.0 | 2.0 | 5.0 |
| · Ohio | 102 | 3.7 | 0.9 | 0.0 | 0.0 | 3.0 |
| · Other | 120 | 6.3 | 1.0 | 0.0 | 2.0 | 5.0 |
| West North Central | 232 | 5.7 | 0.7 | 0.0 | 2.0 | 5.0 |
| South Atlantic | 557 | 6.6 | 0.5 | 0.0 | 2.0 | 6.0 |
| · Florida | 155 | 6.0 | 0.9 | 0.0 | 2.0 | 7.0 |
| · Other | 402 | 6.8 | 0.6 | 0.0 | 2.0 | 6.0 |
| East South Central | 185 | 7.6 | 1.1 | 0.0 | 1.0 | 6.0 |
| West South Central | 281 | 7.1 | 0.7 | 0.0 | 2.0 | 6.0 |
| · Texas | 186 | 7.5 | 0.9 | 0.0 | 2.0 | 8.0 |
| · Other | 95 | 6.1 | 0.9 | 0.0 | 2.0 | 5.0 |
| Mountain | 181 | 6.8 | 0.9 | 0.0 | 1.0 | 6.0 |
| Pacific | 500 | 6.1 | 0.5 | 0.0 | 1.0 | 5.0 |
| · California | 349 | 6.0 | 0.6 | 0.0 | 1.0 | 5.0 |
| · Other | 151 | 6.3 | 1.0 | 0.0 | 1.0 | 5.0 |
| *Practice Arrangement* | | | | | | |
| Self-Employed | 1801 | 4.1 | 0.2 | 0.0 | 1.0 | 5.0 |
| · Solo Practice | 843 | 3.5 | 0.2 | 0.0 | 1.0 | 5.0 |
| · Two Physician Practice | 237 | 3.7 | 0.4 | 0.0 | 2.0 | 5.0 |
| · Three Physician Practice | 186 | 4.3 | 0.7 | 0.0 | 1.0 | 5.0 |
| · 4-8 Physician Practice | 386 | 4.0 | 0.4 | 0.0 | 2.0 | 5.0 |
| · Over 8 Physician Practice | 147 | 8.8 | 1.1 | 0.0 | 2.0 | 10.0 |
| Employee | 1111 | 7.3 | 0.4 | 0.0 | 2.0 | 8.0 |
| Independent Contractor | 147 | 19.2 | 2.2 | 0.0 | 3.0 | 40.0 |

Source: 1995 Socioeconomic Monitoring System survey of nonfederal patient care physicians. See the beginning of this section, the introduction, and appendices for a discussion of the survey sample, definitions, and computation procedures. Statistics are not reported if the number of responses is less than 25.

## Table 8. Hours in Surgery per Week, for Nonfederal Physicians (excluding Physicians in Radiology, Psychiatry, Anesthesiology, and Pathology), 1995

| | Number of Responses | Mean | Standard Error | 25th Percentile | Median | 75th Percentile |
|---|---|---|---|---|---|---|
| All Physicians | 3063 | 6.5 | 0.2 | 0.0 | 0.0 | 10.0 |
| *Specialty* | | | | | | |
| General/Family Practice | 508 | 1.1 | 0.1 | 0.0 | 0.0 | 0.0 |
| Internal Medicine | 760 | 2.9 | 0.3 | 0.0 | 0.0 | 0.0 |
| · General Internal Medicine | 520 | 0.7 | 0.2 | 0.0 | 0.0 | 0.0 |
| · Cardiovascular Diseases | 100 | 8.6 | 1.3 | 0.0 | 2.0 | 15.0 |
| · Other | 140 | 7.5 | 1.0 | 0.0 | 0.0 | 15.0 |
| Surgery | 878 | 15.8 | 0.3 | 8.0 | 15.0 | 20.0 |
| · General Surgery | 215 | 22.0 | 0.7 | 15.0 | 20.0 | 28.0 |
| · Otolaryngology | 76 | 13.4 | 0.8 | 8.0 | 12.0 | 20.0 |
| · Orthopedic Surgery | 185 | 15.6 | 0.6 | 10.0 | 15.0 | 20.0 |
| · Ophthalmology | 187 | 6.3 | 0.3 | 4.0 | 6.0 | 8.0 |
| · Urological Surgery | 98 | 15.2 | 0.7 | 9.0 | 15.0 | 20.0 |
| · Other | 117 | 18.9 | 1.1 | 10.0 | 20.0 | 29.0 |
| Pediatrics | 305 | 1.5 | 0.2 | 0.0 | 0.0 | 1.0 |
| Obstetrics/Gynecology | 244 | 13.3 | 0.7 | 6.0 | 10.0 | 20.0 |
| Other Specialty | 368 | 1.1 | 0.3 | 0.0 | 0.0 | 0.0 |
| · Emergency Medicine | 133 | 0.1 | 0.0 | 0.0 | 0.0 | 0.0 |
| · Other | 235 | 1.7 | 0.4 | 0.0 | 0.0 | 0.0 |
| *Geographic Area* | | | | | | |
| New England | 191 | 5.1 | 0.6 | 0.0 | 0.0 | 8.0 |
| · Massachusetts | 89 | 4.8 | 0.9 | 0.0 | 0.0 | 6.0 |
| · Other | 102 | 5.4 | 0.8 | 0.0 | 0.0 | 8.0 |
| Middle Atlantic | 474 | 5.6 | 0.5 | 0.0 | 0.0 | 8.0 |
| · New Jersey | 87 | 4.3 | 1.0 | 0.0 | 0.0 | 3.0 |
| · New York | 185 | 5.6 | 0.7 | 0.0 | 0.0 | 8.0 |
| · Pennsylvania | 202 | 6.5 | 0.8 | 0.0 | 0.0 | 10.0 |
| East North Central | 458 | 6.8 | 0.5 | 0.0 | 0.0 | 12.0 |
| · Illinois | 151 | 6.7 | 0.9 | 0.0 | 0.0 | 10.0 |
| · Michigan | 86 | 8.2 | 1.2 | 0.0 | 0.0 | 20.0 |
| · Ohio | 102 | 5.4 | 0.9 | 0.0 | 0.0 | 10.0 |
| · Other | 119 | 7.1 | 0.8 | 0.0 | 1.0 | 15.0 |
| West North Central | 231 | 7.2 | 0.7 | 0.0 | 2.0 | 12.0 |
| South Atlantic | 561 | 7.4 | 0.5 | 0.0 | 0.0 | 14.0 |
| · Florida | 156 | 8.8 | 1.0 | 0.0 | 0.0 | 20.0 |
| · Other | 405 | 6.8 | 0.5 | 0.0 | 0.0 | 12.0 |
| East South Central | 185 | 6.4 | 0.7 | 0.0 | 0.0 | 11.0 |
| West South Central | 284 | 6.8 | 0.6 | 0.0 | 0.0 | 12.0 |
| · Texas | 187 | 6.3 | 0.8 | 0.0 | 0.0 | 10.0 |
| · Other | 97 | 7.8 | 1.0 | 0.0 | 4.0 | 13.0 |
| Mountain | 180 | 5.7 | 0.6 | 0.0 | 0.0 | 10.0 |
| Pacific | 499 | 6.2 | 0.5 | 0.0 | 0.0 | 10.0 |
| · California | 348 | 6.5 | 0.6 | 0.0 | 0.0 | 10.0 |
| · Other | 151 | 5.3 | 0.6 | 0.0 | 0.0 | 10.0 |
| *Practice Arrangement* | | | | | | |
| Self-Employed | 1806 | 7.5 | 0.2 | 0.0 | 2.0 | 13.0 |
| · Solo Practice | 848 | 7.1 | 0.4 | 0.0 | 0.0 | 12.0 |
| · Two Physician Practice | 237 | 7.4 | 0.7 | 0.0 | 3.0 | 12.0 |
| · Three Physician Practice | 186 | 8.3 | 0.6 | 0.0 | 6.0 | 15.0 |
| · 4-8 Physician Practice | 386 | 8.9 | 0.5 | 0.0 | 5.0 | 15.0 |
| · Over 8 Physician Practice | 147 | 5.9 | 0.8 | 0.0 | 0.0 | 10.0 |
| Employee | 1110 | 5.3 | 0.3 | 0.0 | 0.0 | 6.0 |
| Independent Contractor | 147 | 3.4 | 0.7 | 0.0 | 0.0 | 1.0 |

Source: 1995 Socioeconomic Monitoring System survey of nonfederal patient care physicians. See the beginning of this section, the introduction, and appendices for a discussion of the survey sample, definitions, and computation procedures. Statistics are not reported if the number of responses is less than 25.

Table 9. **Hours in Selected Patient Care Activities per Week per Nonfederal Physician in Radiology, Psychiatry, Anesthesiology, and Pathology, 1995**

| | Number of Responses | Mean | Standard Error | 25th Percentile | Median | 75th Percentile |
|---|---|---|---|---|---|---|
| *Radiology* | | | | | | |
| Radiodiagnostic procedures | 263 | 9.8 | 0.6 | 3.0 | 7.0 | 10.0 |
| Radiotherapy patients | 267 | 4.1 | 0.7 | 0.0 | 0.0 | 0.0 |
| Consultations with other physicians | 266 | 4.5 | 0.2 | 2.0 | 4.0 | 5.0 |
| Reading films | 267 | 27.5 | 0.8 | 18.0 | 30.0 | 40.0 |
| *Psychiatry* | | | | | | |
| Individual patient sessions | 271 | 33.0 | 0.8 | 23.0 | 32.0 | 40.0 |
| Family group sessions | 271 | 2.4 | 0.2 | 0.0 | 1.0 | 3.0 |
| Nonfamily group sessions | 272 | 1.0 | 0.2 | 0.0 | 0.0 | 0.0 |
| *Anesthesiology* | | | | | | |
| Patients personally anesthetized | 222 | 31.6 | 1.2 | 15.0 | 35.0 | 45.0 |
| Patients anesthetized by nurse anesthetists under physician supervision | 222 | 11.3 | 1.0 | 0.0 | 2.0 | 22.0 |
| Pre-anesthesia and inpatient visits | 220 | 5.2 | 0.3 | 2.0 | 5.0 | 7.0 |
| *Pathology* | | | | | | |
| Surgical consultations | 118 | 4.8 | 0.5 | 1.0 | 3.0 | 5.0 |
| Examinations of surgical specimens | 118 | 20.0 | 1.0 | 13.0 | 20.0 | 26.0 |
| Non-surgical laboratory procedures | 116 | 6.7 | 0.6 | 1.0 | 5.0 | 10.0 |
| Autopsies | 118 | 3.0 | 0.6 | 0.0 | 0.0 | 3.0 |

Source: 1995 Socioeconomic Monitoring System survey of nonfederal patient care physicians. See the beginning of this section, the introduction, and appendices for a discussion of the survey sample, definitions, and computation procedures. Statistics are not reported if the number of responses is less than 25.

## Table 10. **Total Patient Visit Hours per Week, for Nonfederal Physicians, 1995 – General/Family Practice**

| | Number of Responses | Mean | Standard Error | 25th Percentile | Median | 75th Percentile |
|---|---|---|---|---|---|---|
| All Physicians | 506 | 46.9 | 0.6 | 39 | 46 | 55 |
| *Geographic Area* | | | | | | |
| New England | 29 | 42.1 | 1.9 | 34 | 44 | 48 |
| Middle Atlantic | 59 | 47.6 | 1.8 | 40 | 48 | 55 |
| East North Central | 82 | 50.3 | 1.5 | 42 | 50 | 60 |
| West North Central | 60 | 47.3 | 1.8 | 39 | 44 | 56 |
| South Atlantic | 77 | 46.0 | 1.5 | 38 | 46 | 55 |
| East South Central | 32 | 52.3 | 2.7 | 39 | 48 | 67 |
| West South Central | 43 | 47.5 | 1.6 | 40 | 45 | 55 |
| Mountain | 45 | 44.5 | 2.1 | 38 | 46 | 53 |
| Pacific | 79 | 43.9 | 1.6 | 36 | 42 | 50 |
| *Practice Arrangement* | | | | | | |
| Self-Employed | 263 | 49.2 | 0.8 | 41 | 48 | 56 |
| · Solo Practice | 152 | 51.1 | 1.0 | 43 | 50 | 60 |
| · Two Physician Practice | 38 | 46.4 | 2.2 | 37 | 48 | 57 |
| · Three Physician Practice | 19 | · | · | · | · | · |
| · 4-8 Physician Practice | 41 | 47.8 | 1.8 | 40 | 47 | 52 |
| · Over 8 Physician Practice | 13 | · | · | · | · | · |
| Employee | 215 | 43.6 | 0.9 | 35 | 42 | 50 |
| Independent Contractor | 28 | 49.1 | 3.3 | 40 | 48 | 60 |

Source: 1995 Socioeconomic Monitoring System survey of nonfederal patient care physicians. See the beginning of this section, the introduction, and appendices for a discussion of the survey sample, definitions, and computation procedures. Statistics are not reported if the number of responses is less than 25.

## Table 11. **Total Patient Visit Hours per Week, for Nonfederal Physicians, 1995 – Internal Medicine**

| | Number of Responses | Mean | Standard Error | 25th Percentile | Median | 75th Percentile |
|---|---|---|---|---|---|---|
| All Physicians | 756 | 45.0 | 0.6 | 35 | 45 | 55 |
| *Geographic Area* | | | | | | |
| New England | 64 | 41.0 | 1.8 | 32 | 42 | 49 |
| Middle Atlantic | 137 | 45.5 | 1.1 | 38 | 45 | 55 |
| East North Central | 109 | 45.0 | 1.9 | 32 | 45 | 55 |
| West North Central | 42 | 42.0 | 2.3 | 30 | 40 | 52 |
| South Atlantic | 133 | 47.2 | 1.5 | 38 | 45 | 57 |
| East South Central | 51 | 47.7 | 2.1 | 38 | 50 | 58 |
| West South Central | 63 | 47.5 | 1.9 | 40 | 50 | 55 |
| Mountain | 34 | 43.1 | 2.5 | 32 | 40 | 50 |
| Pacific | 123 | 43.1 | 1.3 | 35 | 41 | 51 |
| *Practice Arrangement* | | | | | | |
| Self-Employed | 435 | 47.9 | 0.7 | 39 | 48 | 57 |
| · Solo Practice | 198 | 47.7 | 1.2 | 38 | 48 | 56 |
| · Two Physician Practice | 44 | 46.7 | 2.1 | 38 | 47 | 58 |
| · Three Physician Practice | 50 | 46.4 | 2.3 | 35 | 45 | 55 |
| · 4-8 Physician Practice | 93 | 47.8 | 1.4 | 39 | 48 | 57 |
| · Over 8 Physician Practice | 50 | 51.5 | 1.8 | 41 | 52 | 60 |
| Employee | 298 | 41.2 | 0.9 | 30 | 40 | 51 |
| Independent Contractor | 23 | · | · | · | · | · |

Source: 1995 Socioeconomic Monitoring System survey of nonfederal patient care physicians. See the beginning of this section, the introduction, and appendices for a discussion of the survey sample, definitions, and computation procedures. Statistics are not reported if the number of responses is less than 25.

Table 12. **Total Patient Visit Hours per Week, for Nonfederal Physicians, 1995 – Surgery**

| | Number of Responses | Mean | Standard Error | 25th Percentile | Median | 75th Percentile |
|---|---|---|---|---|---|---|
| All Physicians | 872 | 33.9 | 0.4 | 25 | 33 | 40 |
| *Geographic Area* | | | | | | |
| New England | 49 | 34.5 | 1.7 | 25 | 36 | 42 |
| Middle Atlantic | 133 | 33.3 | 1.2 | 24 | 32 | 39 |
| East North Central | 125 | 30.7 | 1.0 | 23 | 29 | 38 |
| West North Central | 69 | 33.9 | 1.4 | 26 | 32 | 37 |
| South Atlantic | 182 | 34.9 | 0.9 | 27 | 34 | 40 |
| East South Central | 49 | 31.9 | 1.3 | 23 | 31 | 38 |
| West South Central | 83 | 38.5 | 1.3 | 30 | 36 | 45 |
| Mountain | 41 | 36.6 | 2.2 | 24 | 38 | 43 |
| Pacific | 141 | 32.7 | 0.8 | 26 | 32 | 40 |
| *Practice Arrangement* | | | | | | |
| Self-Employed | 623 | 34.9 | 0.5 | 26 | 34 | 41 |
| · Solo Practice | 282 | 35.7 | 0.8 | 25 | 35 | 44 |
| · Two Physician Practice | 99 | 36.0 | 1.0 | 30 | 34 | 42 |
| · Three Physician Practice | 75 | 35.5 | 1.4 | 28 | 34 | 42 |
| · 4-8 Physician Practice | 131 | 32.9 | 0.8 | 26 | 32 | 40 |
| · Over 8 Physician Practice | 35 | 30.1 | 1.2 | 24 | 30 | 35 |
| Employee | 222 | 31.6 | 0.8 | 24 | 30 | 38 |
| Independent Contractor | 27 | 31.5 | 1.6 | 23 | 30 | 36 |

Source: 1995 Socioeconomic Monitoring System survey of nonfederal patient care physicians. See the beginning of this section, the introduction, and appendices for a discussion of the survey sample, definitions, and computation procedures. Statistics are not reported if the number of responses is less than 25.

Table 13. **Total Patient Visit Hours per Week, for Nonfederal Physicians, 1995 – Pediatrics**

| | Number of Responses | Mean | Standard Error | 25th Percentile | Median | 75th Percentile |
|---|---|---|---|---|---|---|
| All Physicians | 303 | 43.4 | 0.8 | 34 | 42 | 52 |
| *Geographic Area* | | | | | | |
| New England | 18 | . | . | . | . | . |
| Middle Atlantic | 58 | 37.3 | 1.7 | 29 | 39 | 50 |
| East North Central | 35 | 42.6 | 2.0 | 34 | 43 | 53 |
| West North Central | 19 | . | . | . | . | . |
| South Atlantic | 62 | 45.4 | 2.1 | 35 | 40 | 55 |
| East South Central | 15 | . | . | . | . | . |
| West South Central | 36 | 49.1 | 2.0 | 40 | 48 | 56 |
| Mountain | 18 | . | . | . | . | . |
| Pacific | 42 | 44.0 | 1.8 | 40 | 42 | 50 |
| *Practice Arrangement* | | | | | | |
| Self-Employed | 152 | 47.6 | 1.1 | 40 | 47 | 54 |
| · Solo Practice | 68 | 48.4 | 1.7 | 40 | 49 | 53 |
| · Two Physician Practice | 24 | . | . | . | . | . |
| · Three Physician Practice | 16 | . | . | . | . | . |
| · 4-8 Physician Practice | 34 | 45.5 | 2.2 | 35 | 42 | 55 |
| · Over 8 Physician Practice | 9 | . | . | . | . | . |
| Employee | 141 | 38.9 | 1.1 | 30 | 38 | 47 |
| Independent Contractor | 10 | . | . | . | . | . |

Source: 1995 Socioeconomic Monitoring System survey of nonfederal patient care physicians. See the beginning of this section, the introduction, and appendices for a discussion of the survey sample, definitions, and computation procedures. Statistics are not reported if the number of responses is less than 25.

## Table 14. **Total Patient Visit Hours per Week, for Nonfederal Physicians, 1995 – Obstetrics/Gynecology**

|  | Number of Responses | Mean | Standard Error | 25th Percentile | Median | 75th Percentile |
|---|---|---|---|---|---|---|
| All Physicians | 243 | 36.6 | 0.8 | 30 | 36 | 44 |
| *Geographic Area* | | | | | | |
| New England | 12 | . | . | . | . | . |
| Middle Atlantic | 35 | 35.2 | 2.3 | 32 | 35 | 40 |
| East North Central | 46 | 35.3 | 1.4 | 29 | 33 | 40 |
| West North Central | 14 | . | . | . | . | . |
| South Atlantic | 38 | 41.0 | 2.0 | 34 | 40 | 50 |
| East South Central | 17 | . | . | . | . | . |
| West South Central | 25 | 40.6 | 1.8 | 37 | 38 | 45 |
| Mountain | 20 | . | . | . | . | . |
| Pacific | 36 | 35.8 | 2.1 | 24 | 38 | 45 |
| *Practice Arrangement* | | | | | | |
| Self-Employed | 162 | 38.1 | 0.9 | 33 | 37 | 45 |
| · Solo Practice | 73 | 36.9 | 1.7 | 29 | 37 | 43 |
| · Two Physician Practice | 21 | . | . | . | . | . |
| · Three Physician Practice | 14 | . | . | . | . | . |
| · 4-8 Physician Practice | 42 | 37.9 | 1.1 | 33 | 37 | 44 |
| · Over 8 Physician Practice | 12 | . | . | . | . | . |
| Employee | 73 | 34.5 | 1.4 | 26 | 33 | 41 |
| Independent Contractor | 8 | . | . | . | . | . |

Source: 1995 Socioeconomic Monitoring System survey of nonfederal patient care physicians. See the beginning of this section, the introduction, and appendices for a discussion of the survey sample, definitions, and computation procedures. Statistics are not reported if the number of responses is less than 25.

## Table 15. **Total Patient Visit Hours per Week, for Nonfederal Physicians, 1995 – Other Specialty**

|  | Number of Responses | Mean | Standard Error | 25th Percentile | Median | 75th Percentile |
|---|---|---|---|---|---|---|
| All Physicians | 365 | 42.6 | 1.1 | 33 | 40 | 48 |
| *Geographic Area* | | | | | | |
| New England | 19 | . | . | . | . | . |
| Middle Atlantic | 51 | 39.1 | 1.6 | 28 | 40 | 49 |
| East North Central | 57 | 40.1 | 1.8 | 30 | 40 | 48 |
| West North Central | 26 | 44.3 | 2.9 | 35 | 40 | 53 |
| South Atlantic | 64 | 42.3 | 1.9 | 36 | 40 | 45 |
| East South Central | 19 | . | . | . | . | . |
| West South Central | 29 | 39.0 | 2.6 | 30 | 40 | 43 |
| Mountain | 23 | . | . | . | . | . |
| Pacific | 77 | 48.4 | 4.1 | 35 | 40 | 50 |
| *Practice Arrangement* | | | | | | |
| Self-Employed | 158 | 45.5 | 2.1 | 35 | 40 | 50 |
| · Solo Practice | 65 | 42.4 | 1.7 | 35 | 40 | 50 |
| · Two Physician Practice | 11 | . | . | . | . | . |
| · Three Physician Practice | 11 | . | . | . | . | . |
| · 4-8 Physician Practice | 44 | 41.9 | 1.6 | 35 | 42 | 49 |
| · Over 8 Physician Practice | 27 | 39.0 | 2.0 | 35 | 40 | 40 |
| Employee | 157 | 38.1 | 1.0 | 30 | 38 | 45 |
| Independent Contractor | 50 | 48.4 | 2.3 | 40 | 48 | 60 |

Source: 1995 Socioeconomic Monitoring System survey of nonfederal patient care physicians. See the beginning of this section, the introduction, and appendices for a discussion of the survey sample, definitions, and computation procedures. Statistics are not reported if the number of responses is less than 25.

# Physician Service and Hospital Utilization for Nonfederal Physicians

Total Patient Visits

Visits by Type

Surgical Procedures Including and Excluding Assists

Selected Specialty-Specific Services and Procedures

Hospital Discharges and Lengths of Stays

Specialty Specific Total Patient Visits,
by Census Division and Practice Arrangement

## Physician Service and Hospital Utilization for Nonfederal Physicians

Physician service utilization refers to the quantity of services provided by physicians to their patients. The number of patient visits is a measure that captures a large proportion of overall physician utilization in most specialties. Total patient visits may be decomposed into different types of visits. The types of visits for which statistics are reported below include total office visits, new patient office visits, visits made on hospital rounds, and visits made in outpatient clinics and hospital emergency rooms. Surgical services account for another important share of physician services. The number of surgical procedures, both including and excluding assists, is indicated in the tables that follow. While patient visit and surgical service measures cover a broad range of the practice activities of physicians, they do not reflect the full heterogeneity of physician services. For this reason, additional tables are provided that give more detail on selected services and procedures on a specialty-specific basis.

The questions from which physician service utilization information in Tables 16-22 and 27-32 were derived are as follows:

1. During your last complete week of practice, how many:

*All specialties except radiology, psychiatry, anesthesiology, and pathology*

a. patient visits did you personally have during the hours you spent in the office or in freestanding primary or urgent care centers? Please count as one visit every time you saw a patient. Do not include patient visits in outpatient clinics located in hospitals or in hospital emergency rooms.

aa. How many of these visits were with new patients?

b. patient visits did you personally have during the hours you spent in hospital emergency rooms and outpatient clinics located in hospitals? Please count as one visit every time you saw a patient.

c. patient visits did you personally have during the hours you spent seeing patients in nursing homes, convalescent homes, and other extended care facilities? Please count as one visit every time you saw a patient.

d. operations and deliveries did you perform during the hours you spent in the operating, labor or delivery room? Do not include assists in this question.

e. assists did you perform?

f. inpatient visits did you make during the hours you spent on hospital rounds? Please count as one visit every time you saw a patient.

*Radiology*

g. radiodiagnostic procedures did you personally perform?

h. patients did you personally provide with radiotherapy?

i. consultations did you have with other physicians?

*Psychiatry*

j. sessions did you have during the hours you spent with individual patients?

k. sessions did you have during the hours you spent with nonfamily groups?

l. sessions did you have during the hours you spent with family groups?

*Anesthesiology*

m. patients did you personally anesthetize?

n. patients were anesthetized by nurse anesthetists under your supervision?

o. pre-anesthesia and inpatient visits did you make? (Do not include visits to patients in intensive care units.)

*Pathology*

p. consultations during surgery did you perform?

q. surgical specimens did you examine other than frozen sections examined during surgical consultations?

r. autopsies did you personally perform?

s. nonsurgical laboratory procedures did you personally perform?

Total patient visits (Tables 16 and 27-32) is based on the sum of responses to parts a, b, c, and f of Question 1. Information in Tables 17 through 22 reflects responses to individual parts of Question 1. Only responses from physicians who saw patients in the office in their last complete week of practice and who accept new patients were used in the calculation of new patient visits per week (Table 18). Surgical procedures including assists (Table 21) reflects the sum of responses to parts d and e of the same question.

Tables 23-24 are based on the following questions:

2. During the last month, how many times did you:

*General/family practice, internal medicine*

a. personally interpret electrocardiograms (EKGs) - CPT 93000?

b. perform a periodic or annual type of exam with an adult established patient – CPT 99395-99397?

   (By periodic or annual exam, I mean a routine checkup, if this is applicable to your practice.)

*General/family practice, obstetrics/gynecology*

c. perform any vaginal deliveries which included antepartum and postpartum care –CPT 59400?

*General surgery*

d. perform an appendectomy – CPT 44950 or 44960?

e. perform a single inguinal hernia repair on a person age 5 or older – CPT 49505? (The procedure may also be described as hernioplasty, herniography, herniotomy)?

f. perform a cholecystectomy (gall bladder removal) – CPT 47600?

*Otolaryngology*

g. perform a tonsillectomy with an adenoidectomy on a child 12 years of age or under – CPT 42820?

*Orthopedic surgery*

h. perform a total hip replacement – CPT 27130 (arthroplasty, acetabular and proximal femoral prosthetic replacement with no unusual complications)?

i. suture and perform a secondary repair of a torn, ruptured or severed knee, collateral and cruciate ligaments (with or without meniscectomy and no complications) – CPT 27427?

*Ophthalmology*

j. perform an operation to remove a cataract and insert a lens – CPT 66984?

*Urological surgery*

k. perform a transurethral resection of the prostate – CPT 52601? (This includes vasectomy, meatotomy, cystourethroscopy, urethral calibration and/or dilation and internal urethrotomy. This may also be called a prostatectomy).

*Pediatrics*

l. perform a periodic or annual type of exam with an established patient in early childhood, 1-4 years old – CPT 99392? (By periodic or annual type of exam, I mean a routine checkup, if this is applicable to your practice.)

m. provide routine newborn care in the hospital – CPT 99431 or 99433?

*Obstetrics/gynecology*

n. perform a total hysterectomy with or without removal of tubes, and/or ovaries corpus and cervix – CPT 58150?

o. perform a cesarean section which included antepartum and postpartum care – CPT 59510?

*Radiology*

p. interpret or perform a radiologic exam of the upper gastrointestinal tract without KUB (with or without delayed films) – CPT 74240?

q. interpret or perform a radiologic exam of the chest (postero-anterior and lateral) – CPT 71020?

r. interpret or perform a CAT scan of the head with intravenous contrast (also called computerized axial tomography) – CPT 70460?

*Psychiatry*

s. perform a psychiatric diagnostic evaluation – CPT 90801?

*Pathology*

t. personally interpret or direct technicians who interpreted cervical pap smears – CPT 88150? (This may also be described as cytopathology, including screenings and interpretation of up to three smears).

*Anesthesiology*

Anesthesia services are usually charged for on the basis of time units reflecting the actual amount of time spent in providing anesthesia services for a procedure and a base charge which is determined by the complexity of service. Table 23 reports time units billed in the last month based on responses to the following questions asked of anesthesiologists only:

3. How much total anesthesia time did you bill for during your last complete week of practice? Do not include base charge units.

4. How many minutes are there in a unit of anesthesia time?

The amount of anesthesia time provided in response to these questions is converted to be expressed in terms of 15-minute units of anesthesia time. Monthly figures were obtained by multiplying the weekly rate given in response to the first question by four. If necessary at any point in the process of eliciting responses to these questions, the interviewer may have added the following: The last month refers to the last 30 days.

## Hospital Utilization

Hospital utilization refers to the utilization of hospital resources by physicians. Two measures indicating the extent of hospital utilization reported below are the number of patients discharged from the hospital and the average length of their hospital stays. The following questions were used to obtain the hospital utilization information:

5. During your most recent complete week of practice, how many patients did you personally discharge from the hospital?

6. For the patients you discharged from the hospital that week, what was the average length of stay in days in the hospital?

Hospital utilization statistics are reported in Tables 25 and 26.

Figure 11. **Mean and Median Total Patient Visits per Week, for Nonfederal Physicians, for Selected Specialties, 1995**

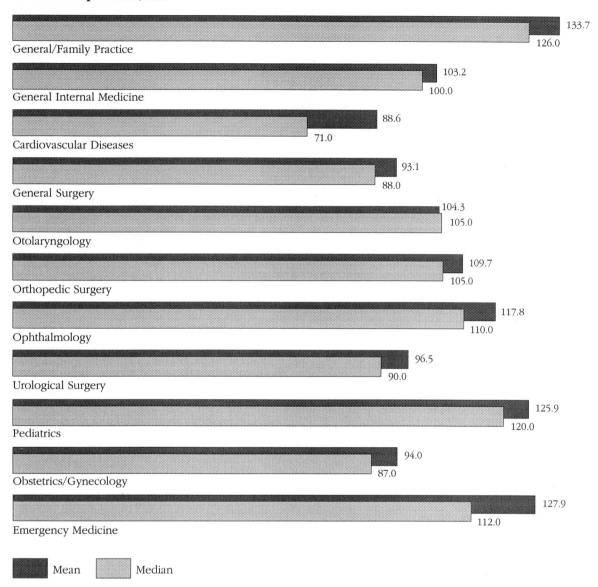

General/Family Practice — 133.7 / 126.0

General Internal Medicine — 103.2 / 100.0

Cardiovascular Diseases — 88.6 / 71.0

General Surgery — 93.1 / 88.0

Otolaryngology — 104.3 / 105.0

Orthopedic Surgery — 109.7 / 105.0

Ophthalmology — 117.8 / 110.0

Urological Surgery — 96.5 / 90.0

Pediatrics — 125.9 / 120.0

Obstetrics/Gynecology — 94.0 / 87.0

Emergency Medicine — 127.9 / 112.0

■ Mean  ☐ Median

Figure 12. **Mean and Median Total Patient Care Visits per Week for Nonfederal Physicians, for Selected States, 1995**[a]

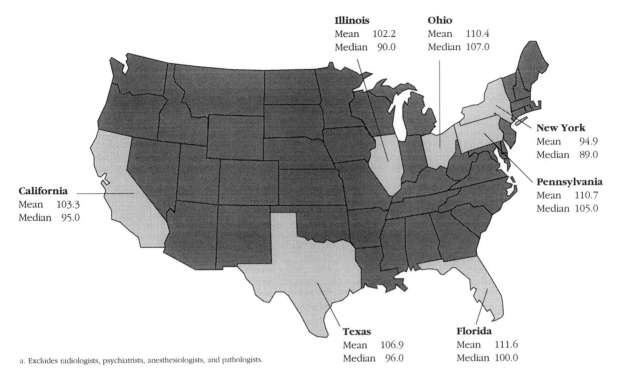

**Illinois**
Mean 102.2
Median 90.0

**Ohio**
Mean 110.4
Median 107.0

**New York**
Mean 94.9
Median 89.0

**Pennsylvania**
Mean 110.7
Median 105.0

**California**
Mean 103.3
Median 95.0

**Texas**
Mean 106.9
Median 96.0

**Florida**
Mean 111.6
Median 100.0

a. Excludes radiologists, psychiatrists, anesthesiologists, and pathologists.

Figure 13. **Mean and Median Total Patient Visits per Week per Self-Employed Nonfederal Physician, by Size of Practice, 1995**[a]

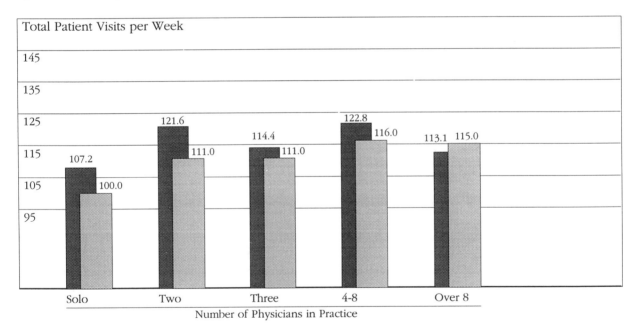

a. Excludes radiologists, psychiatrists, anesthesiologists, and pathologists.

Table 16. **Total Patients Visits per Week, for Nonfederal Physicians (excluding Physicians in Radiology, Psychiatry, Anesthesiology, and Pathology), 1995**

| | Number of Responses | Mean | Standard Error | 25th Percentile | Median | 75th Percentile |
|---|---|---|---|---|---|---|
| All Physicians | 2863 | 107.6 | 1.1 | 70.0 | 100.0 | 137.0 |
| *Specialty* | | | | | | |
| General/Family Practice | 476 | 133.7 | 2.8 | 96.0 | 126.0 | 160.0 |
| Internal Medicine | 709 | 99.7 | 2.0 | 64.0 | 95.0 | 128.0 |
| · General Internal Medicine | 491 | 103.2 | 2.4 | 69.0 | 100.0 | 130.0 |
| · Cardiovascular Diseases | 89 | 88.6 | 6.0 | 57.0 | 71.0 | 108.0 |
| · Other | 129 | 93.1 | 4.3 | 60.0 | 88.0 | 124.0 |
| Surgery | 811 | 97.1 | 1.6 | 63.0 | 92.0 | 125.0 |
| · General Surgery | 195 | 83.2 | 2.9 | 56.0 | 77.0 | 102.0 |
| · Otolaryngology | 72 | 104.3 | 4.0 | 75.0 | 105.0 | 130.0 |
| · Orthopedic Surgery | 166 | 109.7 | 3.4 | 75.0 | 105.0 | 136.0 |
| · Ophthalmology | 182 | 117.8 | 3.7 | 80.0 | 110.0 | 150.0 |
| · Urological Surgery | 93 | 96.5 | 3.3 | 72.0 | 90.0 | 120.0 |
| · Other | 103 | 71.0 | 4.0 | 40.0 | 70.0 | 94.0 |
| Pediatrics | 289 | 125.9 | 3.9 | 81.0 | 120.0 | 160.0 |
| Obstetrics/Gynecology | 227 | 94.0 | 3.2 | 61.0 | 87.0 | 119.0 |
| Other Specialty | 351 | 109.2 | 3.2 | 69.0 | 100.0 | 140.0 |
| · Emergency Medicine | 131 | 127.9 | 5.7 | 85.0 | 112.0 | 152.0 |
| · Other | 220 | 98.7 | 3.7 | 60.0 | 90.0 | 131.0 |
| *Geographic Area* | | | | | | |
| New England | 180 | 99.2 | 3.7 | 74.0 | 90.0 | 122.0 |
| · Massachusetts | 84 | 99.1 | 5.6 | 75.0 | 95.0 | 124.0 |
| · Other | 96 | 99.3 | 5.0 | 71.0 | 87.0 | 122.0 |
| Middle Atlantic | 444 | 102.3 | 2.7 | 61.0 | 100.0 | 132.0 |
| · New Jersey | 81 | 101.2 | 7.3 | 61.0 | 105.0 | 136.0 |
| · New York | 170 | 94.9 | 3.9 | 56.0 | 89.0 | 130.0 |
| · Pennsylvania | 193 | 110.7 | 4.1 | 71.0 | 105.0 | 136.0 |
| East North Central | 430 | 108.9 | 2.7 | 70.0 | 100.0 | 140.0 |
| · Illinois | 142 | 102.2 | 4.6 | 63.0 | 90.0 | 130.0 |
| · Michigan | 77 | 111.9 | 7.5 | 71.0 | 100.0 | 134.0 |
| · Ohio | 97 | 110.4 | 5.2 | 73.0 | 107.0 | 148.0 |
| · Other | 114 | 115.2 | 5.0 | 80.0 | 102.0 | 151.0 |
| West North Central | 209 | 121.2 | 4.2 | 80.0 | 116.0 | 146.0 |
| South Atlantic | 522 | 107.7 | 2.6 | 68.0 | 100.0 | 140.0 |
| · Florida | 141 | 111.6 | 4.9 | 68.0 | 100.0 | 142.0 |
| · Other | 381 | 106.2 | 3.0 | 68.0 | 100.0 | 139.0 |
| East South Central | 177 | 129.8 | 5.2 | 82.0 | 118.0 | 154.0 |
| West South Central | 252 | 109.0 | 3.3 | 72.0 | 100.0 | 142.0 |
| · Texas | 167 | 106.9 | 4.1 | 70.0 | 96.0 | 140.0 |
| · Other | 85 | 113.8 | 5.6 | 80.0 | 109.0 | 143.0 |
| Mountain | 171 | 104.9 | 3.8 | 70.0 | 95.0 | 131.0 |
| Pacific | 478 | 101.5 | 2.3 | 64.0 | 95.0 | 127.0 |
| · California | 332 | 103.3 | 2.9 | 64.0 | 95.0 | 130.0 |
| · Other | 146 | 96.5 | 3.7 | 61.0 | 90.0 | 125.0 |
| *Practice Arrangement* | | | | | | |
| Self-Employed | 1675 | 113.1 | 1.4 | 74.0 | 107.0 | 143.0 |
| · Solo Practice | 790 | 107.2 | 2.1 | 65.0 | 100.0 | 141.0 |
| · Two Physician Practice | 220 | 121.6 | 4.0 | 80.0 | 111.0 | 150.0 |
| · Three Physician Practice | 175 | 114.4 | 3.8 | 75.0 | 111.0 | 140.0 |
| · 4-8 Physician Practice | 354 | 122.8 | 2.7 | 87.0 | 116.0 | 143.0 |
| · Over 8 Physician Practice | 134 | 113.1 | 4.1 | 77.0 | 115.0 | 142.0 |
| Employee | 1047 | 98.1 | 1.7 | 61.0 | 90.0 | 125.0 |
| Independent Contractor | 141 | 114.4 | 5.7 | 70.0 | 100.0 | 145.0 |

Source: 1995 Socioeconomic Monitoring System survey of nonfederal patient care physicians. See the beginning of this section, the introduction, and appendices for a discussion of the survey sample, definitions, and computation procedures. Statistics are not reported if the number of responses is less than 25.

## Table 17. **Total Office Visits per Week, for Nonfederal Physicians (excluding Physicians in Radiology, Psychiatry, Anesthesiology, and Pathology), 1995**

| | Number of Responses | Mean | Standard Error | 25th Percentile | Median | 75th Percentile |
|---|---|---|---|---|---|---|
| All Physicians | 3039 | 73.7 | 1.0 | 35.0 | 70.0 | 100.0 |
| *Specialty* | | | | | | |
| General/Family Practice | 501 | 108.3 | 2.7 | 80.0 | 105.0 | 140.0 |
| Internal Medicine | 755 | 59.1 | 1.6 | 30.0 | 55.0 | 80.0 |
| · General Internal Medicine | 519 | 65.0 | 2.0 | 35.0 | 65.0 | 90.0 |
| · Cardiovascular Diseases | 98 | 43.5 | 3.5 | 18.0 | 35.0 | 60.0 |
| · Other | 138 | 46.8 | 2.8 | 30.0 | 40.0 | 60.0 |
| Surgery | 876 | 70.4 | 1.6 | 35.0 | 60.0 | 100.0 |
| · General Surgery | 215 | 42.0 | 1.8 | 24.0 | 40.0 | 55.0 |
| · Otolaryngology | 76 | 89.6 | 4.2 | 60.0 | 100.0 | 120.0 |
| · Orthopedic Surgery | 184 | 80.7 | 2.9 | 54.0 | 80.0 | 100.0 |
| · Ophthalmology | 186 | 113.1 | 4.0 | 70.0 | 108.0 | 150.0 |
| · Urological Surgery | 98 | 68.1 | 2.7 | 50.0 | 65.0 | 80.0 |
| · Other | 117 | 42.4 | 3.1 | 20.0 | 35.0 | 58.0 |
| Pediatrics | 301 | 99.9 | 4.0 | 50.0 | 100.0 | 143.0 |
| Obstetrics/Gynecology | 242 | 78.0 | 3.0 | 45.0 | 75.0 | 100.0 |
| Other Specialty | 364 | 47.8 | 3.3 | 0.0 | 25.0 | 80.0 |
| · Emergency Medicine | 133 | 14.8 | 4.5 | 0.0 | 0.0 | 0.0 |
| · Other | 231 | 65.7 | 4.0 | 16.0 | 55.0 | 100.0 |
| *Geographic Area* | | | | | | |
| New England | 189 | 65.0 | 3.6 | 30.0 | 60.0 | 90.0 |
| · Massachusetts | 87 | 59.9 | 4.9 | 20.0 | 60.0 | 90.0 |
| · Other | 102 | 70.0 | 5.1 | 32.0 | 64.0 | 100.0 |
| Middle Atlantic | 468 | 67.6 | 2.6 | 30.0 | 60.0 | 100.0 |
| · New Jersey | 86 | 67.9 | 5.6 | 35.0 | 65.0 | 100.0 |
| · New York | 184 | 62.5 | 4.3 | 20.0 | 50.0 | 100.0 |
| · Pennsylvania | 198 | 73.2 | 3.8 | 35.0 | 66.0 | 100.0 |
| East North Central | 459 | 73.1 | 2.6 | 32.0 | 68.0 | 105.0 |
| · Illinois | 151 | 68.0 | 4.7 | 25.0 | 60.0 | 100.0 |
| · Michigan | 84 | 72.8 | 5.9 | 44.0 | 64.0 | 100.0 |
| · Ohio | 103 | 73.7 | 5.3 | 35.0 | 70.0 | 110.0 |
| · Other | 121 | 80.4 | 4.8 | 40.0 | 75.0 | 120.0 |
| West North Central | 225 | 92.2 | 4.8 | 45.0 | 85.0 | 120.0 |
| South Atlantic | 552 | 73.2 | 2.5 | 33.0 | 60.0 | 100.0 |
| · Florida | 152 | 73.0 | 5.0 | 35.0 | 60.0 | 100.0 |
| · Other | 400 | 73.3 | 2.9 | 30.0 | 70.0 | 100.0 |
| East South Central | 185 | 83.6 | 4.7 | 45.0 | 76.0 | 120.0 |
| West South Central | 283 | 77.7 | 3.1 | 40.0 | 70.0 | 115.0 |
| · Texas | 187 | 77.3 | 3.8 | 40.0 | 70.0 | 115.0 |
| · Other | 96 | 78.7 | 5.2 | 35.0 | 80.0 | 120.0 |
| Mountain | 181 | 72.0 | 3.7 | 36.0 | 70.0 | 100.0 |
| Pacific | 497 | 71.8 | 2.4 | 35.0 | 65.0 | 100.0 |
| · California | 347 | 70.8 | 2.9 | 35.0 | 60.0 | 100.0 |
| · Other | 150 | 74.6 | 3.8 | 45.0 | 75.0 | 100.0 |
| *Practice Arrangement* | | | | | | |
| Self-Employed | 1791 | 84.1 | 1.3 | 45.0 | 75.0 | 115.0 |
| · Solo Practice | 841 | 81.7 | 1.8 | 45.0 | 70.0 | 110.0 |
| · Two Physician Practice | 235 | 94.9 | 3.8 | 55.0 | 80.0 | 120.0 |
| · Three Physician Practice | 186 | 89.4 | 4.3 | 45.0 | 80.0 | 120.0 |
| · 4-8 Physician Practice | 381 | 85.0 | 2.7 | 48.0 | 80.0 | 120.0 |
| · Over 8 Physician Practice | 146 | 73.9 | 4.3 | 35.0 | 75.0 | 110.0 |
| Employee | 1105 | 60.3 | 1.6 | 16.0 | 52.0 | 93.0 |
| Independent Contractor | 143 | 56.9 | 6.8 | 0.0 | 40.0 | 90.0 |

Source: 1995 Socioeconomic Monitoring System survey of nonfederal patient care physicians. See the beginning of this section, the introduction, and appendices for a discussion of the survey sample, definitions, and computation procedures. Statistics are not reported if the number of responses is less than 25.

## Table 18. **Office Visits with New Patients per Week, for Nonfederal Physicians (excluding Physicians in Radiology, Psychiatry, Anesthesiology, and Pathology), 1995**

| | Number of Responses | Mean | Standard Error | 25th Percentile | Median | 75th Percentile |
|---|---|---|---|---|---|---|
| All Physicians | 2255 | 14.6 | 0.3 | 5.0 | 11.0 | 20.0 |
| *Specialty* | | | | | | |
| General/Family Practice | 385 | 13.6 | 0.8 | 5.0 | 8.0 | 20.0 |
| Internal Medicine | 565 | 10.1 | 0.5 | 4.0 | 6.0 | 15.0 |
| · General Internal Medicine | 376 | 9.4 | 0.6 | 4.0 | 6.0 | 15.0 |
| · Cardiovascular Diseases | 79 | 7.2 | 0.7 | 4.0 | 6.0 | 8.0 |
| · Other | 110 | 14.9 | 1.6 | 6.0 | 12.0 | 20.0 |
| Surgery | 713 | 17.5 | 0.5 | 8.0 | 15.0 | 20.0 |
| · General Surgery | 171 | 11.8 | 0.7 | 5.0 | 8.0 | 15.0 |
| · Otolaryngology | 66 | 27.1 | 1.5 | 18.0 | 25.0 | 35.0 |
| · Orthopedic Surgery | 154 | 22.0 | 1.4 | 15.0 | 20.0 | 25.0 |
| · Ophthalmology | 157 | 22.1 | 1.0 | 15.0 | 20.0 | 26.0 |
| · Urological Surgery | 68 | 15.2 | 0.7 | 12.0 | 15.0 | 20.0 |
| · Other | 97 | 11.3 | 1.0 | 4.0 | 8.0 | 15.0 |
| Pediatrics | 194 | 12.7 | 1.0 | 5.0 | 8.0 | 20.0 |
| Obstetrics/Gynecology | 198 | 12.8 | 1.1 | 5.0 | 8.0 | 15.0 |
| Other Specialty | 200 | 26.8 | 2.0 | 8.0 | 20.0 | 35.0 |
| · Emergency Medicine | 21 | . | . | . | . | . |
| · Other | 179 | 24.0 | 1.7 | 8.0 | 20.0 | 30.0 |
| *Geographic Area* | | | | | | |
| New England | 136 | 11.4 | 1.0 | 5.0 | 7.0 | 15.0 |
| · Massachusetts | 65 | 9.9 | 1.0 | 4.0 | 8.0 | 15.0 |
| · Other | 71 | 12.8 | 1.7 | 5.0 | 6.0 | 20.0 |
| Middle Atlantic | 358 | 11.7 | 0.7 | 4.0 | 6.0 | 17.0 |
| · New Jersey | 61 | 10.9 | 1.5 | 5.0 | 6.0 | 15.0 |
| · New York | 140 | 12.9 | 1.2 | 4.0 | 8.0 | 18.0 |
| · Pennsylvania | 157 | 11.0 | 1.0 | 4.0 | 6.0 | 18.0 |
| East North Central | 338 | 13.8 | 0.8 | 5.0 | 11.0 | 20.0 |
| · Illinois | 102 | 13.3 | 1.2 | 5.0 | 12.0 | 16.0 |
| · Michigan | 68 | 17.3 | 1.8 | 6.0 | 15.0 | 25.0 |
| · Ohio | 76 | 11.2 | 1.2 | 5.0 | 8.0 | 15.0 |
| · Other | 92 | 14.2 | 2.1 | 5.0 | 8.0 | 15.0 |
| West North Central | 163 | 15.5 | 1.2 | 5.0 | 11.0 | 20.0 |
| South Atlantic | 422 | 15.4 | 0.9 | 6.0 | 12.0 | 20.0 |
| · Florida | 111 | 15.9 | 1.8 | 6.0 | 12.0 | 20.0 |
| · Other | 311 | 15.2 | 1.1 | 5.0 | 12.0 | 20.0 |
| East South Central | 134 | 17.0 | 1.6 | 5.0 | 14.0 | 20.0 |
| West South Central | 207 | 15.8 | 1.2 | 5.0 | 15.0 | 20.0 |
| · Texas | 133 | 16.2 | 1.6 | 5.0 | 15.0 | 20.0 |
| · Other | 74 | 15.0 | 1.5 | 5.0 | 12.0 | 20.0 |
| Mountain | 139 | 18.1 | 1.7 | 7.0 | 15.0 | 20.0 |
| Pacific | 358 | 15.7 | 0.8 | 5.0 | 12.0 | 20.0 |
| · California | 247 | 15.3 | 1.0 | 5.0 | 12.0 | 20.0 |
| · Other | 111 | 17.0 | 1.5 | 5.0 | 15.0 | 20.0 |
| *Practice Arrangement* | | | | | | |
| Self-Employed | 1433 | 14.1 | 0.4 | 5.0 | 11.0 | 20.0 |
| · Solo Practice | 683 | 13.4 | 0.6 | 5.0 | 8.0 | 20.0 |
| · Two Physician Practice | 193 | 14.3 | 0.8 | 5.0 | 14.0 | 20.0 |
| · Three Physician Practice | 154 | 16.3 | 1.3 | 6.0 | 14.0 | 20.0 |
| · 4-8 Physician Practice | 300 | 14.5 | 0.8 | 5.0 | 12.0 | 20.0 |
| · Over 8 Physician Practice | 102 | 14.4 | 1.4 | 5.0 | 12.0 | 20.0 |
| Employee | 745 | 14.8 | 0.7 | 5.0 | 8.0 | 20.0 |
| Independent Contractor | 77 | 22.1 | 3.6 | 6.0 | 15.0 | 20.0 |

Source: 1995 Socioeconomic Monitoring System survey of nonfederal patient care physicians. See the beginning of this section, the introduction, and appendices for a discussion of the survey sample, definitions, and computation procedures. Statistics are not reported if the number of responses is less than 25.

Table 19. **Visits on Hospital Rounds per Week, for Nonfederal Physicians (excluding Physicians in Radiology, Psychiatry, Anesthesiology, and Pathology), 1995**

| | Number of Responses | Mean | Standard Error | 25th Percentile | Median | 75th Percentile |
|---|---|---|---|---|---|---|
| All Physicians | 2940 | 18.9 | 0.5 | 0.0 | 10.0 | 25.0 |
| *Specialty* | | | | | | |
| General/Family Practice | 496 | 11.9 | 0.7 | 0.0 | 7.0 | 18.0 |
| Internal Medicine | 725 | 28.2 | 1.4 | 4.0 | 20.0 | 40.0 |
| · General Internal Medicine | 500 | 24.3 | 1.6 | 2.0 | 15.0 | 30.0 |
| · Cardiovascular Diseases | 94 | 42.2 | 4.8 | 15.0 | 35.0 | 50.0 |
| · Other | 131 | 34.0 | 3.4 | 10.0 | 25.0 | 50.0 |
| Surgery | 834 | 18.0 | 0.8 | 2.0 | 10.0 | 25.0 |
| · General Surgery | 200 | 31.7 | 2.2 | 12.0 | 25.0 | 40.0 |
| · Otolaryngology | 73 | 7.7 | 0.9 | 2.0 | 5.0 | 12.0 |
| · Orthopedic Surgery | 176 | 17.9 | 1.3 | 5.0 | 15.0 | 24.0 |
| · Ophthalmology | 186 | 1.3 | 0.2 | 0.0 | 0.0 | 1.0 |
| · Urological Surgery | 93 | 20.7 | 1.9 | 8.0 | 15.0 | 25.0 |
| · Other | 106 | 20.9 | 2.6 | 3.0 | 14.0 | 25.0 |
| Pediatrics | 294 | 20.3 | 2.0 | 4.0 | 10.0 | 20.0 |
| Obstetrics/Gynecology | 230 | 12.1 | 0.7 | 4.0 | 10.0 | 16.0 |
| Other Specialty | 361 | 11.1 | 1.5 | 0.0 | 0.0 | 7.0 |
| · Emergency Medicine | 133 | 1.9 | 1.3 | 0.0 | 0.0 | 0.0 |
| · Other | 228 | 16.2 | 2.1 | 0.0 | 2.0 | 20.0 |
| *Geographic Area* | | | | | | |
| New England | 183 | 14.7 | 1.6 | 0.0 | 7.0 | 20.0 |
| · Massachusetts | 86 | 16.4 | 2.6 | 0.0 | 7.0 | 25.0 |
| · Other | 97 | 12.9 | 1.9 | 0.0 | 7.0 | 16.0 |
| Middle Atlantic | 460 | 22.4 | 1.7 | 0.0 | 10.0 | 30.0 |
| · New Jersey | 83 | 18.4 | 4.6 | 0.0 | 10.0 | 21.0 |
| · New York | 178 | 20.0 | 2.4 | 0.0 | 8.0 | 25.0 |
| · Pennsylvania | 199 | 27.3 | 2.5 | 4.0 | 15.0 | 35.0 |
| East North Central | 439 | 20.7 | 1.3 | 1.0 | 12.0 | 30.0 |
| · Illinois | 145 | 21.4 | 2.6 | 2.0 | 15.0 | 30.0 |
| · Michigan | 80 | 20.0 | 3.2 | 0.0 | 10.0 | 28.0 |
| · Ohio | 99 | 20.7 | 2.4 | 1.0 | 15.0 | 30.0 |
| · Other | 115 | 20.1 | 2.3 | 0.0 | 12.0 | 30.0 |
| West North Central | 219 | 18.4 | 1.6 | 2.0 | 12.0 | 25.0 |
| South Atlantic | 534 | 19.3 | 1.3 | 0.0 | 10.0 | 25.0 |
| · Florida | 146 | 24.4 | 3.1 | 0.0 | 12.0 | 30.0 |
| · Other | 388 | 17.2 | 1.4 | 0.0 | 10.0 | 21.0 |
| East South Central | 180 | 24.5 | 2.1 | 0.0 | 15.0 | 40.0 |
| West South Central | 265 | 17.7 | 1.7 | 0.0 | 9.0 | 20.0 |
| · Texas | 174 | 14.8 | 1.9 | 0.0 | 6.0 | 20.0 |
| · Other | 91 | 24.0 | 3.3 | 1.0 | 15.0 | 30.0 |
| Mountain | 174 | 15.2 | 1.9 | 0.0 | 8.0 | 20.0 |
| Pacific | 486 | 15.0 | 1.1 | 0.0 | 6.0 | 20.0 |
| · California | 339 | 16.1 | 1.5 | 0.0 | 6.0 | 20.0 |
| · Other | 147 | 12.1 | 1.3 | 0.0 | 8.0 | 15.0 |
| *Practice Arrangement* | | | | | | |
| Self-Employed | 1723 | 19.2 | 0.6 | 2.0 | 12.0 | 25.0 |
| · Solo Practice | 809 | 16.1 | 0.8 | 1.0 | 10.0 | 24.0 |
| · Two Physician Practice | 227 | 19.6 | 1.7 | 3.0 | 12.0 | 24.0 |
| · Three Physician Practice | 177 | 23.1 | 1.9 | 5.0 | 15.0 | 30.0 |
| · 4-8 Physician Practice | 369 | 25.5 | 1.7 | 5.0 | 15.0 | 30.0 |
| · Over 8 Physician Practice | 139 | 18.9 | 2.1 | 0.0 | 12.0 | 26.0 |
| Employee | 1073 | 19.5 | 1.0 | 0.0 | 10.0 | 25.0 |
| Independent Contractor | 144 | 11.5 | 2.5 | 0.0 | 0.0 | 10.0 |

Source: 1995 Socioeconomic Monitoring System survey of nonfederal patient care physicians. See the beginning of this section, the introduction, and appendices for a discussion of the survey sample, definitions, and computation procedures. Statistics are not reported if the number of responses is less than 25.

Table 20. **Visits in Outpatient Clinics and Emergency Rooms per Week, for Nonfederal Physicians (excluding Physicians in Radiology, Psychiatry, Anesthesiology, and Pathology), 1995**

| | Number of Responses | Mean | Standard Error | 25th Percentile | Median | 75th Percentile |
|---|---|---|---|---|---|---|
| All Physicians | 2971 | 12.5 | 0.6 | 0.0 | 2.0 | 8.0 |
| *Specialty* | | | | | | |
| General/Family Practice | 494 | 8.4 | 1.1 | 0.0 | 0.0 | 5.0 |
| Internal Medicine | 734 | 9.5 | 0.8 | 0.0 | 2.0 | 8.0 |
| · General Internal Medicine | 508 | 9.4 | 0.9 | 0.0 | 1.0 | 8.0 |
| · Cardiovascular Diseases | 91 | 7.3 | 1.5 | 0.0 | 4.0 | 6.0 |
| · Other | 135 | 11.4 | 2.4 | 0.0 | 2.0 | 14.0 |
| Surgery | 845 | 6.2 | 0.4 | 0.0 | 3.0 | 7.0 |
| · General Surgery | 204 | 6.9 | 0.7 | 2.0 | 4.0 | 9.0 |
| · Otolaryngology | 76 | 5.5 | 1.0 | 0.0 | 3.0 | 5.0 |
| · Orthopedic Surgery | 171 | 8.7 | 0.9 | 1.0 | 5.0 | 10.0 |
| · Ophthalmology | 185 | 4.2 | 0.9 | 0.0 | 0.0 | 2.0 |
| · Urological Surgery | 95 | 5.1 | 1.0 | 0.0 | 2.0 | 6.0 |
| · Other | 114 | 5.6 | 1.0 | 0.0 | 2.0 | 5.0 |
| Pediatrics | 299 | 5.7 | 1.2 | 0.0 | 0.0 | 5.0 |
| Obstetrics/Gynecology | 240 | 5.6 | 0.8 | 0.0 | 2.0 | 5.0 |
| Other Specialty | 359 | 48.7 | 3.4 | 0.0 | 7.0 | 100.0 |
| · Emergency Medicine | 131 | 110.6 | 5.2 | 75.0 | 100.0 | 150.0 |
| · Other | 228 | 15.1 | 2.3 | 0.0 | 0.0 | 8.0 |
| *Geographic Area* | | | | | | |
| New England | 184 | 15.7 | 2.9 | 0.0 | 2.0 | 10.0 |
| · Massachusetts | 88 | 18.8 | 5.3 | 0.0 | 3.0 | 10.0 |
| · Other | 96 | 12.3 | 2.7 | 0.0 | 0.0 | 8.0 |
| Middle Atlantic | 458 | 9.2 | 1.0 | 0.0 | 2.0 | 6.0 |
| · New Jersey | 84 | 9.5 | 2.2 | 0.0 | 2.0 | 6.0 |
| · New York | 176 | 10.4 | 1.9 | 0.0 | 1.0 | 10.0 |
| · Pennsylvania | 198 | 7.9 | 1.4 | 0.0 | 2.0 | 5.0 |
| East North Central | 445 | 11.8 | 1.4 | 0.0 | 1.0 | 8.0 |
| · Illinois | 146 | 9.9 | 2.0 | 0.0 | 0.0 | 6.0 |
| · Michigan | 82 | 13.7 | 3.4 | 0.0 | 2.0 | 8.0 |
| · Ohio | 99 | 10.2 | 2.9 | 0.0 | 0.0 | 4.0 |
| · Other | 118 | 14.4 | 3.4 | 0.0 | 2.0 | 8.0 |
| West North Central | 220 | 11.1 | 1.9 | 0.0 | 2.0 | 8.0 |
| South Atlantic | 547 | 13.2 | 1.5 | 0.0 | 2.0 | 8.0 |
| · Florida | 153 | 11.9 | 2.5 | 0.0 | 2.0 | 10.0 |
| · Other | 394 | 13.7 | 1.8 | 0.0 | 3.0 | 8.0 |
| East South Central | 183 | 17.4 | 2.9 | 0.0 | 2.0 | 10.0 |
| West South Central | 265 | 13.2 | 1.9 | 0.0 | 4.0 | 10.0 |
| · Texas | 174 | 13.9 | 2.6 | 0.0 | 3.0 | 10.0 |
| · Other | 91 | 11.6 | 2.6 | 0.0 | 4.0 | 10.0 |
| Mountain | 175 | 15.4 | 2.9 | 0.0 | 1.0 | 10.0 |
| Pacific | 494 | 11.6 | 1.3 | 0.0 | 1.0 | 7.0 |
| · California | 345 | 12.8 | 1.8 | 0.0 | 0.0 | 7.0 |
| · Other | 149 | 8.1 | 1.4 | 0.0 | 1.0 | 6.0 |
| *Practice Arrangement* | | | | | | |
| Self-Employed | 1745 | 6.8 | 0.4 | 0.0 | 2.0 | 6.0 |
| · Solo Practice | 827 | 4.8 | 0.4 | 0.0 | 1.0 | 5.0 |
| · Two Physician Practice | 227 | 6.0 | 0.7 | 0.0 | 2.0 | 7.0 |
| · Three Physician Practice | 183 | 5.5 | 0.8 | 0.0 | 2.0 | 6.0 |
| · 4-8 Physician Practice | 365 | 8.5 | 1.1 | 0.0 | 2.0 | 6.0 |
| · Over 8 Physician Practice | 141 | 18.2 | 3.0 | 0.0 | 3.0 | 14.0 |
| Employee | 1080 | 16.0 | 1.1 | 0.0 | 2.0 | 12.0 |
| Independent Contractor | 146 | 47.0 | 6.2 | 0.0 | 4.0 | 71.0 |

Source: 1995 Socioeconomic Monitoring System survey of nonfederal patient care physicians. See the beginning of this section, the introduction, and appendices for a discussion of the survey sample, definitions, and computation procedures. Statistics are not reported if the number of responses is less than 25.

Table 21. **Surgical Procedures, Including Assists, per Week, for Nonfederal Physicians (excluding Physicians in Radiology, Psychiatry, Anesthesiology, and Pathology), 1995**

| | Number of Responses | Mean | Standard Error | 25th Percentile | Median | 75th Percentile |
|---|---|---|---|---|---|---|
| All Physicians | 3057 | 3.7 | 0.1 | 0.0 | 0.0 | 6.0 |
| *Specialty* | | | | | | |
| General/Family Practice | 507 | 0.6 | 0.1 | 0.0 | 0.0 | 0.0 |
| Internal Medicine | 760 | 2.4 | 0.3 | 0.0 | 0.0 | 0.0 |
| · General Internal Medicine | 520 | 0.6 | 0.2 | 0.0 | 0.0 | 0.0 |
| · Cardiovascular Diseases | 100 | 5.2 | 0.7 | 0.0 | 0.0 | 9.0 |
| · Other | 140 | 7.3 | 0.9 | 0.0 | 0.0 | 15.0 |
| Surgery | 874 | 8.3 | 0.2 | 5.0 | 8.0 | 11.0 |
| · General Surgery | 213 | 11.0 | 0.4 | 7.0 | 10.0 | 14.0 |
| · Otolaryngology | 75 | 9.3 | 0.7 | 5.0 | 8.0 | 12.0 |
| · Orthopedic Surgery | 185 | 7.6 | 0.3 | 5.0 | 7.0 | 10.0 |
| · Ophthalmology | 187 | 5.6 | 0.4 | 2.0 | 4.0 | 7.0 |
| · Urological Surgery | 97 | 8.7 | 0.4 | 6.0 | 8.0 | 10.0 |
| · Other | 117 | 7.2 | 0.5 | 4.0 | 7.0 | 10.0 |
| Pediatrics | 305 | 0.9 | 0.2 | 0.0 | 0.0 | 0.0 |
| Obstetrics/Gynecology | 243 | 7.1 | 0.4 | 3.0 | 6.0 | 9.0 |
| Other Specialty | 368 | 0.8 | 0.3 | 0.0 | 0.0 | 0.0 |
| · Emergency Medicine | 133 | 0.0 | 0.0 | 0.0 | 0.0 | 0.0 |
| · Other | 235 | 1.1 | 0.4 | 0.0 | 0.0 | 0.0 |
| *Geographic Area* | | | | | | |
| New England | 192 | 2.8 | 0.3 | 0.0 | 0.0 | 5.0 |
| · Massachusetts | 89 | 2.7 | 0.6 | 0.0 | 0.0 | 4.0 |
| · Other | 103 | 2.9 | 0.4 | 0.0 | 0.0 | 5.0 |
| Middle Atlantic | 474 | 2.9 | 0.3 | 0.0 | 0.0 | 4.0 |
| · New Jersey | 87 | 2.4 | 0.6 | 0.0 | 0.0 | 3.0 |
| · New York | 185 | 2.8 | 0.4 | 0.0 | 0.0 | 4.0 |
| · Pennsylvania | 202 | 3.3 | 0.4 | 0.0 | 0.0 | 6.0 |
| East North Central | 457 | 3.8 | 0.3 | 0.0 | 0.0 | 6.0 |
| · Illinois | 150 | 3.4 | 0.5 | 0.0 | 0.0 | 6.0 |
| · Michigan | 86 | 4.9 | 0.7 | 0.0 | 0.0 | 9.0 |
| · Ohio | 102 | 2.9 | 0.6 | 0.0 | 0.0 | 4.0 |
| · Other | 119 | 4.4 | 0.6 | 0.0 | 1.0 | 7.0 |
| West North Central | 229 | 4.2 | 0.4 | 0.0 | 1.0 | 7.0 |
| South Atlantic | 557 | 4.1 | 0.3 | 0.0 | 0.0 | 8.0 |
| · Florida | 156 | 5.4 | 0.6 | 0.0 | 0.0 | 10.0 |
| · Other | 401 | 3.6 | 0.3 | 0.0 | 0.0 | 6.0 |
| East South Central | 185 | 4.3 | 0.5 | 0.0 | 0.0 | 7.0 |
| West South Central | 282 | 3.8 | 0.3 | 0.0 | 0.0 | 6.0 |
| · Texas | 186 | 3.4 | 0.4 | 0.0 | 0.0 | 5.0 |
| · Other | 96 | 4.7 | 0.6 | 0.0 | 3.0 | 8.0 |
| Mountain | 181 | 3.8 | 0.5 | 0.0 | 0.0 | 7.0 |
| Pacific | 500 | 3.6 | 0.3 | 0.0 | 0.0 | 5.0 |
| · California | 350 | 3.7 | 0.4 | 0.0 | 0.0 | 5.0 |
| · Other | 150 | 3.1 | 0.4 | 0.0 | 0.0 | 5.0 |
| *Practice Arrangement* | | | | | | |
| Self-Employed | 1798 | 4.4 | 0.2 | 0.0 | 1.0 | 7.0 |
| · Solo Practice | 848 | 4.1 | 0.2 | 0.0 | 0.0 | 6.0 |
| · Two Physician Practice | 236 | 4.4 | 0.4 | 0.0 | 1.0 | 8.0 |
| · Three Physician Practice | 185 | 5.6 | 0.5 | 0.0 | 3.0 | 10.0 |
| · 4-8 Physician Practice | 381 | 5.2 | 0.3 | 0.0 | 2.0 | 8.0 |
| · Over 8 Physician Practice | 146 | 3.5 | 0.4 | 0.0 | 0.0 | 7.0 |
| Employee | 1112 | 2.8 | 0.2 | 0.0 | 0.0 | 4.0 |
| Independent Contractor | 147 | 1.9 | 0.4 | 0.0 | 0.0 | 0.0 |

Source: 1995 Socioeconomic Monitoring System survey of nonfederal patient care physicians. See the beginning of this section, the introduction, and appendices for a discussion of the survey sample, definitions, and computation procedures. Statistics are not reported if the number of responses is less than 25.

## Table 22. Surgical Procedures, Excluding Assists, per Week, for Nonfederal Physicians (excluding Physicians in Radiology, Psychiatry, Anesthesiology, and Pathology), 1995

| | Number of Responses | Mean | Standard Error | 25th Percentile | Median | 75th Percentile |
|---|---|---|---|---|---|---|
| All Physicians | 3044 | 3.3 | 0.1 | 0.0 | 0.0 | 5.0 |
| *Specialty* | | | | | | |
| General/Family Practice | 505 | 0.4 | 0.1 | 0.0 | 0.0 | 0.0 |
| Internal Medicine | 758 | 2.3 | 0.2 | 0.0 | 0.0 | 0.0 |
| · General Internal Medicine | 520 | 0.6 | 0.2 | 0.0 | 0.0 | 0.0 |
| · Cardiovascular Diseases | 98 | 4.8 | 0.7 | 0.0 | 0.0 | 8.0 |
| · Other | 140 | 7.1 | 0.9 | 0.0 | 0.0 | 15.0 |
| Surgery | 866 | 7.5 | 0.2 | 4.0 | 7.0 | 10.0 |
| · General Surgery | 212 | 9.1 | 0.4 | 5.0 | 8.0 | 12.0 |
| · Otolaryngology | 75 | 8.8 | 0.6 | 4.0 | 8.0 | 12.0 |
| · Orthopedic Surgery | 182 | 7.1 | 0.3 | 4.0 | 7.0 | 10.0 |
| · Ophthalmology | 187 | 5.5 | 0.4 | 2.0 | 4.0 | 7.0 |
| · Urological Surgery | 96 | 8.0 | 0.4 | 5.0 | 8.0 | 10.0 |
| · Other | 114 | 6.6 | 0.4 | 4.0 | 6.0 | 10.0 |
| Pediatrics | 305 | 0.7 | 0.2 | 0.0 | 0.0 | 0.0 |
| Obstetrics/Gynecology | 242 | 6.1 | 0.4 | 3.0 | 5.0 | 8.0 |
| Other Specialty | 368 | 0.6 | 0.3 | 0.0 | 0.0 | 0.0 |
| · Emergency Medicine | 133 | 0.0 | 0.0 | 0.0 | 0.0 | 0.0 |
| · Other | 235 | 1.0 | 0.4 | 0.0 | 0.0 | 0.0 |
| *Geographic Area* | | | | | | |
| New England | 191 | 2.5 | 0.3 | 0.0 | 0.0 | 4.0 |
| · Massachusetts | 89 | 2.5 | 0.5 | 0.0 | 0.0 | 4.0 |
| · Other | 102 | 2.6 | 0.4 | 0.0 | 0.0 | 4.0 |
| Middle Atlantic | 472 | 2.5 | 0.2 | 0.0 | 0.0 | 3.0 |
| · New Jersey | 87 | 2.0 | 0.5 | 0.0 | 0.0 | 3.0 |
| · New York | 183 | 2.5 | 0.4 | 0.0 | 0.0 | 3.0 |
| · Pennsylvania | 202 | 2.9 | 0.4 | 0.0 | 0.0 | 5.0 |
| East North Central | 455 | 3.5 | 0.3 | 0.0 | 0.0 | 6.0 |
| · Illinois | 149 | 3.2 | 0.5 | 0.0 | 0.0 | 6.0 |
| · Michigan | 85 | 4.6 | 0.7 | 0.0 | 0.0 | 9.0 |
| · Ohio | 102 | 2.6 | 0.5 | 0.0 | 0.0 | 4.0 |
| · Other | 119 | 4.2 | 0.5 | 0.0 | 0.0 | 6.0 |
| West North Central | 228 | 3.8 | 0.4 | 0.0 | 1.0 | 6.0 |
| South Atlantic | 554 | 3.8 | 0.3 | 0.0 | 0.0 | 6.0 |
| · Florida | 156 | 5.1 | 0.6 | 0.0 | 0.0 | 10.0 |
| · Other | 398 | 3.2 | 0.3 | 0.0 | 0.0 | 5.0 |
| East South Central | 184 | 4.0 | 0.5 | 0.0 | 0.0 | 6.0 |
| West South Central | 281 | 3.4 | 0.3 | 0.0 | 0.0 | 5.0 |
| · Texas | 185 | 3.1 | 0.4 | 0.0 | 0.0 | 5.0 |
| · Other | 96 | 4.2 | 0.6 | 0.0 | 2.0 | 7.0 |
| Mountain | 181 | 3.0 | 0.3 | 0.0 | 0.0 | 5.0 |
| Pacific | 498 | 3.0 | 0.3 | 0.0 | 0.0 | 4.0 |
| · California | 348 | 3.2 | 0.4 | 0.0 | 0.0 | 4.0 |
| · Other | 150 | 2.4 | 0.3 | 0.0 | 0.0 | 4.0 |
| *Practice Arrangement* | | | | | | |
| Self-Employed | 1794 | 3.9 | 0.1 | 0.0 | 0.0 | 6.0 |
| · Solo Practice | 848 | 3.6 | 0.2 | 0.0 | 0.0 | 5.0 |
| · Two Physician Practice | 236 | 3.8 | 0.3 | 0.0 | 1.0 | 7.0 |
| · Three Physician Practice | 183 | 5.1 | 0.5 | 0.0 | 3.0 | 9.0 |
| · 4-8 Physician Practice | 379 | 4.6 | 0.3 | 0.0 | 2.0 | 8.0 |
| · Over 8 Physician Practice | 146 | 3.3 | 0.4 | 0.0 | 0.0 | 6.0 |
| Employee | 1103 | 2.5 | 0.2 | 0.0 | 0.0 | 3.0 |
| Independent Contractor | 147 | 1.7 | 0.4 | 0.0 | 0.0 | 0.0 |

Source: 1995 Socioeconomic Monitoring System survey of nonfederal patient care physicians. See the beginning of this section, the introduction, and appendices for a discussion of the survey sample, definitions, and computation procedures. Statistics are not reported if the number of responses is less than 25.

Table 23. **Selected Patient Care Services per Week per Nonfederal Physician in Radiology, Psychiatry, Anesthesiology, and Pathology, 1995**

| | Number of Responses | Mean | Standard Error | 25th Percentile | Median | 75th Percentile |
|---|---|---|---|---|---|---|
| *Radiology* | | | | | | |
| Radiodiagnostic procedures | 249 | 96.9 | 8.2 | 5.0 | 25.0 | 100.0 |
| Radiotherapy patients | 265 | 5.8 | 1.1 | 0.0 | 0.0 | 0.0 |
| Consultations with other physicians | 252 | 29.8 | 2.8 | 10.0 | 20.0 | 30.0 |
| *Psychiatry* | | | | | | |
| Individual patient sessions | 267 | 47.2 | 1.9 | 29.0 | 40.0 | 60.0 |
| Family group sessions | 268 | 3.0 | 0.3 | 0.0 | 1.0 | 4.0 |
| Nonfamily group sessions | 271 | 1.2 | 0.6 | 0.0 | 0.0 | 0.0 |
| *Anesthesiology* | | | | | | |
| Patients personally anesthetized | 220 | 17.9 | 0.8 | 8.0 | 20.0 | 25.0 |
| Patients anesthetized by nurse anesthetists under physician supervision | 216 | 14.3 | 3.9 | 0.0 | 3.0 | 16.0 |
| Pre-anesthesia and inpatient visits | 218 | 19.9 | 1.3 | 6.0 | 15.0 | 30.0 |
| *Pathology* | | | | | | |
| Surgical consultations | 116 | 9.0 | 0.9 | 4.0 | 8.0 | 10.0 |
| Examinations of surgical specimens | 114 | 94.5 | 6.5 | 60.0 | 80.0 | 120.0 |
| Non-surgical laboratory procedures | 104 | 40.4 | 7.6 | 1.0 | 5.0 | 25.0 |
| Autopsies | 119 | 0.6 | 0.1 | 0.0 | 0.0 | 0.0 |

Source: 1995 Socioeconomic Monitoring System survey of nonfederal patient care physicians. See the beginning of this section, the introduction, and appendices for a discussion of the survey sample, definitions, and computation procedures. Statistics are not reported if the number of responses is less than 25.

## Table 24. **Selected Services and Procedures per Month, for Nonfederal Physicians, 1995**

| | Number of Responses | Mean | Standard Error | 25th Percentile | Median | 75th Percentile |
|---|---|---|---|---|---|---|
| *General/family practice* | | | | | | |
| Periodic or annual type exam | 447 | 27.0 | 1.9 | 5.0 | 16.0 | 35.0 |
| Electrocardiogram | 452 | 17.5 | 1.7 | 4.0 | 10.0 | 20.0 |
| Obstetrical care – vaginal delivery | 471 | 0.8 | 0.1 | 0.0 | 0.0 | 0.0 |
| *Internal medicine* | | | | | | |
| Periodic or annual exam | 653 | 17.6 | 1.7 | 0.0 | 4.0 | 20.0 |
| Electrocardiogram | 646 | 49.0 | 4.3 | 1.0 | 15.0 | 45.0 |
| *General surgery* | | | | | | |
| Single inguinal hernia repair | 193 | 5.5 | 0.4 | 2.0 | 4.0 | 8.0 |
| Cholecystectomy | 193 | 4.3 | 0.4 | 0.0 | 3.0 | 6.0 |
| Appendectomy | 194 | 2.5 | 0.2 | 1.0 | 2.0 | 4.0 |
| *Otolaryngology* | | | | | | |
| Tonsillectomy | 66 | 8.6 | 1.2 | 0.0 | 6.0 | 12.0 |
| *Orthopedic Surgery* | | | | | | |
| Total hip replacement | 165 | 1.9 | 0.3 | 0.0 | 1.0 | 2.0 |
| Knee ligament repair | 159 | 1.3 | 0.3 | 0.0 | 0.0 | 1.0 |
| *Ophthalmology* | | | | | | |
| Cataract removal and lens insertion | 175 | 13.4 | 1.1 | 2.0 | 10.0 | 20.0 |
| *Urological surgery* | | | | | | |
| Transurethral resection of prostate | 92 | 3.1 | 0.3 | 1.0 | 2.0 | 4.0 |
| *Pediatrics* | | | | | | |
| Periodic or annual type exam | 261 | 70.0 | 4.9 | 10.0 | 40.0 | 100.0 |
| Routine newborn care | 270 | 17.6 | 1.3 | 1.0 | 10.0 | 25.0 |
| *Obstetrics/gynecology* | | | | | | |
| Obstetrical care – vaginal delivery | 218 | 9.1 | 0.6 | 0.0 | 8.0 | 13.0 |
| Obstetrical care – cesarean section | 144 | 3.0 | 0.2 | 2.0 | 2.0 | 4.0 |
| Total hysterectomy | 215 | 2.6 | 0.2 | 0.0 | 2.0 | 4.0 |
| *Radiology* | | | | | | |
| Radiologic exam of chest | 227 | 267.8 | 16.3 | 20.0 | 200.0 | 400.0 |
| Radiologic exam of upper GI tract | 244 | 19.9 | 1.8 | 0.0 | 5.0 | 25.0 |
| CT scan of head | 238 | 40.6 | 5.1 | 0.0 | 15.0 | 50.0 |
| *Psychiatry* | | | | | | |
| Psychiatric diagnostic evaluation | 103 | 13.6 | 1.2 | 4.0 | 10.0 | 20.0 |
| *Anesthesiology* | | | | | | |
| 15 minute unit of anesthesia time | 105 | 719.4 | 50.4 | 403.0 | 606.7 | 936.0 |
| *Pathology* | | | | | | |
| Pap smear interpretation | 36 | 358.0 | 83.6 | 0.0 | 130.0 | 520.0 |

Source: 1995 Socioeconomic Monitoring System survey of nonfederal patient care physicians. See the beginning of this section, the introduction, and appendices for a discussion of the survey sample, definitions, and computation procedures. Statistics are not reported if the number of responses is less than 25.

Table 25. **Patients Discharged from the Hospital per Week, for Nonfederal Physicians (excluding Physicians in Radiology, Psychiatry, Anesthesiology, and Pathology), 1995**

| | Number of Responses | Mean | Standard Error | 25th Percentile | Median | 75th Percentile |
|---|---|---|---|---|---|---|
| All Physicians | 1877 | 5.4 | 0.1 | 2.0 | 4.0 | 6.0 |
| *Specialty* | | | | | | |
| General/Family Practice | 331 | 5.1 | 0.5 | 2.0 | 3.0 | 5.0 |
| Internal Medicine | 570 | 5.2 | 0.3 | 2.0 | 4.0 | 6.0 |
| · General Internal Medicine | 387 | 4.7 | 0.2 | 2.0 | 4.0 | 6.0 |
| · Cardiovascular Diseases | 81 | 8.3 | 1.1 | 3.0 | 5.0 | 10.0 |
| · Other | 102 | 4.8 | 0.7 | 1.0 | 4.0 | 6.0 |
| Surgery | 629 | 5.7 | 0.2 | 3.0 | 5.0 | 7.0 |
| · General Surgery | 181 | 7.5 | 0.5 | 4.0 | 6.0 | 10.0 |
| · Otolaryngology | 63 | 4.4 | 0.5 | 1.0 | 3.0 | 6.0 |
| · Orthopedic Surgery | 151 | 4.9 | 0.3 | 2.0 | 4.0 | 6.0 |
| · Ophthalmology | 61 | 1.7 | 0.3 | 0.0 | 1.0 | 2.0 |
| · Urological Surgery | 85 | 5.4 | 0.4 | 3.0 | 4.0 | 6.0 |
| · Other | 88 | 6.2 | 0.6 | 3.0 | 5.0 | 8.0 |
| Pediatrics | 46 | 7.9 | 1.6 | 3.0 | 5.0 | 10.0 |
| Obstetrics/Gynecology | 191 | 6.0 | 0.4 | 3.0 | 5.0 | 7.0 |
| Other Specialty | 110 | 3.3 | 0.7 | 0.0 | 2.0 | 4.0 |
| · Emergency Medicine | 5 | . | . | . | . | . |
| · Other | 105 | 2.6 | 0.3 | 0.0 | 2.0 | 4.0 |
| *Geographic Area* | | | | | | |
| New England | 114 | 4.1 | 0.3 | 2.0 | 3.0 | 6.0 |
| · Massachusetts | 56 | 4.8 | 0.5 | 2.0 | 4.0 | 7.0 |
| · Other | 58 | 3.2 | 0.4 | 1.0 | 2.0 | 5.0 |
| Middle Atlantic | 301 | 5.0 | 0.3 | 2.0 | 4.0 | 6.0 |
| · New Jersey | 52 | 4.5 | 0.6 | 2.0 | 3.0 | 5.0 |
| · New York | 110 | 4.8 | 0.5 | 2.0 | 3.0 | 5.0 |
| · Pennsylvania | 139 | 5.5 | 0.4 | 2.0 | 4.0 | 7.0 |
| East North Central | 301 | 5.8 | 0.4 | 2.0 | 5.0 | 8.0 |
| · Illinois | 104 | 6.4 | 0.7 | 2.0 | 5.0 | 8.0 |
| · Michigan | 56 | 5.5 | 1.2 | 2.0 | 4.0 | 6.0 |
| · Ohio | 64 | 4.4 | 0.5 | 1.0 | 4.0 | 5.0 |
| · Other | 77 | 6.5 | 0.6 | 3.0 | 5.0 | 8.0 |
| West North Central | 150 | 6.0 | 0.6 | 2.0 | 5.0 | 8.0 |
| South Atlantic | 321 | 5.2 | 0.3 | 2.0 | 4.0 | 7.0 |
| · Florida | 81 | 5.5 | 0.7 | 2.0 | 3.0 | 6.0 |
| · Other | 240 | 5.1 | 0.3 | 2.0 | 4.0 | 7.0 |
| East South Central | 123 | 6.9 | 0.8 | 3.0 | 5.0 | 8.0 |
| West South Central | 161 | 6.2 | 0.6 | 2.0 | 5.0 | 7.0 |
| · Texas | 103 | 5.5 | 0.5 | 3.0 | 5.0 | 6.0 |
| · Other | 58 | 7.9 | 1.5 | 2.0 | 4.0 | 10.0 |
| Mountain | 110 | 5.0 | 0.5 | 2.0 | 4.0 | 6.0 |
| Pacific | 296 | 4.6 | 0.4 | 2.0 | 3.0 | 6.0 |
| · California | 207 | 4.6 | 0.5 | 2.0 | 3.0 | 5.0 |
| · Other | 89 | 4.7 | 0.3 | 2.0 | 4.0 | 6.0 |
| *Practice Arrangement* | | | | | | |
| Self-Employed | 1214 | 5.6 | 0.2 | 2.0 | 4.0 | 7.0 |
| · Solo Practice | 544 | 5.1 | 0.2 | 2.0 | 4.0 | 6.0 |
| · Two Physician Practice | 163 | 6.4 | 0.7 | 2.0 | 4.0 | 6.0 |
| · Three Physician Practice | 142 | 4.9 | 0.4 | 2.0 | 4.0 | 5.0 |
| · 4-8 Physician Practice | 272 | 6.8 | 0.5 | 2.0 | 5.0 | 8.0 |
| · Over 8 Physician Practice | 92 | 5.8 | 0.5 | 3.0 | 5.0 | 8.0 |
| Employee | 615 | 4.8 | 0.2 | 2.0 | 4.0 | 6.0 |
| Independent Contractor | 48 | 5.8 | 1.6 | 2.0 | 3.0 | 6.0 |

Source: 1995 Socioeconomic Monitoring System survey of nonfederal patient care physicians. See the beginning of this section, the introduction, and appendices for a discussion of the survey sample, definitions, and computation procedures. Statistics are not reported if the number of responses is less than 25.

Table 26. **Average Length of Hospital Stay of Patients Discharged from the Hospital, for Nonfederal Physicians (excluding Physicians in Radiology, Psychiatry, Anesthesiology, and Pathology), 1995**

| | Number of Responses | Mean | Standard Error | 25th Percentile | Median | 75th Percentile |
|---|---|---|---|---|---|---|
| All Physicians | 1625 | 4.2 | 0.1 | 2.0 | 3.0 | 5.0 |
| *Specialty* | | | | | | |
| General/Family Practice | 300 | 4.2 | 0.2 | 3.0 | 4.0 | 5.0 |
| Internal Medicine | 480 | 5.4 | 0.3 | 3.0 | 4.0 | 5.0 |
| · General Internal Medicine | 325 | 5.3 | 0.3 | 3.0 | 5.0 | 5.0 |
| · Cardiovascular Diseases | 72 | 4.3 | 0.3 | 3.0 | 4.0 | 5.0 |
| · Other | 83 | 6.6 | 1.2 | 3.0 | 4.0 | 5.0 |
| Surgery | 561 | 3.2 | 0.1 | 2.0 | 3.0 | 4.0 |
| · General Surgery | 171 | 3.3 | 0.1 | 2.0 | 3.0 | 4.0 |
| · Otolaryngology | 56 | 2.3 | 0.2 | 1.0 | 2.0 | 3.0 |
| · Orthopedic Surgery | 142 | 3.5 | 0.1 | 2.0 | 3.0 | 4.0 |
| · Ophthalmology | 29 | 1.6 | 0.3 | 1.0 | 1.0 | 1.0 |
| · Urological Surgery | 81 | 2.9 | 0.2 | 2.0 | 3.0 | 3.0 |
| · Other | 82 | 3.6 | 0.2 | 2.0 | 3.0 | 4.0 |
| Pediatrics | 40 | 4.5 | 0.9 | 2.0 | 3.0 | 5.0 |
| Obstetrics/Gynecology | 181 | 2.0 | 0.1 | 1.0 | 2.0 | 2.0 |
| Other Specialty | 63 | 8.5 | 0.9 | 4.0 | 5.0 | 14.0 |
| · Emergency Medicine | 3 | . | . | . | . | . |
| · Other | 60 | 8.7 | 0.9 | 5.0 | 5.0 | 14.0 |
| *Geographic Area* | | | | | | |
| New England | 95 | 4.2 | 0.3 | 2.0 | 4.0 | 5.0 |
| · Massachusetts | 48 | 3.9 | 0.3 | 2.0 | 4.0 | 5.0 |
| · Other | 47 | 4.6 | 0.5 | 2.0 | 4.0 | 6.0 |
| Middle Atlantic | 253 | 4.8 | 0.3 | 3.0 | 4.0 | 5.0 |
| · New Jersey | 40 | 4.3 | 0.5 | 3.0 | 4.0 | 5.0 |
| · New York | 91 | 4.7 | 0.4 | 3.0 | 4.0 | 6.0 |
| · Pennsylvania | 122 | 5.1 | 0.5 | 3.0 | 4.0 | 6.0 |
| East North Central | 256 | 4.4 | 0.4 | 2.0 | 3.0 | 5.0 |
| · Illinois | 88 | 3.4 | 0.2 | 2.0 | 3.0 | 5.0 |
| · Michigan | 44 | 4.8 | 0.7 | 2.0 | 4.0 | 5.0 |
| · Ohio | 53 | 5.4 | 1.4 | 3.0 | 4.0 | 5.0 |
| · Other | 71 | 4.6 | 0.8 | 2.0 | 3.0 | 5.0 |
| West North Central | 129 | 3.6 | 0.2 | 2.0 | 3.0 | 5.0 |
| South Atlantic | 279 | 3.8 | 0.2 | 2.0 | 3.0 | 5.0 |
| · Florida | 71 | 4.3 | 0.6 | 3.0 | 4.0 | 5.0 |
| · Other | 208 | 3.7 | 0.2 | 2.0 | 3.0 | 5.0 |
| East South Central | 114 | 6.1 | 0.9 | 3.0 | 4.0 | 5.0 |
| West South Central | 142 | 3.8 | 0.2 | 2.0 | 3.0 | 5.0 |
| · Texas | 93 | 4.0 | 0.3 | 3.0 | 4.0 | 5.0 |
| · Other | 49 | 3.4 | 0.2 | 2.0 | 3.0 | 5.0 |
| Mountain | 99 | 3.4 | 0.3 | 2.0 | 3.0 | 4.0 |
| Pacific | 258 | 3.8 | 0.2 | 2.0 | 3.0 | 5.0 |
| · California | 179 | 3.9 | 0.3 | 2.0 | 3.0 | 5.0 |
| · Other | 79 | 3.4 | 0.3 | 2.0 | 3.0 | 4.0 |
| *Practice Arrangement* | | | | | | |
| Self-Employed | 1079 | 3.9 | 0.1 | 2.0 | 3.0 | 5.0 |
| · Solo Practice | 484 | 3.8 | 0.1 | 2.0 | 3.0 | 5.0 |
| · Two Physician Practice | 145 | 3.6 | 0.2 | 2.0 | 3.0 | 5.0 |
| · Three Physician Practice | 118 | 3.8 | 0.2 | 2.0 | 4.0 | 5.0 |
| · 4-8 Physician Practice | 246 | 3.5 | 0.1 | 2.0 | 3.0 | 4.0 |
| · Over 8 Physician Practice | 85 | 6.8 | 1.2 | 3.0 | 4.0 | 5.0 |
| Employee | 506 | 4.5 | 0.2 | 3.0 | 3.0 | 5.0 |
| Independent Contractor | 40 | 5.7 | 1.7 | 3.0 | 3.0 | 5.0 |

Source: 1995 Socioeconomic Monitoring System survey of nonfederal patient care physicians. See the beginning of this section, the introduction, and appendices for a discussion of the survey sample, definitions, and computation procedures. Statistics are not reported if the number of responses is less than 25.

Table 27. **Total Patient Visits per Week, for Nonfederal Physicians, 1995 – General/Family Practice**

| | Number of Responses | Mean | Standard Error | 25th Percentile | Median | 75th Percentile |
|---|---|---|---|---|---|---|
| All Physicians | 476 | 133.7 | 2.8 | 96 | 126 | 160 |
| *Geographic Area* | | | | | | |
| New England | 26 | 113.8 | 7.4 | 96 | 107 | 124 |
| Middle Atlantic | 59 | 113.4 | 7.4 | 64 | 117 | 149 |
| East North Central | 77 | 138.4 | 7.0 | 85 | 134 | 185 |
| West North Central | 50 | 146.1 | 9.1 | 114 | 131 | 164 |
| South Atlantic | 73 | 139.5 | 7.1 | 100 | 141 | 179 |
| East South Central | 32 | 188.7 | 15.7 | 119 | 170 | 222 |
| West South Central | 40 | 134.4 | 6.9 | 103 | 127 | 153 |
| Mountain | 43 | 118.4 | 6.7 | 92 | 115 | 145 |
| Pacific | 76 | 127.2 | 6.3 | 100 | 124 | 148 |
| *Practice Arrangement* | | | | | | |
| Self-Employed | 252 | 146.1 | 3.6 | 110 | 142 | 179 |
| · Solo Practice | 147 | 147.9 | 4.4 | 113 | 149 | 181 |
| · Two Physician Practice | 36 | 139.8 | 11.4 | 82 | 132 | 196 |
| · Three Physician Practice | 18 | . | . | . | . | . |
| · 4-8 Physician Practice | 39 | 153.5 | 11.1 | 114 | 130 | 174 |
| · Over 8 Physician Practice | 12 | . | . | . | . | . |
| Employee | 199 | 121.9 | 4.3 | 80 | 114 | 143 |
| Independent Contractor | 25 | 108.7 | 15.1 | 55 | 92 | 146 |

Source: 1995 Socioeconomic Monitoring System survey of nonfederal patient care physicians. See the beginning of this section, the introduction, and appendices for a discussion of the survey sample, definitions, and computation procedures. Statistics are not reported if the number of responses is less than 25.

Table 28. **Total Patient Visits per Week, for Nonfederal Physicians, 1995 – Internal Medicine**

| | Number of Responses | Mean | Standard Error | 25th Percentile | Median | 75th Percentile |
|---|---|---|---|---|---|---|
| All Physicians | 709 | 99.7 | 2.0 | 64 | 95 | 128 |
| *Geographic Area* | | | | | | |
| New England | 62 | 95.7 | 6.4 | 65 | 84 | 132 |
| Middle Atlantic | 125 | 107.6 | 5.3 | 62 | 106 | 136 |
| East North Central | 105 | 101.0 | 5.4 | 66 | 100 | 134 |
| West North Central | 38 | 101.6 | 9.9 | 63 | 104 | 120 |
| South Atlantic | 126 | 94.5 | 4.4 | 59 | 95 | 122 |
| East South Central | 49 | 109.5 | 6.9 | 75 | 107 | 128 |
| West South Central | 54 | 104.1 | 9.2 | 66 | 92 | 111 |
| Mountain | 33 | 93.1 | 7.4 | 70 | 83 | 115 |
| Pacific | 117 | 93.6 | 4.3 | 64 | 90 | 116 |
| *Practice Arrangement* | | | | | | |
| Self-Employed | 402 | 107.0 | 2.7 | 70 | 100 | 132 |
| · Solo Practice | 189 | 101.8 | 4.1 | 64 | 95 | 124 |
| · Two Physician Practice | 40 | 115.7 | 10.0 | 69 | 111 | 144 |
| · Three Physician Practice | 47 | 106.9 | 8.2 | 62 | 101 | 132 |
| · 4-8 Physician Practice | 82 | 114.9 | 5.6 | 81 | 110 | 136 |
| · Over 8 Physician Practice | 44 | 112.1 | 7.1 | 70 | 115 | 138 |
| Employee | 285 | 89.4 | 2.9 | 58 | 85 | 115 |
| Independent Contractor | 22 | . | . | . | . | . |

Source: 1995 Socioeconomic Monitoring System survey of nonfederal patient care physicians. See the beginning of this section, the introduction, and appendices for a discussion of the survey sample, definitions, and computation procedures. Statistics are not reported if the number of responses is less than 25.

Table 29. **Total Patient Visits per Week, for Nonfederal Physicians, 1995 – Surgery**

|  | Number of Responses | Mean | Standard Error | 25th Percentile | Median | 75th Percentile |
|---|---|---|---|---|---|---|
| All Physicians | 811 | 97.1 | 1.6 | 63 | 92 | 125 |
| *Geographic Area* |  |  |  |  |  |  |
| New England | 45 | 92.4 | 4.9 | 73 | 87 | 117 |
| Middle Atlantic | 129 | 91.6 | 4.6 | 60 | 86 | 124 |
| East North Central | 118 | 96.9 | 4.5 | 60 | 80 | 126 |
| West North Central | 65 | 119.3 | 6.7 | 77 | 114 | 155 |
| South Atlantic | 166 | 102.2 | 3.5 | 70 | 98 | 139 |
| East South Central | 46 | 106.7 | 5.8 | 62 | 107 | 140 |
| West South Central | 73 | 98.4 | 4.4 | 70 | 95 | 122 |
| Mountain | 36 | 87.9 | 6.2 | 52 | 80 | 127 |
| Pacific | 133 | 85.1 | 3.1 | 55 | 82 | 106 |
| *Practice Arrangement* |  |  |  |  |  |  |
| Self-Employed | 576 | 99.6 | 1.9 | 67 | 95 | 130 |
| · Solo Practice | 259 | 90.3 | 3.1 | 57 | 78 | 124 |
| · Two Physician Practice | 91 | 110.8 | 4.2 | 78 | 103 | 135 |
| · Three Physician Practice | 72 | 103.5 | 4.8 | 71 | 101 | 126 |
| · 4-8 Physician Practice | 122 | 112.6 | 3.6 | 84 | 108 | 134 |
| · Over 8 Physician Practice | 31 | 100.7 | 5.9 | 78 | 101 | 124 |
| Employee | 208 | 89.9 | 2.9 | 60 | 85 | 113 |
| Independent Contractor | 27 | 100.7 | 11.8 | 70 | 92 | 100 |

Source: 1995 Socioeconomic Monitoring System survey of nonfederal patient care physicians. See the beginning of this section, the introduction, and appendices for a discussion of the survey sample, definitions, and computation procedures. Statistics are not reported if the number of responses is less than 25.

Table 30. **Total Patient Visits per Week, for Nonfederal Physicians, 1995 – Pediatrics**

|  | Number of Responses | Mean | Standard Error | 25th Percentile | Median | 75th Percentile |
|---|---|---|---|---|---|---|
| All Physicians | 289 | 125.9 | 3.9 | 81 | 120 | 160 |
| *Geographic Area* |  |  |  |  |  |  |
| New England | 17 | . | . | . | . | . |
| Middle Atlantic | 54 | 102.7 | 7.2 | 73 | 104 | 140 |
| East North Central | 35 | 129.5 | 10.6 | 90 | 127 | 168 |
| West North Central | 18 | . | . | . | . | . |
| South Atlantic | 60 | 118.6 | 9.4 | 60 | 109 | 166 |
| East South Central | 15 | . | . | . | . | . |
| West South Central | 32 | 135.9 | 9.3 | 87 | 131 | 175 |
| Mountain | 17 | . | . | . | . | . |
| Pacific | 41 | 132.5 | 9.3 | 103 | 135 | 160 |
| *Practice Arrangement* |  |  |  |  |  |  |
| Self-Employed | 143 | 147.4 | 5.4 | 107 | 143 | 170 |
| · Solo Practice | 60 | 139.5 | 8.1 | 95 | 140 | 168 |
| · Two Physician Practice | 24 | . | . | . | . | . |
| · Three Physician Practice | 15 | . | . | . | . | . |
| · 4-8 Physician Practice | 34 | 161.1 | 10.0 | 115 | 156 | 195 |
| · Over 8 Physician Practice | 9 | . | . | . | . | . |
| Employee | 136 | 104.5 | 5.3 | 65 | 91 | 135 |
| Independent Contractor | 10 | . | . | . | . | . |

Source: 1995 Socioeconomic Monitoring System survey of nonfederal patient care physicians. See the beginning of this section, the introduction, and appendices for a discussion of the survey sample, definitions, and computation procedures. Statistics are not reported if the number of responses is less than 25.

Table 31. **Total Patient Visits per Week, for Nonfederal Physicians, 1995 – Obstetrics/Gynecology**

| | Number of Responses | Mean | Standard Error | 25th Percentile | Median | 75th Percentile |
|---|---|---|---|---|---|---|
| All Physicians | 227 | 94.0 | 3.2 | 61 | 87 | 119 |
| *Geographic Area* | | | | | | |
| New England | 12 | . | . | . | . | . |
| Middle Atlantic | 31 | 93.9 | 11.1 | 50 | 96 | 133 |
| East North Central | 41 | 105.5 | 6.5 | 80 | 98 | 140 |
| West North Central | 13 | . | . | . | . | . |
| South Atlantic | 33 | 99.0 | 8.1 | 69 | 91 | 110 |
| East South Central | 16 | . | . | . | . | . |
| West South Central | 25 | 95.2 | 8.0 | 56 | 89 | 121 |
| Mountain | 20 | . | . | . | . | . |
| Pacific | 36 | 76.2 | 5.9 | 49 | 68 | 96 |
| *Practice Arrangement* | | | | | | |
| Self-Employed | 151 | 98.6 | 4.1 | 68 | 91 | 121 |
| · Solo Practice | 72 | 86.1 | 6.5 | 52 | 77 | 101 |
| · Two Physician Practice | 19 | . | . | . | . | . |
| · Three Physician Practice | 12 | . | . | . | . | . |
| · 4-8 Physician Practice | 37 | 120.3 | 6.5 | 91 | 116 | 141 |
| · Over 8 Physician Practice | 11 | . | . | . | . | . |
| Employee | 68 | 87.8 | 5.4 | 51 | 86 | 115 |
| Independent Contractor | 8 | . | . | . | . | . |

Source: 1995 Socioeconomic Monitoring System survey of nonfederal patient care physicians. See the beginning of this section, the introduction, and appendices for a discussion of the survey sample, definitions, and computation procedures. Statistics are not reported if the number of responses is less than 25.

Table 32. **Total Patient Visits per Week, for Nonfederal Physicians, 1995 – Other Specialty**

| | Number of Responses | Mean | Standard Error | 25th Percentile | Median | 75th Percentile |
|---|---|---|---|---|---|---|
| All Physicians | 351 | 109.2 | 3.2 | 69 | 100 | 140 |
| *Geographic Area* | | | | | | |
| New England | 18 | . | . | . | . | . |
| Middle Atlantic | 46 | 107.0 | 9.1 | 65 | 98 | 120 |
| East North Central | 54 | 103.6 | 7.2 | 75 | 100 | 125 |
| West North Central | 25 | 103.3 | 10.5 | 65 | 102 | 125 |
| South Atlantic | 64 | 114.2 | 9.5 | 65 | 100 | 145 |
| East South Central | 19 | . | . | . | . | . |
| West South Central | 28 | 97.5 | 10.0 | 75 | 83 | 122 |
| Mountain | 22 | . | . | . | . | . |
| Pacific | 75 | 108.3 | 6.5 | 60 | 100 | 140 |
| *Practice Arrangement* | | | | | | |
| Self-Employed | 151 | 109.4 | 4.8 | 69 | 100 | 140 |
| · Solo Practice | 63 | 105.7 | 7.5 | 65 | 100 | 150 |
| · Two Physician Practice | 10 | . | . | . | . | . |
| · Three Physician Practice | 11 | . | . | . | . | . |
| · 4-8 Physician Practice | 40 | 110.2 | 7.7 | 77 | 100 | 125 |
| · Over 8 Physician Practice | 27 | 97.8 | 8.3 | 75 | 100 | 120 |
| Employee | 151 | 99.1 | 4.4 | 60 | 90 | 125 |
| Independent Contractor | 49 | 139.7 | 10.2 | 90 | 125 | 170 |

Source: 1995 Socioeconomic Monitoring System survey of nonfederal patient care physicians. See the beginning of this section, the introduction, and appendices for a discussion of the survey sample, definitions, and computation procedures. Statistics are not reported if the number of responses is less than 25.

# Selected Medicare Statistics for Nonfederal Physicians

Office Visits with Medicare Patients

Visits on Hospital Rounds with Medicare Patients

Surgical Procedures with Medicare Patients

Hospital Utilization of Medicare Patients

## Selected Medicare Statistics for Nonfederal Physicians

Information on services provided to Medicare patients was derived from the following questions asked of physicians in all specialties except radiology, psychiatry, anesthesiology, and pathology:

1. During your last complete week of practice, how many of the [NUMBER]:

   a. patient visits that you personally had during the hours you spent in the office or in freestanding primary or urgent care centers were with Medicare patients? (Do not include patient visits in outpatient clinics located in hospitals or in hospital emergency rooms.)

   b. operations and deliveries that you performed during the hours you spent in the operating, labor or delivery room were with Medicare patients? Do not include assists in this question.

   c. assists that you performed were with Medicare patients?

   e. inpatient visits that you had during the hours you spent on hospital rounds were with Medicare patients?

2a. During your most recent complete week of practice, how many of the [Number] patients did you personally discharged from the hospital were Medicare patients?

2b. For the Medicare patients you discharged from the hospital that week, what was the average length of stay in days in the hospital?

Information reported in Table 33 (Medicare office visits) was derived from responses to Question 1a. Figures 14-16 highlight statistics reported in Table 33 for selected specialties, states, and practice arrangements. Information reported in Table 34

(Medicare hospital visits) was derived from responses to Question 1b. Information reported in Table 35 was based on the sum of responses to Questions 1b and 1c. Table 36 was derived from responses to Question 1b. Information reported in Tables 37 and 38 was derived from responses from Questions 2a and 2b, respectively.

Information on patient visits in the hospital emergency rooms and outpatient clinics located in hospitals with Medicare patients was not collected in 1995. Therefore, this information and information on total Medicare visits (which is calculated as the sum of each type of visit) are not reported in the 1995 edition of *Physician Marketplace Statistics.*

Figure 14. **Mean and Median Office Visits with Medicare Patient per Week, for Nonfederal Physicians (excluding Physicians in Radiology, Psychiatry, Anesthesiology, and Pathology), for Selected Specialties, 1995**

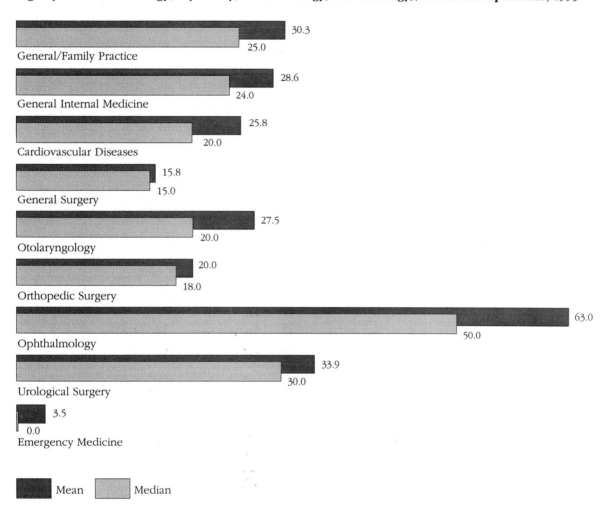

Figure 15. **Mean and Median Medicare Office Visits per Week, for Nonfederal Physicians, for Selected States, 1995**[a]

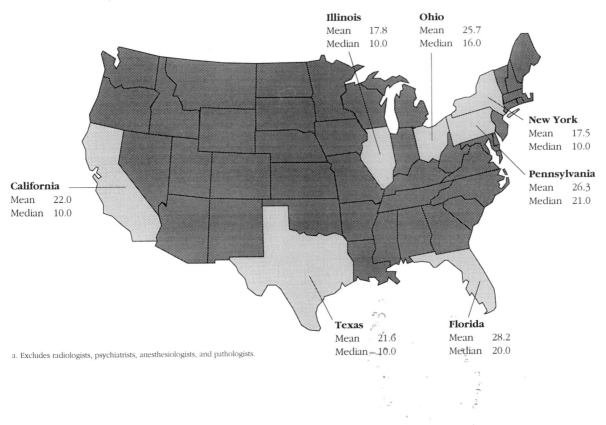

| Illinois | | Ohio | |
|---|---|---|---|
| Mean | 17.8 | Mean | 25.7 |
| Median | 10.0 | Median | 16.0 |

**New York**
Mean 17.5
Median 10.0

**Pennsylvania**
Mean 26.3
Median 21.0

**California**
Mean 22.0
Median 10.0

**Texas**
Mean 21.6
Median 10.0

**Florida**
Mean 28.2
Median 20.0

a. Excludes radiologists, psychiatrists, anesthesiologists, and pathologists.

Figure 16. **Mean and Median Medicare Office Visits per Week per Self-Employed Nonfederal Physician, by Size of Practice, 1995**[a]

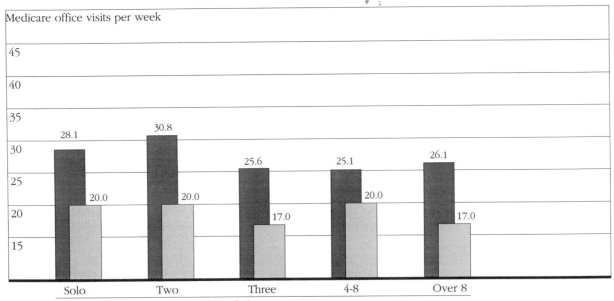

Medicare office visits per week

| | Solo | Two | Three | 4-8 | Over 8 |
|---|---|---|---|---|---|
| Mean | 28.1 | 30.8 | 25.6 | 25.1 | 26.1 |
| Median | 20.0 | 20.0 | 17.0 | 20.0 | 17.0 |

Number of Physicians in Practice

◼ Mean ▢ Median

a. Excludes radiologists, psychiatrists, anesthesiologists, and pathologists.

Table 33. **Office Visits with Medicare Patients per Week, for Nonfederal Physicians (excluding Physicians in Radiology, Psychiatry, Anesthesiology, and Pathology), 1995**

|  | Number of Responses | Mean | Standard Error | 25th Percentile | Median | 75th Percentile |
|---|---|---|---|---|---|---|
| All Physicians | 2870 | 22.3 | 0.5 | 2.0 | 15.0 | 30.0 |
| *Specialty* | | | | | | |
| General/Family Practice | 484 | 30.3 | 1.2 | 10.0 | 25.0 | 43.0 |
| Internal Medicine | 721 | 26.8 | 1.1 | 8.0 | 21.0 | 38.0 |
| · General Internal Medicine | 498 | 28.6 | 1.4 | 8.0 | 24.0 | 40.0 |
| · Cardiovascular Diseases | 91 | 25.8 | 2.5 | 10.0 | 20.0 | 38.0 |
| · Other | 132 | 20.8 | 1.6 | 10.0 | 18.0 | 30.0 |
| Surgery | 811 | 28.8 | 1.1 | 9.0 | 20.0 | 36.0 |
| · General Surgery | 192 | 15.8 | 0.9 | 7.0 | 15.0 | 24.0 |
| · Otolaryngology | 70 | 27.5 | 3.0 | 10.0 | 20.0 | 36.0 |
| · Orthopedic Surgery | 173 | 20.0 | 1.1 | 10.0 | 18.0 | 30.0 |
| · Ophthalmology | 178 | 63.0 | 3.3 | 30.0 | 50.0 | 85.0 |
| · Urological Surgery | 95 | 33.9 | 2.0 | 20.0 | 30.0 | 48.0 |
| · Other | 103 | 11.9 | 1.3 | 3.0 | 8.0 | 15.0 |
| Pediatrics | 281 | 2.0 | 0.6 | 0.0 | 0.0 | 0.0 |
| Obstetrics/Gynecology | 231 | 8.1 | 0.6 | 2.0 | 5.0 | 10.0 |
| Other Specialty | 342 | 13.6 | 1.3 | 0.0 | 0.0 | 20.0 |
| · Emergency Medicine | 132 | 3.5 | 1.2 | 0.0 | 0.0 | 0.0 |
| · Other | 210 | 19.5 | 1.9 | 0.0 | 10.0 | 28.0 |
| *Geographic Area* | | | | | | |
| New England | 176 | 21.4 | 1.8 | 1.0 | 18.0 | 30.0 |
| · Massachusetts | 80 | 21.0 | 2.9 | 2.0 | 15.0 | 30.0 |
| · Other | 96 | 21.8 | 2.4 | 1.0 | 18.0 | 30.0 |
| Middle Atlantic | 443 | 20.8 | 1.3 | 0.0 | 13.0 | 30.0 |
| · New Jersey | 84 | 18.2 | 2.4 | 0.0 | 10.0 | 35.0 |
| · New York | 177 | 17.5 | 2.2 | 0.0 | 10.0 | 25.0 |
| · Pennsylvania | 182 | 26.3 | 2.0 | 5.0 | 21.0 | 38.0 |
| East North Central | 432 | 22.1 | 1.2 | 3.0 | 15.0 | 32.0 |
| · Illinois | 146 | 17.8 | 1.9 | 1.0 | 10.0 | 30.0 |
| · Michigan | 79 | 22.1 | 3.0 | 1.0 | 15.0 | 35.0 |
| · Ohio | 98 | 25.7 | 2.8 | 5.0 | 16.0 | 40.0 |
| · Other | 109 | 25.4 | 2.4 | 6.0 | 20.0 | 38.0 |
| West North Central | 212 | 28.4 | 2.4 | 4.0 | 18.0 | 39.0 |
| South Atlantic | 526 | 23.1 | 1.2 | 2.0 | 16.0 | 30.0 |
| · Florida | 147 | 28.2 | 2.8 | 1.0 | 20.0 | 40.0 |
| · Other | 379 | 20.9 | 1.3 | 2.0 | 15.0 | 29.0 |
| East South Central | 175 | 26.5 | 1.8 | 6.0 | 24.0 | 40.0 |
| West South Central | 267 | 22.7 | 1.8 | 0.0 | 10.0 | 35.0 |
| · Texas | 174 | 21.6 | 2.2 | 0.0 | 10.0 | 30.0 |
| · Other | 93 | 25.1 | 3.4 | 4.0 | 12.0 | 35.0 |
| Mountain | 174 | 16.7 | 1.5 | 0.0 | 10.0 | 25.0 |
| Pacific | 465 | 20.9 | 1.4 | 2.0 | 11.0 | 30.0 |
| · California | 325 | 22.0 | 1.9 | 2.0 | 10.0 | 30.0 |
| · Other | 140 | 17.9 | 1.8 | 2.0 | 12.0 | 20.0 |
| *Practice Arrangement* | | | | | | |
| Self-Employed | 1723 | 27.4 | 0.7 | 7.0 | 20.0 | 40.0 |
| · Solo Practice | 814 | 28.1 | 1.1 | 7.0 | 20.0 | 40.0 |
| · Two Physician Practice | 228 | 30.8 | 2.3 | 7.0 | 20.0 | 41.0 |
| · Three Physician Practice | 180 | 25.6 | 1.9 | 7.0 | 17.0 | 36.0 |
| · 4-8 Physician Practice | 363 | 25.1 | 1.3 | 7.0 | 20.0 | 35.0 |
| · Over 8 Physician Practice | 136 | 26.1 | 2.6 | 3.0 | 17.0 | 40.0 |
| Employee | 1010 | 15.4 | 0.7 | 0.0 | 8.0 | 24.0 |
| Independent Contractor | 137 | 12.3 | 1.8 | 0.0 | 4.0 | 20.0 |

Source: 1995 Socioeconomic Monitoring System survey of nonfederal patient care physicians. See the beginning of this section, the introduction, and appendices for a discussion of the survey sample, definitions, and computation procedures. Statistics are not reported if the number of responses is less than 25.

## Table 34. Visits on Hospital Rounds with Medicare Patients per Week, for Nonfederal Physicians (excluding Physicians in Radiology, Psychiatry, Anesthesiology, and Pathology), 1995

| | Number of Responses | Mean | Standard Error | 25th Percentile | Median | 75th Percentile |
|---|---|---|---|---|---|---|
| All Physicians | 2836 | 8.6 | 0.3 | 0.0 | 2.0 | 10.0 |
| *Specialty* | | | | | | |
| General/Family Practice | 486 | 7.4 | 0.5 | 0.0 | 3.0 | 10.0 |
| Internal Medicine | 693 | 16.8 | 0.9 | 0.0 | 10.0 | 25.0 |
| · General Internal Medicine | 481 | 14.5 | 1.0 | 0.0 | 8.0 | 20.0 |
| · Cardiovascular Diseases | 85 | 26.1 | 3.5 | 6.0 | 20.0 | 36.0 |
| · Other | 127 | 19.5 | 2.2 | 2.0 | 12.0 | 30.0 |
| Surgery | 797 | 7.4 | 0.4 | 0.0 | 3.0 | 10.0 |
| · General Surgery | 187 | 13.9 | 1.4 | 4.0 | 8.0 | 20.0 |
| · Otolaryngology | 70 | 2.3 | 0.4 | 0.0 | 1.0 | 2.0 |
| · Orthopedic Surgery | 171 | 7.3 | 0.7 | 1.0 | 5.0 | 10.0 |
| · Ophthalmology | 182 | 0.7 | 0.1 | 0.0 | 0.0 | 0.0 |
| · Urological Surgery | 93 | 11.5 | 1.3 | 4.0 | 8.0 | 15.0 |
| · Other | 94 | 5.6 | 0.8 | 0.0 | 3.0 | 8.0 |
| Pediatrics | 288 | 0.6 | 0.2 | 0.0 | 0.0 | 0.0 |
| Obstetrics/Gynecology | 222 | 1.9 | 0.4 | 0.0 | 0.0 | 2.0 |
| Other Specialty | 350 | 4.4 | 0.7 | 0.0 | 0.0 | 0.0 |
| · Emergency Medicine | 133 | 1.3 | 0.9 | 0.0 | 0.0 | 0.0 |
| · Other | 217 | 6.2 | 1.0 | 0.0 | 0.0 | 5.0 |
| *Geographic Area* | | | | | | |
| New England | 171 | 7.4 | 0.9 | 0.0 | 2.0 | 10.0 |
| · Massachusetts | 77 | 8.7 | 1.6 | 0.0 | 2.0 | 10.0 |
| · Other | 94 | 6.2 | 1.0 | 0.0 | 1.0 | 8.0 |
| Middle Atlantic | 446 | 10.6 | 1.0 | 0.0 | 2.0 | 15.0 |
| · New Jersey | 80 | 7.6 | 1.8 | 0.0 | 0.0 | 12.0 |
| · New York | 175 | 9.3 | 1.4 | 0.0 | 1.0 | 14.0 |
| · Pennsylvania | 191 | 13.6 | 1.7 | 0.0 | 5.0 | 20.0 |
| East North Central | 413 | 9.8 | 0.8 | 0.0 | 2.0 | 15.0 |
| · Illinois | 140 | 8.6 | 1.1 | 0.0 | 2.0 | 13.0 |
| · Michigan | 75 | 10.9 | 2.2 | 0.0 | 1.0 | 14.0 |
| · Ohio | 93 | 11.1 | 1.8 | 0.0 | 1.0 | 18.0 |
| · Other | 105 | 9.4 | 1.3 | 0.0 | 4.0 | 15.0 |
| West North Central | 210 | 8.7 | 0.9 | 0.0 | 4.0 | 12.0 |
| South Atlantic | 519 | 8.5 | 0.8 | 0.0 | 2.0 | 10.0 |
| · Florida | 142 | 12.2 | 2.0 | 0.0 | 2.0 | 16.0 |
| · Other | 377 | 7.1 | 0.8 | 0.0 | 1.0 | 7.0 |
| East South Central | 173 | 12.1 | 1.3 | 0.0 | 4.0 | 16.0 |
| West South Central | 260 | 9.0 | 1.3 | 0.0 | 1.0 | 8.0 |
| · Texas | 170 | 7.1 | 1.4 | 0.0 | 1.0 | 5.0 |
| · Other | 90 | 13.2 | 2.6 | 0.0 | 2.0 | 10.0 |
| Mountain | 171 | 5.0 | 0.7 | 0.0 | 0.0 | 6.0 |
| Pacific | 473 | 5.8 | 0.6 | 0.0 | 0.0 | 7.0 |
| · California | 329 | 6.4 | 0.8 | 0.0 | 0.0 | 8.0 |
| · Other | 144 | 4.2 | 0.5 | 0.0 | 1.0 | 6.0 |
| *Practice Arrangement* | | | | | | |
| Self-Employed | 1691 | 9.8 | 0.4 | 0.0 | 3.0 | 12.0 |
| · Solo Practice | 799 | 8.7 | 0.5 | 0.0 | 3.0 | 10.0 |
| · Two Physician Practice | 223 | 9.5 | 1.1 | 0.0 | 2.0 | 15.0 |
| · Three Physician Practice | 173 | 11.7 | 1.2 | 0.0 | 5.0 | 15.0 |
| · 4-8 Physician Practice | 359 | 11.9 | 1.1 | 0.0 | 5.0 | 15.0 |
| · Over 8 Physician Practice | 135 | 9.6 | 1.3 | 0.0 | 3.0 | 13.0 |
| Employee | 1005 | 7.4 | 0.5 | 0.0 | 0.0 | 8.0 |
| Independent Contractor | 140 | 4.3 | 1.3 | 0.0 | 0.0 | 2.0 |

Source: 1995 Socioeconomic Monitoring System survey of nonfederal patient care physicians. See the beginning of this section, the introduction, and appendices for a discussion of the survey sample, definitions, and computation procedures. Statistics are not reported if the number of responses is less than 25.

Table 35. **Surgical Procedures, Including Assists, Performed on Medicare Patients per Week, for Nonfederal Physicians (excluding Physicians in Radiology, Psychiatry, Anesthesiology, and Pathology), 1995**

| | Number of Responses | Mean | Standard Error | 25th Percentile | Median | 75th Percentile |
|---|---|---|---|---|---|---|
| All Physicians | 2942 | 1.3 | 0.1 | 0.0 | 0.0 | 1.0 |
| *Specialty* | | | | | | |
| General/Family Practice | 500 | 0.2 | 0.0 | 0.0 | 0.0 | 0.0 |
| Internal Medicine | 748 | 1.1 | 0.1 | 0.0 | 0.0 | 0.0 |
| · General Internal Medicine | 519 | 0.1 | 0.0 | 0.0 | 0.0 | 0.0 |
| · Cardiovascular Diseases | 90 | 2.7 | 0.4 | 0.0 | 0.0 | 5.0 |
| · Other | 139 | 4.0 | 0.6 | 0.0 | 0.0 | 8.0 |
| Surgery | 806 | 3.5 | 0.1 | 1.0 | 3.0 | 5.0 |
| · General Surgery | 186 | 4.8 | 0.4 | 2.0 | 4.0 | 7.0 |
| · Otolaryngology | 69 | 1.6 | 0.2 | 1.0 | 1.0 | 2.0 |
| · Orthopedic Surgery | 175 | 2.4 | 0.1 | 1.0 | 2.0 | 3.0 |
| · Ophthalmology | 181 | 4.1 | 0.3 | 1.0 | 3.0 | 6.0 |
| · Urological Surgery | 93 | 4.6 | 0.3 | 3.0 | 4.0 | 6.0 |
| · Other | 102 | 2.2 | 0.2 | 0.0 | 2.0 | 3.0 |
| Pediatrics | 300 | 0.0 | 0.0 | 0.0 | 0.0 | 0.0 |
| Obstetrics/Gynecology | 222 | 0.7 | 0.1 | 0.0 | 0.0 | 1.0 |
| Other Specialty | 366 | 0.2 | 0.1 | 0.0 | 0.0 | 0.0 |
| · Emergency Medicine | 133 | 0.0 | 0.0 | 0.0 | 0.0 | 0.0 |
| · Other | 233 | 0.4 | 0.2 | 0.0 | 0.0 | 0.0 |
| *Geographic Area* | | | | | | |
| New England | 181 | 1.0 | 0.2 | 0.0 | 0.0 | 1.0 |
| · Massachusetts | 82 | 1.0 | 0.2 | 0.0 | 0.0 | 1.0 |
| · Other | 99 | 1.0 | 0.2 | 0.0 | 0.0 | 2.0 |
| Middle Atlantic | 457 | 1.0 | 0.1 | 0.0 | 0.0 | 0.0 |
| · New Jersey | 86 | 0.9 | 0.3 | 0.0 | 0.0 | 0.0 |
| · New York | 178 | 0.9 | 0.2 | 0.0 | 0.0 | 1.0 |
| · Pennsylvania | 193 | 1.1 | 0.2 | 0.0 | 0.0 | 0.0 |
| East North Central | 434 | 1.4 | 0.1 | 0.0 | 0.0 | 1.0 |
| · Illinois | 142 | 1.2 | 0.2 | 0.0 | 0.0 | 1.0 |
| · Michigan | 79 | 1.6 | 0.3 | 0.0 | 0.0 | 2.0 |
| · Ohio | 98 | 1.3 | 0.3 | 0.0 | 0.0 | 0.0 |
| · Other | 115 | 1.5 | 0.3 | 0.0 | 0.0 | 2.0 |
| West North Central | 218 | 1.6 | 0.2 | 0.0 | 0.0 | 2.0 |
| South Atlantic | 541 | 1.6 | 0.2 | 0.0 | 0.0 | 2.0 |
| · Florida | 154 | 2.7 | 0.4 | 0.0 | 0.0 | 4.0 |
| · Other | 387 | 1.1 | 0.1 | 0.0 | 0.0 | 1.0 |
| East South Central | 180 | 1.5 | 0.2 | 0.0 | 0.0 | 1.0 |
| West South Central | 273 | 1.3 | 0.2 | 0.0 | 0.0 | 1.0 |
| · Texas | 179 | 1.1 | 0.2 | 0.0 | 0.0 | 0.0 |
| · Other | 94 | 1.7 | 0.3 | 0.0 | 0.0 | 2.0 |
| Mountain | 172 | 1.1 | 0.2 | 0.0 | 0.0 | 1.0 |
| Pacific | 486 | 1.2 | 0.2 | 0.0 | 0.0 | 1.0 |
| · California | 339 | 1.4 | 0.3 | 0.0 | 0.0 | 1.0 |
| · Other | 147 | 0.9 | 0.1 | 0.0 | 0.0 | 1.0 |
| *Practice Arrangement* | | | | | | |
| Self-Employed | 1736 | 1.8 | 0.1 | 0.0 | 0.0 | 2.0 |
| · Solo Practice | 826 | 1.7 | 0.1 | 0.0 | 0.0 | 2.0 |
| · Two Physician Practice | 228 | 1.5 | 0.2 | 0.0 | 0.0 | 2.0 |
| · Three Physician Practice | 176 | 2.3 | 0.3 | 0.0 | 0.0 | 3.0 |
| · 4-8 Physician Practice | 366 | 2.1 | 0.3 | 0.0 | 0.0 | 3.0 |
| · Over 8 Physician Practice | 138 | 1.2 | 0.2 | 0.0 | 0.0 | 1.0 |
| Employee | 1063 | 0.7 | 0.1 | 0.0 | 0.0 | 0.0 |
| Independent Contractor | 143 | 0.5 | 0.1 | 0.0 | 0.0 | 0.0 |

Source: 1995 Socioeconomic Monitoring System survey of nonfederal patient care physicians. See the beginning of this section, the introduction, and appendices for a discussion of the survey sample, definitions, and computation procedures. Statistics are not reported if the number of responses is less than 25.

Table 36. **Surgical Procedures, Excluding Assists, Performed on Medicare Patients per Week, for Nonfederal Physicians (excluding Physicians in Radiology, Psychiatry, Anesthesiology, and Pathology), 1995**

| | Number of Responses | Mean | Standard Error | 25th Percentile | Median | 75th Percentile |
|---|---|---|---|---|---|---|
| All Physicians | 2976 | 1.2 | 0.1 | 0.0 | 0.0 | 1.0 |
| *Specialty* | | | | | | |
| General/Family Practice | 504 | 0.1 | 0.0 | 0.0 | 0.0 | 0.0 |
| Internal Medicine | 749 | 1.1 | 0.1 | 0.0 | 0.0 | 0.0 |
| · General Internal Medicine | 519 | 0.1 | 0.0 | 0.0 | 0.0 | 0.0 |
| · Cardiovascular Diseases | 91 | 2.5 | 0.4 | 0.0 | 0.0 | 4.0 |
| · Other | 139 | 3.9 | 0.5 | 0.0 | 0.0 | 6.0 |
| Surgery | 826 | 3.2 | 0.1 | 1.0 | 2.0 | 4.0 |
| · General Surgery | 194 | 4.1 | 0.4 | 1.0 | 3.0 | 6.0 |
| · Otolaryngology | 71 | 1.5 | 0.2 | 0.0 | 1.0 | 2.0 |
| · Orthopedic Surgery | 177 | 2.1 | 0.1 | 1.0 | 2.0 | 3.0 |
| · Ophthalmology | 183 | 4.0 | 0.3 | 1.0 | 3.0 | 5.0 |
| · Urological Surgery | 95 | 4.2 | 0.3 | 2.0 | 4.0 | 6.0 |
| · Other | 106 | 2.0 | 0.2 | 0.0 | 2.0 | 3.0 |
| Pediatrics | 301 | 0.0 | 0.0 | 0.0 | 0.0 | 0.0 |
| Obstetrics/Gynecology | 230 | 0.6 | 0.1 | 0.0 | 0.0 | 1.0 |
| Other Specialty | 366 | 0.2 | 0.1 | 0.0 | 0.0 | 0.0 |
| · Emergency Medicine | 133 | 0.0 | 0.0 | 0.0 | 0.0 | 0.0 |
| · Other | 233 | 0.3 | 0.2 | 0.0 | 0.0 | 0.0 |
| *Geographic Area* | | | | | | |
| New England | 183 | 1.0 | 0.1 | 0.0 | 0.0 | 1.0 |
| · Massachusetts | 83 | 1.0 | 0.2 | 0.0 | 0.0 | 1.0 |
| · Other | 100 | 0.9 | 0.2 | 0.0 | 0.0 | 2.0 |
| Middle Atlantic | 462 | 0.9 | 0.1 | 0.0 | 0.0 | 0.0 |
| · New Jersey | 87 | 0.8 | 0.2 | 0.0 | 0.0 | 0.0 |
| · New York | 180 | 0.8 | 0.1 | 0.0 | 0.0 | 1.0 |
| · Pennsylvania | 195 | 1.1 | 0.2 | 0.0 | 0.0 | 0.0 |
| East North Central | 438 | 1.3 | 0.1 | 0.0 | 0.0 | 1.0 |
| · Illinois | 143 | 1.1 | 0.2 | 0.0 | 0.0 | 1.0 |
| · Michigan | 82 | 1.5 | 0.3 | 0.0 | 0.0 | 2.0 |
| · Ohio | 98 | 1.2 | 0.3 | 0.0 | 0.0 | 0.0 |
| · Other | 115 | 1.4 | 0.3 | 0.0 | 0.0 | 2.0 |
| West North Central | 223 | 1.4 | 0.2 | 0.0 | 0.0 | 2.0 |
| South Atlantic | 545 | 1.5 | 0.1 | 0.0 | 0.0 | 2.0 |
| · Florida | 154 | 2.6 | 0.4 | 0.0 | 0.0 | 3.0 |
| · Other | 391 | 1.1 | 0.1 | 0.0 | 0.0 | 1.0 |
| East South Central | 181 | 1.4 | 0.2 | 0.0 | 0.0 | 1.0 |
| West South Central | 277 | 1.2 | 0.2 | 0.0 | 0.0 | 1.0 |
| · Texas | 182 | 1.1 | 0.2 | 0.0 | 0.0 | 0.0 |
| · Other | 95 | 1.5 | 0.3 | 0.0 | 0.0 | 2.0 |
| Mountain | 177 | 0.8 | 0.1 | 0.0 | 0.0 | 0.0 |
| Pacific | 490 | 1.0 | 0.2 | 0.0 | 0.0 | 0.0 |
| · California | 342 | 1.2 | 0.2 | 0.0 | 0.0 | 0.0 |
| · Other | 148 | 0.7 | 0.1 | 0.0 | 0.0 | 0.0 |
| *Practice Arrangement* | | | | | | |
| Self-Employed | 1762 | 1.6 | 0.1 | 0.0 | 0.0 | 2.0 |
| · Solo Practice | 835 | 1.5 | 0.1 | 0.0 | 0.0 | 2.0 |
| · Two Physician Practice | 233 | 1.4 | 0.2 | 0.0 | 0.0 | 2.0 |
| · Three Physician Practice | 180 | 2.1 | 0.3 | 0.0 | 0.0 | 3.0 |
| · 4-8 Physician Practice | 370 | 1.9 | 0.2 | 0.0 | 0.0 | 2.0 |
| · Over 8 Physician Practice | 142 | 1.2 | 0.2 | 0.0 | 0.0 | 1.0 |
| Employee | 1070 | 0.7 | 0.1 | 0.0 | 0.0 | 0.0 |
| Independent Contractor | 144 | 0.4 | 0.1 | 0.0 | 0.0 | 0.0 |

Source: 1995 Socioeconomic Monitoring System survey of nonfederal patient care physicians. See the beginning of this section, the introduction, and appendices for a discussion of the survey sample, definitions, and computation procedures. Statistics are not reported if the number of responses is less than 25.

Table 37. **Medicare Patients Discharged from the Hospital per Week, for Nonfederal Physicians (excluding Physicians in Radiology, Psychiatry, Anesthesiology, and Pathology), 1995**

| | Number of Responses | Mean | Standard Error | 25th Percentile | Median | 75th Percentile |
|---|---|---|---|---|---|---|
| All Physicians | 1813 | 2.6 | 0.1 | 0.0 | 2.0 | 3.0 |
| *Specialty* | | | | | | |
| General/Family Practice | 326 | 3.0 | 0.3 | 1.0 | 2.0 | 4.0 |
| Internal Medicine | 554 | 3.2 | 0.2 | 1.0 | 2.0 | 4.0 |
| · General Internal Medicine | 378 | 2.9 | 0.2 | 1.0 | 2.0 | 4.0 |
| · Cardiovascular Diseases | 76 | 5.0 | 0.7 | 2.0 | 4.0 | 7.0 |
| · Other | 100 | 2.7 | 0.3 | 1.0 | 2.0 | 4.0 |
| Surgery | 600 | 2.6 | 0.1 | 1.0 | 2.0 | 3.0 |
| · General Surgery | 167 | 3.5 | 0.3 | 2.0 | 2.0 | 4.0 |
| · Otolaryngology | 59 | 0.8 | 0.1 | 0.0 | 1.0 | 1.0 |
| · Orthopedic Surgery | 150 | 2.4 | 0.3 | 1.0 | 2.0 | 3.0 |
| · Ophthalmology | 60 | 1.2 | 0.3 | 0.0 | 0.0 | 2.0 |
| · Urological Surgery | 84 | 3.2 | 0.2 | 2.0 | 3.0 | 4.0 |
| · Other | 80 | 2.0 | 0.3 | 1.0 | 1.0 | 2.0 |
| Pediatrics | 43 | 2.5 | 0.9 | 0.0 | 0.0 | 2.0 |
| Obstetrics/Gynecology | 185 | 0.7 | 0.1 | 0.0 | 0.0 | 1.0 |
| Other Specialty | 105 | 1.9 | 0.3 | 0.0 | 0.0 | 4.0 |
| · Emergency Medicine | 5 | · | · | · | · | · |
| · Other | 100 | 1.7 | 0.2 | 0.0 | 0.0 | 3.0 |
| *Geographic Area* | | | | | | |
| New England | 107 | 2.3 | 0.2 | 1.0 | 2.0 | 4.0 |
| · Massachusetts | 49 | 2.9 | 0.3 | 1.0 | 2.0 | 5.0 |
| · Other | 58 | 1.8 | 0.2 | 0.0 | 1.0 | 3.0 |
| Middle Atlantic | 289 | 2.3 | 0.2 | 0.0 | 2.0 | 3.0 |
| · New Jersey | 51 | 2.0 | 0.4 | 0.0 | 2.0 | 2.0 |
| · New York | 108 | 2.1 | 0.3 | 0.0 | 1.0 | 3.0 |
| · Pennsylvania | 130 | 2.7 | 0.2 | 0.0 | 2.0 | 4.0 |
| East North Central | 287 | 2.9 | 0.2 | 0.0 | 2.0 | 4.0 |
| · Illinois | 99 | 3.0 | 0.4 | 0.0 | 2.0 | 3.0 |
| · Michigan | 52 | 2.8 | 0.8 | 0.0 | 1.0 | 4.0 |
| · Ohio | 63 | 2.5 | 0.4 | 0.0 | 2.0 | 4.0 |
| · Other | 73 | 3.1 | 0.4 | 1.0 | 2.0 | 4.0 |
| West North Central | 145 | 2.9 | 0.3 | 1.0 | 2.0 | 4.0 |
| South Atlantic | 312 | 2.5 | 0.2 | 0.0 | 2.0 | 4.0 |
| · Florida | 80 | 2.9 | 0.4 | 1.0 | 2.0 | 4.0 |
| · Other | 232 | 2.4 | 0.2 | 0.0 | 2.0 | 3.0 |
| East South Central | 120 | 3.0 | 0.3 | 1.0 | 2.0 | 4.0 |
| West South Central | 159 | 3.0 | 0.3 | 0.0 | 2.0 | 4.0 |
| · Texas | 101 | 2.8 | 0.3 | 0.0 | 2.0 | 4.0 |
| · Other | 58 | 3.5 | 0.6 | 0.0 | 2.0 | 4.0 |
| Mountain | 108 | 1.9 | 0.2 | 0.0 | 1.0 | 2.0 |
| Pacific | 286 | 2.4 | 0.3 | 0.0 | 1.0 | 3.0 |
| · California | 201 | 2.5 | 0.4 | 0.0 | 1.0 | 3.0 |
| · Other | 85 | 2.2 | 0.2 | 1.0 | 2.0 | 3.0 |
| *Practice Arrangement* | | | | | | |
| Self-Employed | 1195 | 2.8 | 0.1 | 1.0 | 2.0 | 4.0 |
| · Solo Practice | 537 | 2.7 | 0.2 | 1.0 | 2.0 | 4.0 |
| · Two Physician Practice | 162 | 3.1 | 0.3 | 0.0 | 2.0 | 4.0 |
| · Three Physician Practice | 139 | 2.7 | 0.3 | 0.0 | 2.0 | 4.0 |
| · 4-8 Physician Practice | 266 | 3.0 | 0.3 | 1.0 | 2.0 | 4.0 |
| · Over 8 Physician Practice | 90 | 2.9 | 0.3 | 1.0 | 2.0 | 4.0 |
| Employee | 573 | 2.1 | 0.1 | 0.0 | 2.0 | 3.0 |
| Independent Contractor | 45 | 2.4 | 0.5 | 0.0 | 2.0 | 3.0 |

Source: 1995 Socioeconomic Monitoring System survey of nonfederal patient care physicians. See the beginning of this section, the introduction, and appendices for a discussion of the survey sample, definitions, and computation procedures. Statistics are not reported if the number of responses is less than 25.

Table 38. **Average Length of Stay of Medicare Patients Discharged from the Hospital, for Nonfederal Physicians (excluding Physicians in Radiology, Psychiatry, Anesthesiology, and Pathology), 1995**

| | Number of Responses | Mean | Standard Error | 25th Percentile | Median | 75th Percentile |
|---|---|---|---|---|---|---|
| All Physicians | 1037 | 4.9 | 0.2 | 3.0 | 4.0 | 5.0 |
| *Specialty* | | | | | | |
| General/Family Practice | 215 | 4.6 | 0.2 | 3.0 | 4.0 | 5.0 |
| Internal Medicine | 384 | 5.7 | 0.3 | 4.0 | 5.0 | 6.0 |
| · General Internal Medicine | 261 | 5.5 | 0.3 | 4.0 | 5.0 | 6.0 |
| · Cardiovascular Diseases | 58 | 4.9 | 0.4 | 3.0 | 4.0 | 5.0 |
| · Other | 65 | 7.2 | 1.5 | 4.0 | 4.0 | 6.0 |
| Surgery | 359 | 3.9 | 0.3 | 2.0 | 3.0 | 5.0 |
| · General Surgery | 128 | 3.9 | 0.2 | 2.0 | 3.0 | 5.0 |
| · Otolaryngology | 16 | · | · | · | · | · |
| · Orthopedic Surgery | 91 | 4.7 | 0.2 | 4.0 | 5.0 | 6.0 |
| · Ophthalmology | 20 | · | · | · | · | · |
| · Urological Surgery | 69 | 3.2 | 0.2 | 2.0 | 3.0 | 4.0 |
| · Other | 35 | 3.7 | 0.3 | 3.0 | 3.0 | 5.0 |
| Pediatrics | 8 | · | · | · | · | · |
| Obstetrics/Gynecology | 32 | 2.4 | 0.2 | 2.0 | 2.0 | 3.0 |
| Other Specialty | 39 | 9.0 | 1.2 | 5.0 | 5.0 | 15.0 |
| · Emergency Medicine | 3 | · | · | · | · | · |
| · Other | 36 | 9.5 | 1.3 | 5.0 | 5.0 | 15.0 |
| *Geographic Area* | | | | | | |
| New England | 59 | 4.9 | 0.5 | 3.0 | 5.0 | 6.0 |
| · Massachusetts | 29 | 4.4 | 0.5 | 2.0 | 4.0 | 6.0 |
| · Other | 30 | 5.7 | 0.7 | 3.0 | 5.0 | 7.0 |
| Middle Atlantic | 167 | 5.3 | 0.2 | 4.0 | 5.0 | 7.0 |
| · New Jersey | 30 | 5.0 | 0.6 | 3.0 | 5.0 | 6.0 |
| · New York | 53 | 6.3 | 0.5 | 4.0 | 5.0 | 7.0 |
| · Pennsylvania | 84 | 4.8 | 0.2 | 3.0 | 4.0 | 6.0 |
| East North Central | 162 | 5.2 | 0.5 | 3.0 | 4.0 | 5.0 |
| · Illinois | 58 | 4.1 | 0.3 | 3.0 | 4.0 | 5.0 |
| · Michigan | 20 | · | · | · | · | · |
| · Ohio | 35 | 6.5 | 2.0 | 3.0 | 4.0 | 6.0 |
| · Other | 49 | 4.8 | 0.6 | 3.0 | 4.0 | 5.0 |
| West North Central | 87 | 4.4 | 0.2 | 3.0 | 4.0 | 5.0 |
| South Atlantic | 182 | 4.4 | 0.3 | 3.0 | 4.0 | 5.0 |
| · Florida | 56 | 5.0 | 0.7 | 3.0 | 4.0 | 5.0 |
| · Other | 126 | 4.2 | 0.2 | 2.0 | 4.0 | 5.0 |
| East South Central | 79 | 7.6 | 1.3 | 3.0 | 5.0 | 6.0 |
| West South Central | 90 | 4.7 | 0.4 | 3.0 | 4.0 | 5.0 |
| · Texas | 62 | 4.4 | 0.3 | 3.0 | 4.0 | 5.0 |
| · Other | 28 | 5.4 | 1.1 | 3.0 | 5.0 | 5.0 |
| Mountain | 53 | 5.4 | 1.7 | 3.0 | 3.0 | 5.0 |
| Pacific | 158 | 4.0 | 0.2 | 3.0 | 4.0 | 5.0 |
| · California | 108 | 3.9 | 0.2 | 3.0 | 4.0 | 5.0 |
| · Other | 50 | 4.3 | 0.4 | 3.0 | 3.0 | 5.0 |
| *Practice Arrangement* | | | | | | |
| Self-Employed | 721 | 4.8 | 0.2 | 3.0 | 4.0 | 5.0 |
| · Solo Practice | 333 | 4.4 | 0.3 | 3.0 | 4.0 | 5.0 |
| · Two Physician Practice | 86 | 4.7 | 0.2 | 3.0 | 5.0 | 5.0 |
| · Three Physician Practice | 82 | 4.5 | 0.3 | 3.0 | 4.0 | 5.0 |
| · 4-8 Physician Practice | 167 | 4.4 | 0.2 | 3.0 | 4.0 | 5.0 |
| · Over 8 Physician Practice | 53 | 8.8 | 1.8 | 3.0 | 5.0 | 7.0 |
| Employee | 294 | 5.0 | 0.3 | 3.0 | 4.0 | 6.0 |
| Independent Contractor | 22 | · | · | · | · | · |

Source: 1995 Socioeconomic Monitoring System survey of nonfederal patient care physicians. See the beginning of this section, the introduction, and appendices for a discussion of the survey sample, definitions, and computation procedures. Statistics are not reported if the number of responses is less than 25.

# Fees for Selected Nonfederal Physician Visits and Procedures

Office Visit with an Established Patient

Office Visit with a New Patient

Follow-up Hospital Visit

Selected Surgical and Other Procedures

Specialty Specific Fees for Office Visits
With Established and New Patients,
by Census Division and Practice Arrangement

## Fees for Selected Nonfederal Physician Visits and Procedures

Physicians responding to the SMS survey were asked to provide fees charged for selected services and procedures. Physicians were asked only for their fees charged to privately insured patients. However, the fees may not reflect the amount actually reimbursed by private insurers. In addition, the fees for privately insured patients may differ from fees charged to Medicare or Medicaid patients (the fees charged may also differ from the reimbursement amounts received from these sources). The fee questions make specific reference to AMA Current Procedural Terminology (CPT) codes that are applicable to each service or procedure. For some procedures or services a range of CPT codes is indicated. For example, there are four CPT codes for an office visit with an established patient. The codes represent differences in the length of time spent with the patient. However, rather than ask four different fee questions, physicians were asked to provide a single fee for the visit. If necessary, a probe that asked the physicians to give the fee for the procedure they did most often was used.

Prior to asking any fee questions, all physicians except anesthesiologists were asked the following question to ascertain whether the fee questions were pertinent to their practice:

1. Does this practice provide at least some medical care on a fee-for-service basis? (By fee-for-service, we mean that your practice charges patients fees for specific medical services rather than charging a lump sum or premium for comprehensive medical services. Patients typically are covered for comprehensive medical services in HMOs and on a fee-for-service basis in other settings.)

Anesthesia services are usually charged for on the basis of time units reflecting the actual amount of time spent in providing anesthesia services for a procedure and a base charge that is determined by the complexity of service. For this reason, instead of Question 1, anesthesiologists were asked:

2. Is your fee based upon both the complexity of the procedure and the number of units of anesthesia time required?

Questions on fees were asked only of those physicians who responded affirmatively to Question 1 or 2. The question on a fee for an individual service or procedure was omitted for physicians who indicated that they had not performed it in the last week or last month as determined from the response to the relevant question given at the beginning of the section on physician service utilization. The intent was to collect fee information for any service or procedure only from physicians who performed it as a regular part of their practices.

The specific questions used to collect the fee information used in calculating statistics reported in this section are as follows:

3. What do you typically charge a privately insured patient for:

Probe: Private insurers include all insurers except Medicare and Medicaid.

All specialties except ophthalmology, radiology, psychiatry, anesthesiology, and pathology

a. an office visit with a new patient that includes an evaluation history, examination, and medical decision-making – CPT 99201-99205?

b. an office visit with an established patient that includes an evaluation history, examination and medical decision-making – CPT 99211-99215?

*All specialties except, radiology, psychiatry, anesthesiology, and pathology*

c. subsequent hospital care when you charge a separate fee for hospital visits – CPT 99231-99233?

*Ophthalmology*

d. an established patient office visit to initiate or continue an ophthalmological diagnostic and treatment program – CPT 92012 or CPT 92014?

e. a new patient office visit to initiate an ophthalmological diagnostic or treatment program – CPT 92002 or CPT 92004?

4. What do you typically charge a privately insured patient for:

Probe: Private insurers include all insurers except Medicare and Medicaid.

*General/family practice, internal medicine*

a. an electrocardiogram including the fee for the use of the electrocardiograph, interpretation and report – CPT 93000?

b. a periodic or annual type of exam (a routine check-up) with an adult established patient, excluding any lab or x-ray charges – CPT 99395-99397?

*General/family practice, obstetrics/gynecology*

c. complete obstetrical care leading to a vaginal delivery including antepartum care, vaginal delivery and postpartum care (with or without low forceps and/or episiotomy) – CPT 59400?

*General surgery*

d. an appendectomy – CPT 44950 or CPT 44960?

e. a single inguinal hernia repair on a person age 5 or older – CPT 49505?

f. a cholecystectomy (gall bladder removal) – CPT 47600?

*Otolaryngology*

g. tonsillectomy with an adenoidectomy on a child 12 years of age or under – CPT 42820?

*Orthopedic surgery*

h. a secondary repair of a torn, ruptured or severed knee, collateral and cruciate ligaments – CPT 27427?

i. a total hip replacement – CPT 27130?

*Ophthalmology*

j. cataract extraction and lens insertion – CPT 66984?

*Urological surgery*

k. a transurethral resection of the prostate – CPT 52601?

*Pediatrics*

l. a periodic or annual type of exam with a patient in early childhood, 1-4 years old, excluding any lab or x-ray charges – CPT 99382?

m. routine newborn care in the hospital excluding any lab or x-ray charges – CPT 99431 or 99433?

*Obstetrics/gynecology*

n. a cesarean section with antepartum and postpartum care – CPT 59510?

o. a total hysterectomy with or without removal of tubes and/or ovaries – CPT 58150?

*Radiology*

p. a radiological exam of the upper gastrointestinal tract without KUB – CPT 74240?

q. a radiologic exam of the chest – CPT 71020?

r. a CAT scan of the head with intravenous contrast – CPT 70460?

*Psychiatry*

s. an individual psychotherapy session which lasts 45-60 minutes – CPT 90841?

t. a family psychotherapy session for two family members which lasts 45-60 minutes – CPT 90847? (This may also be called conjoint therapy).

u. a psychiatric diagnostic evaluation – CPT 90801?

*Anesthesiology*

v. a unit of anesthesia time? How many minutes are there in a unit of anesthesia time?

*Pathology*

w. a consultation during surgery including frozen section – CPT 88331?

x. a pathological examination of a surgical specimen, gross and microscopic (e.g., uterine tubes, vas derns, sympathetic ganglion) – CPT 88302?

y. interpretation of cervical pap smears, including lab fees – CPT 88150?

Tables 39 and 43-48, 40 and 49-54, 41, and 42 are, respectively, based on responses to Questions 3a and 3d, Questions 3b and 3e, Question 3c, and Question 4.

Following questions on fees for services provided by radiologists (4p, 4q and 4r), the physician was also asked:

5. Does that charge include the technical or nonphysician component? (The technical or nonphysician component may also be called the hospital component.)

Fees that did not include the technical or nonphysician component were excluded for purposes of calculating statistics on fees for radiologic services. For services provided by radiologists and pathologists, if the physician indicated that his or her fee varied by hospital, the interviewer was instructed to ask for the fee charged in the location in which the physician performed the most of each procedure.

For anesthesiologists, fees for anesthesia time are all standardized in terms of 15-minute units of anesthesia time for purposes of calculating the fee statistics on anesthesia time.

Figure 17. **Mean and Median Fees (in dollars) for Selected Surgical Procedures, for Nonfederal Physicians, 1995**

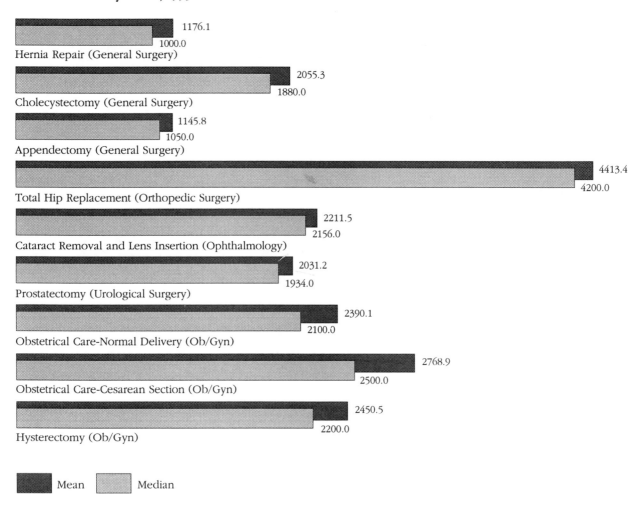

1176.1
1000.0
Hernia Repair (General Surgery)

2055.3
1880.0
Cholecystectomy (General Surgery)

1145.8
1050.0
Appendectomy (General Surgery)

4413.4
4200.0
Total Hip Replacement (Orthopedic Surgery)

2211.5
2156.0
Cataract Removal and Lens Insertion (Ophthalmology)

2031.2
1934.0
Prostatectomy (Urological Surgery)

2390.1
2100.0
Obstetrical Care-Normal Delivery (Ob/Gyn)

2768.9
2500.0
Obstetrical Care-Cesarean Section (Ob/Gyn)

2450.5
2200.0
Hysterectomy (Ob/Gyn)

■ Mean    ▨ Median

Figure 18. **Mean and Median Fee (in dollars) for an Established Patient Office Visit, for Nonfederal Physicians, for Selected States, 1995**[a]

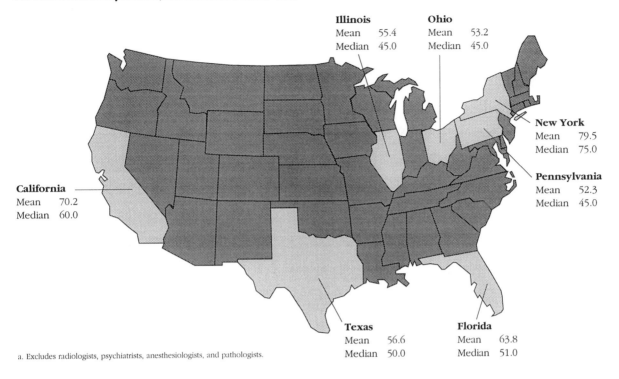

**Illinois**
Mean     55.4
Median   45.0

**Ohio**
Mean     53.2
Median   45.0

**New York**
Mean     79.5
Median   75.0

**Pennsylvania**
Mean     52.3
Median   45.0

**California**
Mean     70.2
Median   60.0

**Texas**
Mean     56.6
Median   50.0

**Florida**
Mean     63.8
Median   51.0

a. Excludes radiologists, psychiatrists, anesthesiologists, and pathologists.

Figure 19. **Mean and Median Fee (in dollars) for an Established Patient Office Visit per Self-Employed Nonfederal Physician, by Size of Practice, 1995**[a]

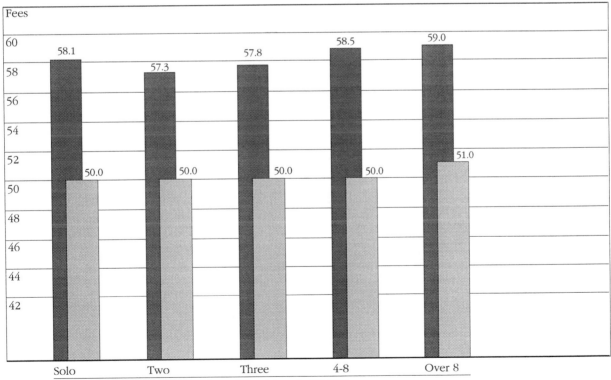

a. Excludes radiologists, psychiatrists, anesthesiologists, and pathologists.

**Table 39. Fee (in dollars) for an Office Visit with an Established Patient, for Nonfederal Physicians (excluding Physicians in Radiology, Psychiatry, Anesthesiology, and Pathology), 1995**

| | Number of Responses | Mean | Standard Error | 25th Percentile | Median | 75th Percentile |
|---|---|---|---|---|---|---|
| All Physicians | 2378 | 59.4 | 0.7 | 40.0 | 50.0 | 70.0 |
| *Specialty* | | | | | | |
| General/Family Practice | 429 | 45.9 | 0.9 | 35.0 | 40.0 | 50.0 |
| Internal Medicine | 603 | 64.4 | 1.6 | 45.0 | 55.0 | 75.0 |
| · General Internal Medicine | 398 | 63.8 | 1.6 | 45.0 | 55.0 | 75.0 |
| · Cardiovascular Diseases | 84 | 73.9 | 6.5 | 50.0 | 60.0 | 85.0 |
| · Other | 121 | 60.1 | 4.1 | 45.0 | 55.0 | 67.0 |
| Surgery | 737 | 60.8 | 1.3 | 40.0 | 52.0 | 70.0 |
| · General Surgery | 172 | 54.0 | 2.2 | 40.0 | 45.0 | 65.0 |
| · Otolaryngology | 65 | 60.9 | 7.6 | 38.0 | 46.0 | 67.0 |
| · Orthopedic Surgery | 157 | 53.3 | 1.8 | 40.0 | 50.0 | 60.0 |
| · Ophthalmology | 166 | 70.0 | 1.6 | 55.0 | 65.0 | 84.0 |
| · Urological Surgery | 83 | 57.0 | 3.2 | 40.0 | 50.0 | 65.0 |
| · Other | 94 | 73.1 | 5.7 | 44.0 | 60.0 | 80.0 |
| Pediatrics | 234 | 49.2 | 1.1 | 40.0 | 45.0 | 55.0 |
| Obstetrics/Gynecology | 197 | 69.5 | 2.0 | 50.0 | 63.0 | 80.0 |
| Other Specialty | 178 | 65.6 | 2.5 | 44.0 | 56.0 | 75.0 |
| · Emergency Medicine | 0 | · | · | · | · | · |
| · Other | 178 | 65.6 | 2.5 | 44.0 | 56.0 | 75.0 |
| *Geographic Area* | | | | | | |
| New England | 151 | 71.8 | 4.1 | 49.0 | 59.0 | 85.0 |
| · Massachusetts | 62 | 80.9 | 8.5 | 50.0 | 65.0 | 90.0 |
| · Other | 89 | 64.1 | 3.4 | 45.0 | 55.0 | 70.0 |
| Middle Atlantic | 372 | 64.6 | 1.8 | 40.0 | 60.0 | 75.0 |
| · New Jersey | 69 | 66.6 | 4.7 | 50.0 | 60.0 | 65.0 |
| · New York | 138 | 78.1 | 3.3 | 50.0 | 75.0 | 95.0 |
| · Pennsylvania | 165 | 51.4 | 1.7 | 38.0 | 41.0 | 60.0 |
| East North Central | 365 | 55.8 | 2.1 | 40.0 | 46.0 | 60.0 |
| · Illinois | 121 | 54.1 | 3.5 | 40.0 | 45.0 | 60.0 |
| · Michigan | 64 | 56.6 | 3.1 | 40.0 | 50.0 | 70.0 |
| · Ohio | 88 | 55.3 | 3.3 | 40.0 | 45.0 | 60.0 |
| · Other | 92 | 58.5 | 5.6 | 38.0 | 50.0 | 60.0 |
| West North Central | 181 | 49.6 | 1.7 | 35.0 | 44.0 | 55.0 |
| South Atlantic | 445 | 57.5 | 1.5 | 40.0 | 50.0 | 69.0 |
| · Florida | 126 | 62.9 | 4.0 | 43.0 | 55.0 | 75.0 |
| · Other | 319 | 55.3 | 1.3 | 40.0 | 50.0 | 65.0 |
| East South Central | 150 | 48.8 | 1.4 | 37.0 | 45.0 | 55.0 |
| West South Central | 224 | 52.9 | 1.6 | 40.0 | 45.0 | 60.0 |
| · Texas | 150 | 55.3 | 2.3 | 40.0 | 48.0 | 65.0 |
| · Other | 74 | 47.5 | 1.7 | 35.0 | 44.0 | 52.0 |
| Mountain | 138 | 54.2 | 1.5 | 41.0 | 50.0 | 63.0 |
| Pacific | 352 | 68.7 | 1.7 | 50.0 | 60.0 | 80.0 |
| · California | 237 | 70.6 | 2.3 | 50.0 | 60.0 | 80.0 |
| · Other | 115 | 63.5 | 2.1 | 49.0 | 55.0 | 75.0 |
| *Practice Arrangement* | | | | | | |
| Self-Employed | 1577 | 57.8 | 0.8 | 40.0 | 50.0 | 68.0 |
| · Solo Practice | 757 | 57.7 | 1.3 | 40.0 | 50.0 | 70.0 |
| · Two Physician Practice | 211 | 57.3 | 1.6 | 40.0 | 50.0 | 65.0 |
| · Three Physician Practice | 169 | 57.9 | 2.0 | 40.0 | 50.0 | 70.0 |
| · 4-8 Physician Practice | 333 | 58.0 | 1.5 | 40.0 | 50.0 | 65.0 |
| · Over 8 Physician Practice | 106 | 58.6 | 2.4 | 45.0 | 50.0 | 65.0 |
| Employee | 733 | 63.1 | 1.4 | 42.0 | 52.0 | 74.0 |
| Independent Contractor | 68 | 55.3 | 2.8 | 40.0 | 47.0 | 70.0 |

Source: 1995 Socioeconomic Monitoring System survey of nonfederal patient care physicians. See the beginning of this section, the introduction, and appendices for a discussion of the survey sample, definitions, and computation procedures. Statistics are not reported if the number of responses is less than 25.

Table 40. **Fee (in dollars) for an Office Visit with a New Patient, for Nonfederal Physicians (excluding Physicians in Radiology, Psychiatry, Anesthesiology, and Pathology), 1995**

| | Number of Responses | Mean | Standard Error | 25th Percentile | Median | 75th Percentile |
|---|---|---|---|---|---|---|
| All Physicians | 2376 | 102.7 | 1.3 | 60.0 | 85.0 | 130.0 |
| *Specialty* | | | | | | |
| General/Family Practice | 418 | 64.9 | 1.3 | 45.0 | 60.0 | 75.0 |
| Internal Medicine | 601 | 133.9 | 3.4 | 81.0 | 125.0 | 160.0 |
| · General Internal Medicine | 393 | 127.6 | 4.3 | 75.0 | 120.0 | 150.0 |
| · Cardiovascular Diseases | 82 | 152.7 | 9.0 | 105.0 | 145.0 | 175.0 |
| · Other | 126 | 142.1 | 6.5 | 100.0 | 138.0 | 165.0 |
| Surgery | 746 | 96.1 | 1.7 | 64.0 | 80.0 | 120.0 |
| · General Surgery | 174 | 92.9 | 4.0 | 58.0 | 75.0 | 115.0 |
| · Otolaryngology | 68 | 86.1 | 4.1 | 60.0 | 75.0 | 105.0 |
| · Orthopedic Surgery | 159 | 90.8 | 2.9 | 60.0 | 80.0 | 120.0 |
| · Ophthalmology | 165 | 87.0 | 2.2 | 70.0 | 80.0 | 95.0 |
| · Urological Surgery | 84 | 101.3 | 4.2 | 75.0 | 95.0 | 120.0 |
| · Other | 96 | 124.6 | 7.0 | 60.0 | 112.0 | 160.0 |
| Pediatrics | 230 | 71.4 | 2.5 | 50.0 | 60.0 | 75.0 |
| Obstetrics/Gynecology | 203 | 100.8 | 2.9 | 75.0 | 91.0 | 120.0 |
| Other Specialty | 178 | 129.8 | 5.3 | 65.0 | 125.0 | 175.0 |
| · Emergency Medicine | 0 | . | . | . | . | . |
| · Other | 178 | 129.8 | 5.3 | 65.0 | 125.0 | 175.0 |
| *Geographic Area* | | | | | | |
| New England | 147 | 107.3 | 5.9 | 65.0 | 90.0 | 130.0 |
| · Massachusetts | 60 | 116.7 | 12.0 | 75.0 | 90.0 | 130.0 |
| · Other | 87 | 99.6 | 5.6 | 59.0 | 80.0 | 130.0 |
| Middle Atlantic | 371 | 115.6 | 4.4 | 65.0 | 100.0 | 150.0 |
| · New Jersey | 69 | 128.5 | 17.9 | 60.0 | 95.0 | 125.0 |
| · New York | 137 | 135.8 | 5.9 | 80.0 | 125.0 | 175.0 |
| · Pennsylvania | 165 | 89.9 | 3.5 | 55.0 | 75.0 | 120.0 |
| East North Central | 364 | 91.0 | 2.5 | 57.0 | 75.0 | 120.0 |
| · Illinois | 121 | 90.7 | 4.3 | 55.0 | 75.0 | 120.0 |
| · Michigan | 63 | 90.1 | 5.7 | 60.0 | 80.0 | 120.0 |
| · Ohio | 88 | 99.8 | 6.1 | 60.0 | 80.0 | 125.0 |
| · Other | 92 | 82.2 | 3.7 | 57.0 | 75.0 | 100.0 |
| West North Central | 187 | 79.9 | 3.0 | 50.0 | 67.0 | 90.0 |
| South Atlantic | 443 | 102.2 | 2.8 | 60.0 | 85.0 | 125.0 |
| · Florida | 127 | 109.9 | 6.2 | 65.0 | 95.0 | 150.0 |
| · Other | 316 | 99.1 | 3.1 | 60.0 | 80.0 | 125.0 |
| East South Central | 148 | 93.3 | 3.9 | 55.0 | 75.0 | 120.0 |
| West South Central | 225 | 95.3 | 3.4 | 57.0 | 75.0 | 125.0 |
| · Texas | 148 | 100.6 | 4.7 | 55.0 | 75.0 | 125.0 |
| · Other | 77 | 83.8 | 4.1 | 58.0 | 71.0 | 110.0 |
| Mountain | 137 | 93.2 | 3.8 | 60.0 | 76.0 | 125.0 |
| Pacific | 354 | 122.1 | 3.4 | 72.0 | 104.0 | 150.0 |
| · California | 241 | 131.8 | 4.5 | 76.0 | 120.0 | 170.0 |
| · Other | 113 | 95.4 | 3.9 | 65.0 | 85.0 | 120.0 |
| *Practice Arrangement* | | | | | | |
| Self-Employed | 1581 | 99.9 | 1.6 | 60.0 | 80.0 | 125.0 |
| · Solo Practice | 756 | 102.3 | 2.7 | 60.0 | 80.0 | 125.0 |
| · Two Physician Practice | 214 | 89.8 | 3.0 | 60.0 | 75.0 | 115.0 |
| · Three Physician Practice | 166 | 96.7 | 3.7 | 60.0 | 85.0 | 120.0 |
| · 4-8 Physician Practice | 334 | 101.7 | 2.9 | 60.0 | 85.0 | 130.0 |
| · Over 8 Physician Practice | 110 | 100.5 | 3.9 | 65.0 | 100.0 | 125.0 |
| Employee | 729 | 110.1 | 2.3 | 63.0 | 95.0 | 140.0 |
| Independent Contractor | 66 | 87.3 | 5.9 | 51.0 | 71.0 | 110.0 |

Source: 1995 Socioeconomic Monitoring System survey of nonfederal patient care physicians. See the beginning of this section, the introduction, and appendices for a discussion of the survey sample, definitions, and computation procedures. Statistics are not reported if the number of responses is less than 25.

Table 41. **Fee (in dollars) for a Follow-up Hospital Visit, for Nonfederal Physicians (excluding Physicians in Radiology, Psychiatry, Anesthesiology, and Pathology), 1995**

| | Number of Responses | Mean | Standard Error | 25th Percentile | Median | 75th Percentile |
|---|---|---|---|---|---|---|
| All Physicians | 1613 | 67.1 | 1.0 | 46.0 | 60.0 | 75.0 |
| *Specialty* | | | | | | |
| General/Family Practice | 261 | 56.6 | 1.3 | 42.0 | 50.0 | 65.0 |
| Internal Medicine | 487 | 67.9 | 1.7 | 50.0 | 60.0 | 75.0 |
| · General Internal Medicine | 319 | 67.6 | 2.0 | 50.0 | 60.0 | 75.0 |
| · Cardiovascular Diseases | 67 | 68.9 | 3.9 | 55.0 | 60.0 | 77.0 |
| · Other | 101 | 68.1 | 4.1 | 50.0 | 60.0 | 75.0 |
| Surgery | 465 | 64.1 | 1.4 | 45.0 | 56.0 | 75.0 |
| · General Surgery | 113 | 59.0 | 2.2 | 45.0 | 50.0 | 74.0 |
| · Otolaryngology | 43 | 65.3 | 3.6 | 41.0 | 66.0 | 75.0 |
| · Orthopedic Surgery | 83 | 58.9 | 2.9 | 40.0 | 50.0 | 75.0 |
| · Ophthalmology | 101 | 70.8 | 3.3 | 45.0 | 65.0 | 85.0 |
| · Urological Surgery | 62 | 59.0 | 2.7 | 45.0 | 53.0 | 74.0 |
| · Other | 63 | 73.2 | 6.2 | 50.0 | 60.0 | 95.0 |
| Pediatrics | 174 | 73.7 | 3.5 | 45.0 | 60.0 | 80.0 |
| Obstetrics/Gynecology | 112 | 76.2 | 6.9 | 50.0 | 65.0 | 85.0 |
| Other Specialty | 114 | 75.2 | 3.6 | 50.0 | 64.0 | 90.0 |
| · Emergency Medicine | 0 | . | . | . | . | . |
| · Other | 114 | 75.2 | 3.6 | 50.0 | 64.0 | 90.0 |
| *Geographic Area* | | | | | | |
| New England | 100 | 67.4 | 3.8 | 45.0 | 60.0 | 75.0 |
| · Massachusetts | 38 | 76.5 | 8.7 | 45.0 | 65.0 | 80.0 |
| · Other | 62 | 59.8 | 2.7 | 45.0 | 55.0 | 70.0 |
| Middle Atlantic | 241 | 69.2 | 2.3 | 50.0 | 65.0 | 80.0 |
| · New Jersey | 54 | 70.0 | 2.8 | 60.0 | 70.0 | 80.0 |
| · New York | 90 | 77.1 | 4.6 | 51.0 | 75.0 | 100.0 |
| · Pennsylvania | 97 | 60.4 | 3.1 | 40.0 | 51.0 | 70.0 |
| East North Central | 246 | 62.7 | 1.9 | 45.0 | 58.0 | 74.0 |
| · Illinois | 88 | 64.5 | 3.4 | 45.0 | 60.0 | 75.0 |
| · Michigan | 37 | 60.2 | 6.1 | 42.0 | 50.0 | 60.0 |
| · Ohio | 59 | 62.2 | 3.1 | 46.0 | 60.0 | 70.0 |
| · Other | 62 | 61.7 | 3.3 | 42.0 | 60.0 | 74.0 |
| West North Central | 128 | 63.2 | 6.2 | 40.0 | 50.0 | 68.0 |
| South Atlantic | 304 | 69.3 | 2.2 | 50.0 | 60.0 | 80.0 |
| · Florida | 89 | 71.2 | 4.4 | 50.0 | 65.0 | 81.0 |
| · Other | 215 | 68.6 | 2.6 | 50.0 | 60.0 | 80.0 |
| East South Central | 109 | 53.9 | 2.0 | 40.0 | 50.0 | 64.0 |
| West South Central | 150 | 66.0 | 2.7 | 45.0 | 60.0 | 75.0 |
| · Texas | 102 | 68.3 | 3.6 | 50.0 | 60.0 | 75.0 |
| · Other | 48 | 60.4 | 3.5 | 40.0 | 50.0 | 75.0 |
| Mountain | 103 | 65.6 | 3.0 | 45.0 | 60.0 | 75.0 |
| Pacific | 232 | 74.8 | 2.5 | 50.0 | 65.0 | 88.0 |
| · California | 160 | 77.6 | 3.3 | 50.0 | 65.0 | 90.0 |
| · Other | 72 | 66.2 | 3.0 | 50.0 | 60.0 | 75.0 |
| *Practice Arrangement* | | | | | | |
| Self-Employed | 1135 | 64.8 | 1.1 | 45.0 | 60.0 | 75.0 |
| · Solo Practice | 537 | 66.9 | 1.3 | 50.0 | 60.0 | 75.0 |
| · Two Physician Practice | 153 | 66.3 | 4.9 | 45.0 | 59.0 | 75.0 |
| · Three Physician Practice | 122 | 60.3 | 2.2 | 40.0 | 57.0 | 71.0 |
| · 4-8 Physician Practice | 246 | 62.0 | 2.1 | 45.0 | 55.0 | 74.0 |
| · Over 8 Physician Practice | 77 | 60.5 | 4.6 | 45.0 | 51.0 | 65.0 |
| Employee | 438 | 73.2 | 2.1 | 50.0 | 60.0 | 85.0 |
| Independent Contractor | 40 | 62.1 | 4.1 | 49.0 | 60.0 | 75.0 |

Source: 1995 Socioeconomic Monitoring System survey of nonfederal patient care physicians. See the beginning of this section, the introduction, and appendices for a discussion of the survey sample, definitions, and computation procedures. Statistics are not reported if the number of responses is less than 25.

## Table 42. **Fee (in dollars) for Selected Services and Procedures, for Nonfederal Physicians, 1995**

| | Number of Responses | Mean | Standard Error | 25th Percentile | Median | 75th Percentile |
|---|---|---|---|---|---|---|
| *General/family practice* | | | | | | |
| Periodic or annual exam | 335 | 75.8 | 1.8 | 52.0 | 70.0 | · 90.0 |
| Electrocardiogram | 277 | 50.8 | 1.2 | 40.0 | 50.0 | 60.0 |
| Obstetrical care – vaginal delivery | 74 | 1625.8 | 42.7 | 1300.0 | 1600.0 | 2000.0 |
| *Internal medicine* | | | | | | |
| Periodic or annual exam | 332 | 100.5 | 3.9 | 60.0 | 90.0 | 125.0 |
| Electrocardiogram | 369 | 56.5 | 2.1 | 45.0 | 55.0 | 61.0 |
| *General surgery* | | | | | | |
| Single inguinal hernia repair | 129 | 1176.1 | 90.8 | 850.0 | 1000.0 | 1200.0 |
| Cholecystectomy | 108 | 2055.3 | 113.1 | 1488.0 | 1880.0 | 2500.0 |
| Appendectomy | 124 | 1145.8 | 72.7 | 900.0 | 1050.0 | 1279.0 |
| *Otolaryngology* | | | | | | |
| Tonsillectomy | 42 | 769.8 | 46.9 | 600.0 | 652.0 | 900.0 |
| *Orthopedic Surgery* | | | | | | |
| Total hip replacement | 83 | 4413.4 | 134.9 | 3570.0 | 4200.0 | 5000.0 |
| Knee ligament repair | 49 | 3421.8 | 233.3 | 2200.0 | 3000.0 | 3850.0 |
| *Ophthalmology* | | | | | | |
| Cataract removal and lens insertion | 127 | 2211.5 | 74.6 | 1800.0 | 2156.0 | 2500.0 |
| *Urological surgery* | | | | | | |
| Transurethral resection of prostate | 62 | 2031.2 | 138.5 | 1570.0 | 1934.0 | 2200.0 |
| *Pediatrics* | | | | | | |
| Periodic or annual type exam | 204 | 49.7 | 1.1 | 40.0 | 45.0 | 55.0 |
| Routine newborn care | 182 | 988.2 | 203.6 | 100.0 | 130.0 | 180.0 |
| *Obstetrics/gynecology* | | | | | | |
| Obstetrical care – vaginal delivery | 146 | 2390.1 | 121.0 | 1800.0 | 2100.0 | 2500.0 |
| Obstetrical care – cesarean section | 135 | 2768.9 | 119.5 | 2025.0 | 2500.0 | 3125.0 |
| Total hysterectomy | 138 | 2450.5 | 96.7 | 1900.0 | 2200.0 | 2850.0 |
| *Radiology* | | | | | | |
| Radiologic exam of chest | 72 | 30.6 | 1.4 | 22.0 | 28.0 | 35.0 |
| Radiologic exam of upper GI tract | 45 | 85.1 | 4.0 | 62.0 | 80.0 | 103.0 |
| CT scan of head | 59 | 147.0 | 5.0 | 110.0 | 150.0 | 174.0 |
| *Psychiatry* | | | | | | |
| Individual psychotherapy session | 98 | 127.5 | 3.3 | 110.0 | 125.0 | 136.0 |
| Psychiatric diagnostic evaluation | 88 | 157.7 | 4.3 | 125.0 | 150.0 | 180.0 |
| Family psychotherapy session | 58 | 133.4 | 3.9 | 110.0 | 130.0 | 150.0 |
| *Anesthesiology* | | | | | | |
| 15 minute unit of anesthesia time | 170 | 50.4 | 1.0 | 42.0 | 48.8 | 56.0 |
| *Pathology* | | | | | | |
| Surgical consultation | 23 | · | · | · | · | · |
| Examination of surgical specimen | 19 | · | · | · | · | · |
| Pap smear interpretation | 18 | · | · | · | · | · |

Source: 1995 Socioeconomic Monitoring System survey of nonfederal patient care physicians. See the beginning of this section, the introduction, and appendices for a discussion of the survey sample, definitions, and computation procedures. Statistics are not reported if the number of responses is less than 25.

Table 43. **Fee (in dollars) for an Office Visit with an Established Patient, for Nonfederal Physicians, 1995 – General/Family Practice**

| | Number of Responses | Mean | Standard Error | 25th Percentile | Median | 75th Percentile |
|---|---|---|---|---|---|---|
| All Physicians | 429 | 45.9 | 0.9 | 35 | 40 | 50 |
| *Geographic Area* | | | | | | |
| New England | 26 | 53.0 | 3.1 | 42 | 50 | 60 |
| Middle Atlantic | 51 | 44.8 | 3.3 | 35 | 40 | 42 |
| East North Central | 75 | 42.2 | 1.6 | 35 | 40 | 46 |
| West North Central | 53 | 42.0 | 1.9 | 33 | 38 | 47 |
| South Atlantic | 67 | 43.6 | 1.5 | 35 | 40 | 47 |
| East South Central | 30 | 42.6 | 2.7 | 33 | 40 | 42 |
| West South Central | 31 | 40.1 | 1.4 | 35 | 40 | 45 |
| Mountain | 36 | 49.6 | 2.8 | 40 | 45 | 54 |
| Pacific | 60 | 56.1 | 3.9 | 43 | 50 | 60 |
| *Practice Arrangement* | | | | | | |
| Self-Employed | 245 | 45.6 | 1.2 | 35 | 40 | 50 |
| · Solo Practice | 140 | 43.0 | 1.3 | 35 | 40 | 50 |
| · Two Physician Practice | 34 | 55.3 | 5.6 | 35 | 42 | 64 |
| · Three Physician Practice | 18 | . | . | . | . | . |
| · 4-8 Physician Practice | 41 | 45.0 | 1.6 | 39 | 41 | 50 |
| · Over 8 Physician Practice | 12 | . | . | . | . | . |
| Employee | 162 | 46.3 | 1.5 | 35 | 42 | 52 |
| Independent Contractor | 22 | . | . | . | . | . |

Source: 1995 Socioeconomic Monitoring System survey of nonfederal patient care physicians. See the beginning of this section, the introduction, and appendices for a discussion of the survey sample, definitions, and computation procedures. Statistics are not reported if the number of responses is less than 25.

Table 44. **Fee (in dollars) for an Office Visit with an Established Patient, for Nonfederal Physicians, 1995 – Internal Medicine**

| | Number of Responses | Mean | Standard Error | 25th Percentile | Median | 75th Percentile |
|---|---|---|---|---|---|---|
| All Physicians | 603 | 64.4 | 1.6 | 45 | 55 | 75 |
| *Geographic Area* | | | | | | |
| New England | 50 | 83.6 | 10.6 | 50 | 60 | 85 |
| Middle Atlantic | 111 | 67.7 | 2.8 | 45 | 65 | 75 |
| East North Central | 92 | 55.2 | 3.0 | 42 | 47 | 60 |
| West North Central | 32 | 65.8 | 6.4 | 40 | 49 | 92 |
| South Atlantic | 113 | 62.5 | 4.5 | 43 | 55 | 75 |
| East South Central | 44 | 51.7 | 3.0 | 43 | 50 | 55 |
| West South Central | 51 | 59.1 | 4.0 | 45 | 50 | 65 |
| Mountain | 25 | 60.6 | 4.9 | 45 | 58 | 65 |
| Pacific | 85 | 74.0 | 3.5 | 54 | 65 | 85 |
| *Practice Arrangement* | | | | | | |
| Self-Employed | 386 | 63.0 | 1.8 | 45 | 55 | 75 |
| · Solo Practice | 182 | 65.1 | 3.3 | 45 | 56 | 75 |
| · Two Physician Practice | 41 | 63.0 | 3.8 | 50 | 59 | 70 |
| · Three Physician Practice | 42 | 57.7 | 4.1 | 41 | 45 | 60 |
| · 4-8 Physician Practice | 78 | 61.5 | 3.0 | 40 | 57 | 70 |
| · Over 8 Physician Practice | 43 | 59.9 | 3.9 | 45 | 51 | 70 |
| Employee | 205 | 67.7 | 3.3 | 45 | 55 | 75 |
| Independent Contractor | 12 | . | . | . | . | . |

Source: 1995 Socioeconomic Monitoring System survey of nonfederal patient care physicians. See the beginning of this section, the introduction, and appendices for a discussion of the survey sample, definitions, and computation procedures. Statistics are not reported if the number of responses is less than 25.

Table 45. **Fee (in dollars) for an Office Visit with an Established Patient, for Nonfederal Physicians, 1995 – Surgery**

| | Number of Responses | Mean | Standard Error | 25th Percentile | Median | 75th Percentile |
|---|---|---|---|---|---|---|
| All Physicians | 737 | 60.8 | 1.3 | 40 | 52 | 70 |
| *Geographic Area* | | | | | | |
| New England | 44 | 73.9 | 5.2 | 50 | 65 | 90 |
| Middle Atlantic | 109 | 73.5 | 4.0 | 45 | 60 | 80 |
| East North Central | 107 | 65.1 | 6.0 | 40 | 50 | 71 |
| West North Central | 57 | 47.1 | 2.8 | 33 | 44 | 52 |
| South Atlantic | 153 | 56.3 | 1.8 | 45 | 50 | 68 |
| East South Central | 43 | 45.4 | 2.3 | 33 | 45 | 53 |
| West South Central | 76 | 50.5 | 2.8 | 35 | 45 | 55 |
| Mountain | 35 | 52.4 | 2.3 | 40 | 52 | 61 |
| Pacific | 113 | 65.8 | 2.4 | 45 | 60 | 76 |
| *Practice Arrangement* | | | | | | |
| Self-Employed | 554 | 58.1 | 1.4 | 40 | 50 | 67 |
| · Solo Practice | 247 | 57.2 | 2.4 | 40 | 50 | 65 |
| · Two Physician Practice | 88 | 56.6 | 2.3 | 40 | 50 | 65 |
| · Three Physician Practice | 72 | 63.0 | 3.5 | 44 | 55 | 75 |
| · 4-8 Physician Practice | 119 | 58.3 | 3.1 | 40 | 50 | 64 |
| · Over 8 Physician Practice | 28 | 59.5 | 4.7 | 40 | 55 | 65 |
| Employee | 163 | 68.8 | 3.4 | 45 | 57 | 75 |
| Independent Contractor | 20 | . | . | . | . | . |

Source: 1995 Socioeconomic Monitoring System survey of nonfederal patient care physicians. See the beginning of this section, the introduction, and appendices for a discussion of the survey sample, definitions, and computation procedures. Statistics are not reported if the number of responses is less than 25.

Table 46. **Fee (in dollars) for an Office Visit with an Established Patient, for Nonfederal Physicians, 1995 – Pediatrics**

| | Number of Responses | Mean | Standard Error | 25th Percentile | Median | 75th Percentile |
|---|---|---|---|---|---|---|
| All Physicians | 234 | 49.2 | 1.1 | 40 | 45 | 55 |
| *Geographic Area* | | | | | | |
| New England | 12 | . | . | . | . | . |
| Middle Atlantic | 43 | 54.2 | 2.6 | 40 | 50 | 60 |
| East North Central | 28 | 44.5 | 2.9 | 35 | 40 | 45 |
| West North Central | 15 | . | . | . | . | . |
| South Atlantic | 46 | 54.1 | 3.5 | 38 | 45 | 60 |
| East South Central | 13 | . | . | . | . | . |
| West South Central | 32 | 41.7 | 1.3 | 38 | 42 | 45 |
| Mountain | 17 | . | . | . | . | . |
| Pacific | 28 | 53.0 | 3.7 | 46 | 50 | 60 |
| *Practice Arrangement* | | | | | | |
| Self-Employed | 142 | 48.1 | 1.3 | 40 | 45 | 52 |
| · Solo Practice | 66 | 49.2 | 2.3 | 38 | 45 | 50 |
| · Two Physician Practice | 23 | . | . | . | . | . |
| · Three Physician Practice | 13 | . | . | . | . | . |
| · 4-8 Physician Practice | 31 | 47.7 | 2.0 | 38 | 47 | 51 |
| · Over 8 Physician Practice | 8 | . | . | . | . | . |
| Employee | 86 | 51.3 | 2.1 | 40 | 45 | 59 |
| Independent Contractor | 6 | . | . | . | . | . |

Source: 1995 Socioeconomic Monitoring System survey of nonfederal patient care physicians. See the beginning of this section, the introduction, and appendices for a discussion of the survey sample, definitions, and computation procedures. Statistics are not reported if the number of responses is less than 25.

Table 47. **Fee (in dollars) for an Office Visit with an Established Patient, for Nonfederal Physicians, 1995 – Obstetrics/Gynecology**

| | Number of Responses | Mean | Standard Error | 25th Percentile | Median | 75th Percentile |
|---|---|---|---|---|---|---|
| All Physicians | 197 | 69.5 | 2.0 | 50 | 63 | 80 |
| *Geographic Area* | | | | | | |
| New England | 10 | . | . | . | . | . |
| Middle Atlantic | 29 | 73.6 | 8.6 | 50 | 60 | 85 |
| East North Central | 39 | 60.0 | 3.5 | 50 | 55 | 63 |
| West North Central | 10 | . | . | . | . | . |
| South Atlantic | 33 | 70.2 | 4.1 | 50 | 63 | 80 |
| East South Central | 13 | . | . | . | . | . |
| West South Central | 20 | . | . | . | . | . |
| Mountain | 13 | . | . | . | . | . |
| Pacific | 30 | 84.5 | 4.9 | 65 | 80 | 100 |
| *Practice Arrangement* | | | | | | |
| Self-Employed | 138 | 67.5 | 2.0 | 50 | 60 | 80 |
| · Solo Practice | 62 | 68.8 | 3.4 | 50 | 60 | 85 |
| · Two Physician Practice | 16 | . | . | . | . | . |
| · Three Physician Practice | 14 | . | . | . | . | . |
| · 4-8 Physician Practice | 38 | 68.0 | 3.2 | 51 | 63 | 80 |
| · Over 8 Physician Practice | 8 | . | . | . | . | . |
| Employee | 54 | 75.3 | 5.4 | 51 | 65 | 85 |
| Independent Contractor | 5 | . | . | . | . | . |

Source: 1995 Socioeconomic Monitoring System survey of nonfederal patient care physicians. See the beginning of this section, the introduction, and appendices for a discussion of the survey sample, definitions, and computation procedures. Statistics are not reported if the number of responses is less than 25.

Table 48. **Fee (in dollars) for an Office Visit with an Established Patient, for Nonfederal Physicians, 1995 – Other Specialty**

| | Number of Responses | Mean | Standard Error | 25th Percentile | Median | 75th Percentile |
|---|---|---|---|---|---|---|
| All Physicians | 178 | 65.6 | 2.5 | 44 | 56 | 75 |
| *Geographic Area* | | | | | | |
| New England | 9 | . | . | . | . | . |
| Middle Atlantic | 29 | 63.0 | 4.1 | 45 | 60 | 75 |
| East North Central | 24 | . | . | . | . | . |
| West North Central | 14 | . | . | . | . | . |
| South Atlantic | 33 | 60.3 | 4.5 | 44 | 50 | 75 |
| East South Central | 7 | . | . | . | . | . |
| West South Central | 14 | . | . | . | . | . |
| Mountain | 12 | . | . | . | . | . |
| Pacific | 36 | 83.9 | 8.2 | 50 | 70 | 100 |
| *Practice Arrangement* | | | | | | |
| Self-Employed | 112 | 59.5 | 2.6 | 40 | 50 | 70 |
| · Solo Practice | 60 | 56.3 | 3.2 | 40 | 50 | 70 |
| · Two Physician Practice | 9 | . | . | . | . | . |
| · Three Physician Practice | 10 | . | . | . | . | . |
| · 4-8 Physician Practice | 26 | 64.4 | 6.1 | 42 | 55 | 75 |
| · Over 8 Physician Practice | 7 | . | . | . | . | . |
| Employee | 63 | 75.4 | 5.1 | 50 | 70 | 80 |
| Independent Contractor | 3 | . | . | . | . | . |

Source: 1995 Socioeconomic Monitoring System survey of nonfederal patient care physicians. See the beginning of this section, the introduction, and appendices for a discussion of the survey sample, definitions, and computation procedures. Statistics are not reported if the number of responses is less than 25.

Table 49. **Fee (in dollars) for an Office Visit with a New Patient, for Nonfederal Physicians, 1995 – General/Family Practice**

| | Number of Responses | Mean | Standard Error | 25th Percentile | Median | 75th Percentile |
|---|---|---|---|---|---|---|
| All Physicians | 418 | 64.9 | 1.3 | 45 | 60 | 75 |
| *Geographic Area* | | | | | | |
| New England | 25 | 66.3 | 4.7 | 49 | 60 | 75 |
| Middle Atlantic | 47 | 62.8 | 4.9 | 40 | 55 | 65 |
| East North Central | 70 | 61.5 | 2.8 | 44 | 56 | 70 |
| West North Central | 55 | 59.3 | 3.1 | 43 | 55 | 63 |
| South Atlantic | 65 | 61.7 | 3.2 | 45 | 60 | 70 |
| East South Central | 28 | 65.0 | 4.3 | 44 | 55 | 82 |
| West South Central | 31 | 59.3 | 3.3 | 45 | 55 | 72 |
| Mountain | 36 | 73.1 | 4.6 | 50 | 63 | 86 |
| Pacific | 61 | 75.9 | 4.3 | 55 | 65 | 85 |
| *Practice Arrangement* | | | | | | |
| Self-Employed | 240 | 64.4 | 1.7 | 45 | 60 | 75 |
| · Solo Practice | 138 | 63.7 | 2.2 | 45 | 60 | 75 |
| · Two Physician Practice | 33 | 72.3 | 6.5 | 46 | 60 | 85 |
| · Three Physician Practice | 17 | . | . | . | . | . |
| · 4-8 Physician Practice | 40 | 59.2 | 2.9 | 50 | 59 | 61 |
| · Over 8 Physician Practice | 12 | . | . | . | . | . |
| Employee | 156 | 66.6 | 2.3 | 46 | 60 | 75 |
| Independent Contractor | 22 | . | . | . | . | . |

Source: 1995 Socioeconomic Monitoring System survey of nonfederal patient care physicians. See the beginning of this section, the introduction, and appendices for a discussion of the survey sample, definitions, and computation procedures. Statistics are not reported if the number of responses is less than 25.

Table 50. **Fee (in dollars) for an Office Visit with a New Patient, for Nonfederal Physicians, 1995 – Internal Medicine**

| | Number of Responses | Mean | Standard Error | 25th Percentile | Median | 75th Percentile |
|---|---|---|---|---|---|---|
| All Physicians | 601 | 133.9 | 3.4 | 81 | 125 | 160 |
| *Geographic Area* | | | | | | |
| New England | 47 | 136.4 | 14.5 | 85 | 120 | 160 |
| Middle Atlantic | 111 | 153.9 | 11.2 | 100 | 125 | 175 |
| East North Central | 95 | 103.0 | 5.5 | 60 | 100 | 140 |
| West North Central | 34 | 109.7 | 8.6 | 72 | 100 | 140 |
| South Atlantic | 110 | 129.3 | 7.0 | 86 | 125 | 150 |
| East South Central | 45 | 123.8 | 9.0 | 90 | 120 | 150 |
| West South Central | 51 | 140.2 | 8.7 | 100 | 125 | 166 |
| Mountain | 24 | . | . | . | . | . |
| Pacific | 84 | 164.4 | 7.9 | 102 | 155 | 220 |
| *Practice Arrangement* | | | | | | |
| Self-Employed | 385 | 135.8 | 4.5 | 85 | 125 | 160 |
| · Solo Practice | 181 | 143.5 | 8.6 | 76 | 125 | 170 |
| · Two Physician Practice | 40 | 130.9 | 9.1 | 90 | 120 | 160 |
| · Three Physician Practice | 43 | 119.4 | 7.4 | 85 | 120 | 150 |
| · 4-8 Physician Practice | 78 | 135.6 | 5.7 | 100 | 129 | 175 |
| · Over 8 Physician Practice | 43 | 118.5 | 6.6 | 96 | 120 | 140 |
| Employee | 205 | 131.5 | 5.0 | 80 | 125 | 160 |
| Independent Contractor | 11 | . | . | . | . | . |

Source: 1995 Socioeconomic Monitoring System survey of nonfederal patient care physicians. See the beginning of this section, the introduction, and appendices for a discussion of the survey sample, definitions, and computation procedures. Statistics are not reported if the number of responses is less than 25.

Table 51. **Fee (in dollars) for an Office Visit with a New Patient, for Nonfederal Physicians, 1995 – Surgery**

| | Number of Responses | Mean | Standard Error | 25th Percentile | Median | 75th Percentile |
|---|---|---|---|---|---|---|
| All Physicians | 746 | 96.1 | 1.7 | 64 | 80 | 120 |
| *Geographic Area* | | | | | | |
| New England | 44 | 93.7 | 5.5 | 65 | 85 | 125 |
| Middle Atlantic | 110 | 114.0 | 5.7 | 70 | 95 | 150 |
| East North Central | 107 | 86.6 | 4.1 | 60 | 75 | 90 |
| West North Central | 58 | 79.1 | 4.4 | 55 | 73 | 86 |
| South Atlantic | 158 | 94.3 | 3.5 | 60 | 85 | 120 |
| East South Central | 43 | 76.6 | 4.5 | 55 | 65 | 80 |
| West South Central | 76 | 80.5 | 3.6 | 60 | 70 | 95 |
| Mountain | 34 | 79.1 | 5.2 | 60 | 68 | 91 |
| Pacific | 116 | 119.5 | 4.5 | 80 | 105 | 150 |
| *Practice Arrangement* | | | | | | |
| Self-Employed | 561 | 91.5 | 1.9 | 60 | 77 | 110 |
| · Solo Practice | 249 | 89.6 | 2.9 | 60 | 75 | 110 |
| · Two Physician Practice | 91 | 83.8 | 3.2 | 60 | 75 | 96 |
| · Three Physician Practice | 70 | 100.2 | 6.0 | 65 | 80 | 120 |
| · 4-8 Physician Practice | 121 | 96.9 | 4.2 | 60 | 80 | 120 |
| · Over 8 Physician Practice | 30 | 91.2 | 6.2 | 65 | 75 | 112 |
| Employee | 166 | 109.7 | 3.9 | 74 | 100 | 130 |
| Independent Contractor | 19 | . | . | . | . | . |

Source: 1995 Socioeconomic Monitoring System survey of nonfederal patient care physicians. See the beginning of this section, the introduction, and appendices for a discussion of the survey sample, definitions, and computation procedures. Statistics are not reported if the number of responses is less than 25.

Table 52. **Fee (in dollars) for an Office Visit with a New Patient, for Nonfederal Physicians, 1995 – Pediatrics**

| | Number of Responses | Mean | Standard Error | 25th Percentile | Median | 75th Percentile |
|---|---|---|---|---|---|---|
| All Physicians | 230 | 71.4 | 2.5 | 50 | 60 | 75 |
| *Geographic Area* | | | | | | |
| New England | 12 | . | . | . | . | . |
| Middle Atlantic | 43 | 76.8 | 6.8 | 55 | 65 | 80 |
| East North Central | 28 | 66.2 | 5.1 | 45 | 55 | 71 |
| West North Central | 15 | . | . | . | . | . |
| South Atlantic | 44 | 80.1 | 7.8 | 45 | 60 | 74 |
| East South Central | 13 | . | . | . | . | . |
| West South Central | 31 | 53.7 | 1.8 | 48 | 54 | 60 |
| Mountain | 16 | . | . | . | . | . |
| Pacific | 28 | 84.7 | 7.8 | 61 | 65 | 93 |
| *Practice Arrangement* | | | | | | |
| Self-Employed | 142 | 68.2 | 2.7 | 50 | 60 | 70 |
| · Solo Practice | 66 | 75.4 | 5.3 | 48 | 60 | 85 |
| · Two Physician Practice | 23 | . | . | . | . | . |
| · Three Physician Practice | 13 | . | . | . | . | . |
| · 4-8 Physician Practice | 31 | 61.8 | 2.4 | 50 | 60 | 74 |
| · Over 8 Physician Practice | 8 | . | . | . | . | . |
| Employee | 82 | 78.5 | 5.0 | 50 | 60 | 85 |
| Independent Contractor | 6 | . | . | . | . | . |

Source: 1995 Socioeconomic Monitoring System survey of nonfederal patient care physicians. See the beginning of this section, the introduction, and appendices for a discussion of the survey sample, definitions, and computation procedures. Statistics are not reported if the number of responses is less than 25.

Table 53. **Fee (in dollars) for an Office Visit with a New Patient, for Nonfederal Physicians, 1995 – Obstetrics/Gynecology**

| | Number of Responses | Mean | Standard Error | 25th Percentile | Median | 75th Percentile |
|---|---|---|---|---|---|---|
| All Physicians | 203 | 100.8 | 2.9 | 75 | 91 | 120 |
| *Geographic Area* | | | | | | |
| New England | 10 | . | . | . | . | . |
| Middle Atlantic | 30 | 104.7 | 10.4 | 75 | 95 | 120 |
| East North Central | 39 | 93.3 | 6.1 | 71 | 81 | 100 |
| West North Central | 10 | . | . | . | . | . |
| South Atlantic | 33 | 94.4 | 5.0 | 75 | 95 | 110 |
| East South Central | 14 | . | . | . | . | . |
| West South Central | 22 | . | . | . | . | . |
| Mountain | 14 | . | . | . | . | . |
| Pacific | 31 | 116.9 | 6.4 | 90 | 115 | 150 |
| *Practice Arrangement* | | | | | | |
| Self-Employed | 141 | 94.2 | 2.8 | 75 | 89 | 110 |
| · Solo Practice | 62 | 96.0 | 4.6 | 75 | 90 | 110 |
| · Two Physician Practice | 18 | . | . | . | . | . |
| · Three Physician Practice | 13 | . | . | . | . | . |
| · 4-8 Physician Practice | 39 | 98.0 | 5.3 | 75 | 95 | 110 |
| · Over 8 Physician Practice | 9 | . | . | . | . | . |
| Employee | 57 | 118.0 | 7.2 | 80 | 100 | 150 |
| Independent Contractor | 5 | . | . | . | . | . |

Source: 1995 Socioeconomic Monitoring System survey of nonfederal patient care physicians. See the beginning of this section, the introduction, and appendices for a discussion of the survey sample, definitions, and computation procedures. Statistics are not reported if the number of responses is less than 25.

Table 54. **Fee (in dollars) for an Office Visit with a New Patient, for Nonfederal Physicians, 1995 – Other Specialty**

| | Number of Responses | Mean | Standard Error | 25th Percentile | Median | 75th Percentile |
|---|---|---|---|---|---|---|
| All Physicians | 178 | 129.8 | 5.3 | 65 | 125 | 175 |
| *Geographic Area* | | | | | | |
| New England | 9 | . | . | . | . | . |
| Middle Atlantic | 30 | 135.0 | 11.1 | 75 | 125 | 175 |
| East North Central | 25 | 129.3 | 13.5 | 75 | 125 | 160 |
| West North Central | 15 | . | . | . | . | . |
| South Atlantic | 33 | 140.2 | 14.1 | 65 | 135 | 225 |
| East South Central | 5 | . | . | . | . | . |
| West South Central | 14 | . | . | . | . | . |
| Mountain | 13 | . | . | . | . | . |
| Pacific | 34 | 133.1 | 14.4 | 65 | 120 | 185 |
| *Practice Arrangement* | | | | | | |
| Self-Employed | 112 | 113.3 | 6.1 | 65 | 100 | 150 |
| · Solo Practice | 60 | 110.7 | 7.6 | 60 | 100 | 150 |
| · Two Physician Practice | 9 | . | . | . | . | . |
| · Three Physician Practice | 10 | . | . | . | . | . |
| · 4-8 Physician Practice | 25 | 137.9 | 16.8 | 70 | 120 | 175 |
| · Over 8 Physician Practice | 8 | . | . | . | . | . |
| Employee | 63 | 156.9 | 9.2 | 100 | 150 | 225 |
| Independent Contractor | 3 | . | . | . | . | . |

Source: 1995 Socioeconomic Monitoring System survey of nonfederal patient care physicians. See the beginning of this section, the introduction, and appendices for a discussion of the survey sample, definitions, and computation procedures. Statistics are not reported if the number of responses is less than 25.

# Professional Expenses of Nonfederal Self-Employed Physicians

Total Professional Expenses

Major Expense Components

Specialty Specific Total Professional Expenses by Census Division and Practice Arrangement

# Professional Expenses of Nonfederal Self-Employed Physicians

Professional expense information reported from the Socioeconomic Monitoring System refers to tax-deductible professional expenses from medical practice, not including contributions made for physicians into deferred compensation plans. Physicians with expense sharing arrangements were asked to provide only their share of their practice's total expenses. Information on expenses is obtained only from self-employed physicians.

Question 1 is used to obtain the information on which Tables 57, 59, 60, 63 and 64 are based:

1. To the nearest $1,000, what were your:

a. professional medical liability or malpractice insurance premiums in 1994 (Table 60)?

b. office expenses for 1994 including rent, mortgage interest, depreciation on medical buildings used in your practice, utilities, and telephone (Table 59)?

c. total nonphysician payroll expenses, including fringe benefits for 1994 (Table 57)?

d. 1994 expenses for medical materials and supplies such as drugs, x-ray films, and disposable medical products? Do not include expenses for office supplies in your answer (Table 64).

e. 1994 expenses for depreciation, leases, and rent on medical equipment used in the diagnosis and treatment of patients? Do not include expenses for office equipment and furniture. Do not include the total purchase price or replacement value of your medical equipment. Please report only that portion that was tax-deductible in 1994 (Table 63).

f. 1994 tax-deductible expenses for any other expenses, such as legal services, accounting services, office management services, professional association memberships, journals and continuing education, professional car upkeep and depreciation, and any other professional expenses which have not been mentioned?

Note that prior to Question 1 physicians were asked: "Do you share expenses with other physicians?" If their answer was affirmative, then the wording of question 1 was modified to request their share of their practice's expenses for each item.

For physicians who provided responses to all parts of Question 1, total professional expenses (Tables 55 and 65-74) were calculated as the sum of responses to those questions. Otherwise, the following question was asked to ascertain total professional expenses:

2. Even though we were not able to obtain your 1994 expenses for each expense category, we would like to get an estimate of your total 1994 tax-deductible professional expenses from medical practice to the nearest $1,000. Do not include contributions made for you into compensation plans in this amount.

Physicians who were in practices that had employee physicians were asked the following question:

3. What was your share of the 1994 [employee] physician payroll expenses, including fringe benefits, to the nearest $1,000?

Information based on responses to this question is presented in Table 56.

Physicians were also asked the following question regarding their nonphysician payroll expenses:

4. How much of your 1994 nonphysician payroll expenses were solely for the personnel involved in administrative, secretarial, or clerical activities?

Information based on responses to this question is presented in Table 58.

Physicians were asked to indicate their professional liability premium coverage limit in addition to their annual premium. Two measures, the total limit and the limit per case are shown (in millions of dollars) in Tables 61 and 62, respectively. Specifically, physicians were asked:

4. What is the current annual limit on your total malpractice liability coverage? (Total annual limit would be equivalent to the limit on multiple occurrences.)

5. What is the current limit on your malpractice liability coverage per case? (The amount per case would be for a single occurrence.)

Figure 20. **Mean and Median Professional Expenses (in thousands of dollars) per Self-Employed Nonfederal Physician, for Selected Specialties, 1994**

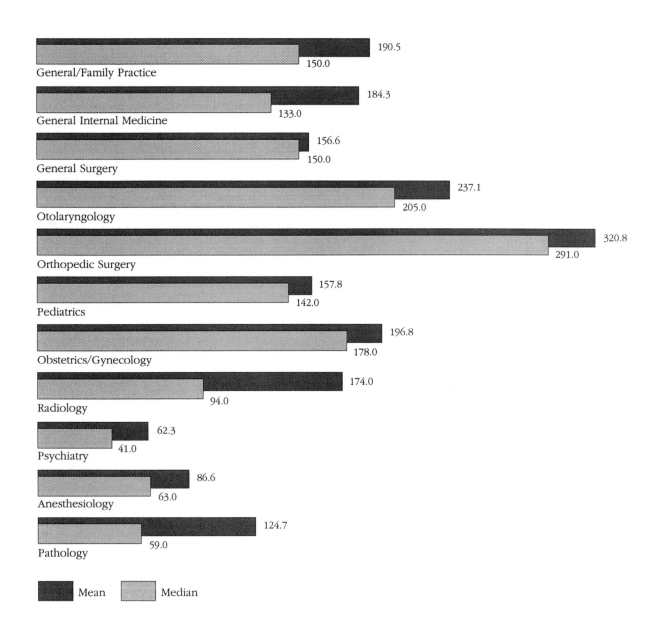

General/Family Practice — 190.5 / 150.0

General Internal Medicine — 184.3 / 133.0

General Surgery — 156.6 / 150.0

Otolaryngology — 237.1 / 205.0

Orthopedic Surgery — 320.8 / 291.0

Pediatrics — 157.8 / 142.0

Obstetrics/Gynecology — 196.8 / 178.0

Radiology — 174.0 / 94.0

Psychiatry — 62.3 / 41.0

Anesthesiology — 86.6 / 63.0

Pathology — 124.7 / 59.0

■ Mean    ▨ Median

Figure 21. **Mean and Median Professional Expenses (in thousands of dollars) per Self-Employed Nonfederal Physician, for Selected States, 1994**

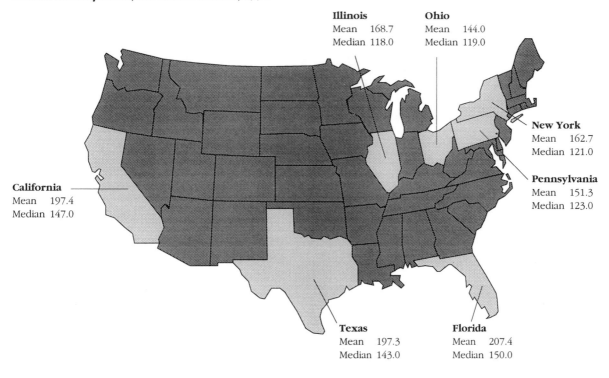

**Illinois**
Mean    168.7
Median  118.0

**Ohio**
Mean    144.0
Median  119.0

**New York**
Mean    162.7
Median  121.0

**Pennsylvania**
Mean    151.3
Median  123.0

**California**
Mean    197.4
Median  147.0

**Texas**
Mean    197.3
Median  143.0

**Florida**
Mean    207.4
Median  150.0

Figure 22. **Mean and Median Professional Expenses (in thousands of dollars) per Self-Employed Nonfederal Physician, by Size of Practice, 1994**

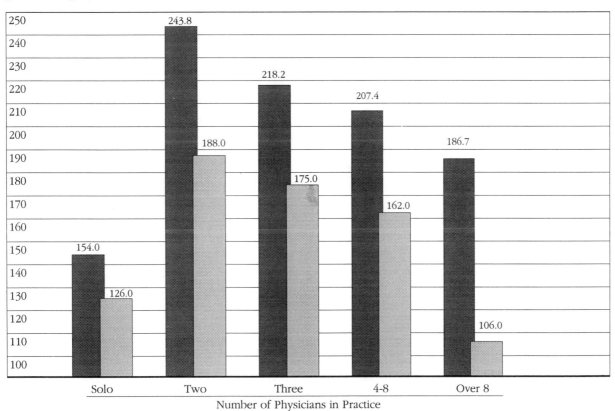

Table 55. **Total Professional Expenses per Self-Employed Nonfederal Physician (in thousands of dollars), 1994**

| | Number of Responses | Mean | Standard Error | 25th Percentile | Median | 75th Percentile |
|---|---|---|---|---|---|---|
| All Physicians | 1601 | 183.1 | 4.3 | 77.0 | 142.0 | 232.0 |
| *Specialty* | | | | | | |
| General/Family Practice | 195 | 190.5 | 10.3 | 100.0 | 150.0 | 243.0 |
| Internal Medicine | 294 | 186.4 | 10.9 | 83.0 | 144.0 | 226.0 |
| · General Internal Medicine | 187 | 184.3 | 14.6 | 82.0 | 133.0 | 218.0 |
| · Cardiovascular Diseases | 42 | 226.6 | 31.4 | 100.0 | 190.0 | 245.0 |
| · Other | 65 | 167.8 | 15.3 | 79.0 | 140.0 | 221.0 |
| Surgery | 444 | 249.9 | 9.4 | 134.0 | 199.0 | 304.0 |
| · General Surgery | 108 | 156.6 | 10.1 | 98.0 | 150.0 | 177.0 |
| · Otolaryngology | 45 | 237.1 | 16.5 | 158.0 | 205.0 | 297.0 |
| · Orthopedic Surgery | 89 | 320.8 | 19.9 | 187.0 | 291.0 | 369.0 |
| · Ophthalmology | 90 | 316.7 | 30.8 | 145.0 | 224.0 | 390.0 |
| · Urological Surgery | 49 | 281.5 | 24.5 | 179.0 | 241.0 | 333.0 |
| · Other | 63 | 257.5 | 21.4 | 154.0 | 216.0 | 285.0 |
| Pediatrics | 104 | 157.8 | 11.4 | 85.0 | 142.0 | 200.0 |
| Obstetrics/Gynecology | 100 | 196.8 | 12.1 | 120.0 | 178.0 | 247.0 |
| Radiology | 95 | 174.0 | 20.2 | 50.0 | 94.0 | 221.0 |
| Psychiatry | 132 | 62.3 | 5.8 | 25.0 | 41.0 | 75.0 |
| Anesthesiology | 93 | 86.6 | 9.9 | 34.0 | 63.0 | 94.0 |
| Pathology | 34 | 124.7 | 21.1 | 28.0 | 59.0 | 111.0 |
| Other Specialty | 110 | 135.2 | 12.0 | 51.0 | 100.0 | 165.0 |
| · Emergency Medicine | 29 | 71.2 | 22.0 | 19.0 | 35.0 | 75.0 |
| · Other | 81 | 156.5 | 13.6 | 87.0 | 127.0 | 188.0 |
| *Geographic Area* | | | | | | |
| New England | 78 | 142.3 | 11.6 | 63.0 | 125.0 | 192.0 |
| · Massachusetts | 36 | 121.8 | 13.2 | 41.0 | 126.0 | 173.0 |
| · Other | 42 | 160.2 | 18.0 | 77.0 | 123.0 | 210.0 |
| Middle Atlantic | 256 | 167.3 | 10.8 | 61.0 | 123.0 | 216.0 |
| · New Jersey | 49 | 196.6 | 28.0 | 82.0 | 155.0 | 218.0 |
| · New York | 101 | 162.7 | 19.7 | 58.0 | 121.0 | 193.0 |
| · Pennsylvania | 106 | 151.3 | 12.7 | 59.0 | 123.0 | 199.0 |
| East North Central | 227 | 171.1 | 9.9 | 76.0 | 125.0 | 222.0 |
| · Illinois | 75 | 168.7 | 20.2 | 70.0 | 118.0 | 201.0 |
| · Michigan | 45 | 182.7 | 17.9 | 99.0 | 147.0 | 232.0 |
| · Ohio | 52 | 144.0 | 15.5 | 75.0 | 119.0 | 175.0 |
| · Other | 55 | 194.1 | 22.2 | 75.0 | 140.0 | 251.0 |
| West North Central | 113 | 195.5 | 17.5 | 80.0 | 150.0 | 249.0 |
| South Atlantic | 292 | 191.7 | 10.7 | 80.0 | 150.0 | 254.0 |
| · Florida | 82 | 207.4 | 28.1 | 83.0 | 150.0 | 261.0 |
| · Other | 210 | 184.6 | 10.0 | 80.0 | 150.0 | 252.0 |
| East South Central | 113 | 221.5 | 19.3 | 84.0 | 159.0 | 282.0 |
| West South Central | 158 | 197.4 | 14.1 | 94.0 | 136.0 | 250.0 |
| · Texas | 99 | 197.3 | 18.0 | 94.0 | 143.0 | 257.0 |
| · Other | 59 | 197.5 | 23.0 | 81.0 | 126.0 | 223.0 |
| Mountain | 85 | 174.6 | 13.0 | 80.0 | 177.0 | 232.0 |
| Pacific | 279 | 187.0 | 10.2 | 75.0 | 146.0 | 225.0 |
| · California | 196 | 197.4 | 13.2 | 80.0 | 147.0 | 250.0 |
| · Other | 83 | 155.3 | 14.1 | 47.0 | 127.0 | 202.0 |
| *Practice Arrangement* | | | | | | |
| Solo Practice | 746 | 154.0 | 5.1 | 70.0 | 126.0 | 199.0 |
| Two Physician Practice | 190 | 243.8 | 13.7 | 114.0 | 188.0 | 313.0 |
| Three Physician Practice | 155 | 218.2 | 14.5 | 94.0 | 175.0 | 279.0 |
| 4-8 Physician Practice | 341 | 207.4 | 10.1 | 89.0 | 162.0 | 261.0 |
| Over 8 Physician Practice | 168 | 186.7 | 15.5 | 45.0 | 106.0 | 246.0 |

Source: 1995 Socioeconomic Monitoring System survey of nonfederal patient care physicians. See the beginning of this section, the introduction, and appendices for a discussion of the survey sample, definitions, and computation procedures. Statistics are not reported if the number of responses is less than 25.

## Table 56. **Employee Physician Payroll Expenses per Self-Employed Nonfederal Physician (in thousands of dollars), 1994**

| | Number of Responses | Mean | Standard Error | 25th Percentile | Median | 75th Percentile |
|---|---|---|---|---|---|---|
| All Physicians | 1435 | 16.6 | 2.0 | 0.0 | 0.0 | 0.0 |
| *Specialty* | | | | | | |
| General/Family Practice | 189 | 8.5 | 2.1 | 0.0 | 0.0 | 0.0 |
| Internal Medicine | 268 | 9.9 | 2.8 | 0.0 | 0.0 | 0.0 |
| · General Internal Medicine | 179 | 6.8 | 2.3 | 0.0 | 0.0 | 0.0 |
| · Cardiovascular Diseases | 37 | 36.1 | 16.0 | 0.0 | 0.0 | 32.0 |
| · Other | 52 | 3.6 | 3.0 | 0.0 | 0.0 | 0.0 |
| Surgery | 392 | 11.7 | 2.6 | 0.0 | 0.0 | 0.0 |
| · General Surgery | 94 | 5.4 | 2.8 | 0.0 | 0.0 | 0.0 |
| · Otolaryngology | 37 | 3.6 | 2.2 | 0.0 | 0.0 | 0.0 |
| · Orthopedic Surgery | 74 | 11.2 | 4.0 | 0.0 | 0.0 | 0.0 |
| · Ophthalmology | 89 | 25.2 | 9.9 | 0.0 | 0.0 | 0.0 |
| · Urological Surgery | 41 | 14.9 | 4.9 | 0.0 | 0.0 | 0.0 |
| · Other | 57 | 9.8 | 3.9 | 0.0 | 0.0 | 0.0 |
| Pediatrics | 102 | 15.4 | 4.2 | 0.0 | 0.0 | 0.0 |
| Obstetrics/Gynecology | 104 | 32.3 | 16.1 | 0.0 | 0.0 | 0.0 |
| Radiology | 54 | 46.4 | 5.3 | 15.0 | 38.0 | 63.0 |
| Psychiatry | 142 | 6.1 | 2.7 | 0.0 | 0.0 | 0.0 |
| Anesthesiology | 65 | 14.6 | 5.3 | 0.0 | 0.0 | 20.0 |
| Pathology | 16 | . | . | . | . | . |
| Other Specialty | 103 | 46.5 | 16.9 | 0.0 | 0.0 | 1.0 |
| · Emergency Medicine | 21 | . | . | . | . | . |
| · Other | 82 | 21.0 | 12.0 | 0.0 | 0.0 | 0.0 |
| *Geographic Area* | | | | | | |
| New England | 80 | 6.0 | 3.0 | 0.0 | 0.0 | 0.0 |
| · Massachusetts | 38 | 4.5 | 4.2 | 0.0 | 0.0 | 0.0 |
| · Other | 42 | 7.3 | 4.4 | 0.0 | 0.0 | 0.0 |
| Middle Atlantic | 244 | 28.1 | 8.2 | 0.0 | 0.0 | 0.0 |
| · New Jersey | 50 | 18.6 | 7.2 | 0.0 | 0.0 | 1.0 |
| · New York | 102 | 42.8 | 18.6 | 0.0 | 0.0 | 0.0 |
| · Pennsylvania | 92 | 16.9 | 5.6 | 0.0 | 0.0 | 0.0 |
| East North Central | 197 | 18.9 | 5.4 | 0.0 | 0.0 | 0.0 |
| · Illinois | 69 | 16.1 | 7.6 | 0.0 | 0.0 | 0.0 |
| · Michigan | 37 | 20.6 | 6.4 | 0.0 | 0.0 | 22.0 |
| · Ohio | 41 | 12.6 | 7.2 | 0.0 | 0.0 | 0.0 |
| · Other | 50 | 28.2 | 16.8 | 0.0 | 0.0 | 14.0 |
| West North Central | 79 | 17.0 | 6.4 | 0.0 | 0.0 | 4.0 |
| South Atlantic | 268 | 11.3 | 2.2 | 0.0 | 0.0 | 0.0 |
| · Florida | 88 | 7.5 | 3.2 | 0.0 | 0.0 | 0.0 |
| · Other | 180 | 13.4 | 2.9 | 0.0 | 0.0 | 0.0 |
| East South Central | 87 | 14.3 | 4.2 | 0.0 | 0.0 | 0.0 |
| West South Central | 147 | 25.6 | 10.2 | 0.0 | 0.0 | 0.0 |
| · Texas | 99 | 32.2 | 14.8 | 0.0 | 0.0 | 0.0 |
| · Other | 48 | 10.7 | 6.3 | 0.0 | 0.0 | 0.0 |
| Mountain | 84 | 8.0 | 2.4 | 0.0 | 0.0 | 0.0 |
| Pacific | 249 | 11.7 | 2.1 | 0.0 | 0.0 | 0.0 |
| · California | 178 | 8.0 | 1.9 | 0.0 | 0.0 | 0.0 |
| · Other | 71 | 24.1 | 5.6 | 0.0 | 0.0 | 20.0 |
| *Practice Arrangement* | | | | | | |
| Solo Practice | 1017 | 0.0 | 0.0 | 0.0 | 0.0 | 0.0 |
| Two Physician Practice | 82 | 46.7 | 6.6 | 0.0 | 20.0 | 63.0 |
| Three Physician Practice | 57 | 59.2 | 10.5 | 0.0 | 35.0 | 73.0 |
| 4-8 Physician Practice | 174 | 59.3 | 8.5 | 0.0 | 28.0 | 60.0 |
| Over 8 Physician Practice | 104 | 83.5 | 20.6 | 10.0 | 22.0 | 45.0 |

Source: 1995 Socioeconomic Monitoring System survey of nonfederal patient care physicians. See the beginning of this section, the introduction, and appendices for a discussion of the survey sample, definitions, and computation procedures. Statistics are not reported if the number of responses is less than 25.

## Table 57. Nonphysician Payroll Expenses per Self-Employed Nonfederal Physician (in thousands of dollars), 1994

| | Number of Responses | Mean | Standard Error | 25th Percentile | Median | 75th Percentile |
|---|---|---|---|---|---|---|
| All Physicians | 1610 | 71.2 | 2.2 | 22.0 | 50.0 | 90.0 |
| *Specialty* | | | | | | |
| General/Family Practice | 190 | 81.0 | 4.5 | 41.0 | 69.0 | 106.0 |
| Internal Medicine | 293 | 72.4 | 4.4 | 30.0 | 55.0 | 90.0 |
| · General Internal Medicine | 191 | 71.2 | 5.3 | 32.0 | 55.0 | 90.0 |
| · Cardiovascular Diseases | 39 | 81.4 | 14.4 | 28.0 | 50.0 | 120.0 |
| · Other | 63 | 70.4 | 8.9 | 33.0 | 59.0 | 80.0 |
| Surgery | 443 | 96.1 | 4.5 | 41.0 | 75.0 | 116.0 |
| · General Surgery | 104 | 59.3 | 5.8 | 31.0 | 50.0 | 80.0 |
| · Otolaryngology | 41 | 97.9 | 7.6 | 65.0 | 90.0 | 122.0 |
| · Orthopedic Surgery | 89 | 124.3 | 6.9 | 67.0 | 111.0 | 165.0 |
| · Ophthalmology | 92 | 145.7 | 16.8 | 55.0 | 100.0 | 170.0 |
| · Urological Surgery | 52 | 95.7 | 6.2 | 58.0 | 86.0 | 120.0 |
| · Other | 65 | 72.1 | 8.7 | 28.0 | 60.0 | 90.0 |
| Pediatrics | 100 | 58.8 | 5.7 | 25.0 | 45.0 | 72.0 |
| Obstetrics/Gynecology | 113 | 88.1 | 14.9 | 30.0 | 60.0 | 82.0 |
| Radiology | 93 | 52.3 | 6.4 | 1.0 | 22.0 | 85.0 |
| Psychiatry | 137 | 16.0 | 2.7 | 0.0 | 4.0 | 20.0 |
| Anesthesiology | 93 | 41.4 | 7.7 | 0.0 | 7.0 | 40.0 |
| Pathology | 34 | 38.2 | 10.9 | 0.0 | 1.0 | 17.0 |
| Other Specialty | 114 | 53.4 | 6.3 | 5.0 | 40.0 | 65.0 |
| · Emergency Medicine | 31 | 23.4 | 12.3 | 0.0 | 3.0 | 20.0 |
| · Other | 83 | 63.7 | 7.0 | 27.0 | 50.0 | 82.0 |
| *Geographic Area* | | | | | | |
| New England | 84 | 57.9 | 6.3 | 15.0 | 52.0 | 80.0 |
| · Massachusetts | 36 | 47.6 | 6.9 | 3.0 | 50.0 | 65.0 |
| · Other | 48 | 65.4 | 9.6 | 17.0 | 52.0 | 96.0 |
| Middle Atlantic | 256 | 70.4 | 7.5 | 13.0 | 42.0 | 88.0 |
| · New Jersey | 48 | 66.4 | 10.0 | 28.0 | 42.0 | 90.0 |
| · New York | 96 | 75.9 | 17.6 | 8.0 | 40.0 | 70.0 |
| · Pennsylvania | 112 | 68.1 | 6.8 | 18.0 | 47.0 | 98.0 |
| East North Central | 230 | 71.1 | 6.4 | 20.0 | 46.0 | 90.0 |
| · Illinois | 74 | 64.1 | 10.0 | 10.0 | 41.0 | 75.0 |
| · Michigan | 46 | 69.4 | 9.6 | 28.0 | 50.0 | 87.0 |
| · Ohio | 53 | 59.7 | 9.4 | 25.0 | 33.0 | 70.0 |
| · Other | 57 | 94.8 | 18.7 | 23.0 | 68.0 | 113.0 |
| West North Central | 102 | 80.7 | 9.2 | 25.0 | 64.0 | 100.0 |
| South Atlantic | 286 | 69.5 | 4.4 | 29.0 | 54.0 | 95.0 |
| · Florida | 83 | 73.7 | 11.9 | 30.0 | 55.0 | 90.0 |
| · Other | 203 | 67.6 | 4.0 | 25.0 | 52.0 | 100.0 |
| East South Central | 116 | 85.7 | 6.6 | 35.0 | 65.0 | 110.0 |
| West South Central | 165 | 78.8 | 6.2 | 30.0 | 50.0 | 100.0 |
| · Texas | 103 | 74.9 | 7.0 | 33.0 | 50.0 | 100.0 |
| · Other | 62 | 85.6 | 11.6 | 26.0 | 48.0 | 100.0 |
| Mountain | 91 | 65.7 | 6.3 | 24.0 | 60.0 | 85.0 |
| Pacific | 280 | 67.1 | 4.3 | 20.0 | 50.0 | 82.0 |
| · California | 198 | 68.7 | 5.6 | 20.0 | 50.0 | 80.0 |
| · Other | 82 | 62.2 | 6.1 | 12.0 | 50.0 | 100.0 |
| *Practice Arrangement* | | | | | | |
| Solo Practice | 767 | 55.2 | 2.3 | 20.0 | 42.0 | 71.0 |
| Two Physician Practice | 192 | 98.0 | 6.2 | 38.0 | 70.0 | 140.0 |
| Three Physician Practice | 155 | 81.5 | 5.7 | 30.0 | 60.0 | 107.0 |
| 4-8 Physician Practice | 335 | 87.5 | 5.2 | 33.0 | 70.0 | 106.0 |
| Over 8 Physician Practice | 161 | 86.0 | 11.2 | 10.0 | 48.0 | 100.0 |

Source: 1995 Socioeconomic Monitoring System survey of nonfederal patient care physicians. See the beginning of this section, the introduction, and appendices for a discussion of the survey sample, definitions, and computation procedures. Statistics are not reported if the number of responses is less than 25.

## Table 58. **Nonphysician Clerical Payroll Expenses per Self-Employed Nonfederal Physician (in thousands of dollars), 1994**

| | Number of Responses | Mean | Standard Error | 25th Percentile | Median | 75th Percentile |
|---|---|---|---|---|---|---|
| All Physicians | 1123 | 46.2 | 1.4 | 21.0 | 35.0 | 58.0 |
| *Specialty* | | | | | | |
| General/Family Practice | 166 | 43.8 | 2.5 | 24.0 | 40.0 | 55.0 |
| Internal Medicine | 240 | 42.2 | 2.7 | 21.0 | 33.0 | 52.0 |
| · General Internal Medicine | 160 | 43.7 | 3.6 | 21.0 | 34.0 | 53.0 |
| · Cardiovascular Diseases | 30 | 47.2 | 7.9 | 25.0 | 31.0 | 50.0 |
| · Other | 50 | 35.8 | 3.3 | 16.0 | 33.0 | 50.0 |
| Surgery | 356 | 59.9 | 2.9 | 30.0 | 48.0 | 72.0 |
| · General Surgery | 77 | 44.0 | 3.8 | 22.0 | 35.0 | 65.0 |
| · Otolaryngology | 38 | 55.5 | 5.2 | 30.0 | 40.0 | 71.0 |
| · Orthopedic Surgery | 78 | 69.4 | 4.3 | 40.0 | 60.0 | 90.0 |
| · Ophthalmology | 75 | 81.3 | 11.1 | 38.0 | 53.0 | 88.0 |
| · Urological Surgery | 44 | 59.9 | 4.5 | 35.0 | 56.0 | 70.0 |
| · Other | 44 | 51.2 | 5.9 | 28.0 | 42.0 | 65.0 |
| Pediatrics | 85 | 32.0 | 3.0 | 15.0 | 25.0 | 40.0 |
| Obstetrics/Gynecology | 95 | 48.5 | 5.9 | 22.0 | 34.0 | 54.0 |
| Radiology | 32 | 41.5 | 6.7 | 15.0 | 26.0 | 52.0 |
| Psychiatry | 49 | 18.6 | 2.2 | 5.0 | 17.0 | 25.0 |
| Anesthesiology | 26 | 19.4 | 5.3 | 8.0 | 12.0 | 16.0 |
| Pathology | 8 | · | · | · | · | · |
| Other Specialty | 66 | 46.2 | 6.0 | 22.0 | 40.0 | 52.0 |
| · Emergency Medicine | 6 | · | · | · | · | · |
| · Other | 60 | 46.8 | 6.1 | 25.0 | 40.0 | 54.0 |
| *Geographic Area* | | | | | | |
| New England | 57 | 46.0 | 3.6 | 24.0 | 48.0 | 60.0 |
| · Massachusetts | 25 | 42.6 | 3.6 | 29.0 | 45.0 | 55.0 |
| · Other | 32 | 48.3 | 5.9 | 19.0 | 50.0 | 75.0 |
| Middle Atlantic | 159 | 47.8 | 3.9 | 20.0 | 33.0 | 60.0 |
| · New Jersey | 31 | 46.5 | 7.9 | 20.0 | 30.0 | 65.0 |
| · New York | 53 | 53.9 | 9.3 | 18.0 | 35.0 | 60.0 |
| · Pennsylvania | 75 | 44.1 | 4.0 | 20.0 | 35.0 | 56.0 |
| East North Central | 163 | 41.4 | 3.3 | 16.0 | 30.0 | 53.0 |
| · Illinois | 51 | 38.8 | 5.7 | 16.0 | 30.0 | 54.0 |
| · Michigan | 33 | 44.9 | 7.5 | 19.0 | 30.0 | 60.0 |
| · Ohio | 38 | 38.8 | 5.1 | 21.0 | 30.0 | 52.0 |
| · Other | 41 | 45.6 | 8.1 | 14.0 | 31.0 | 50.0 |
| West North Central | 77 | 43.9 | 4.9 | 20.0 | 36.0 | 60.0 |
| South Atlantic | 208 | 46.9 | 4.2 | 21.0 | 38.0 | 56.0 |
| · Florida | 62 | 56.0 | 12.5 | 20.0 | 43.0 | 55.0 |
| · Other | 146 | 42.7 | 2.7 | 21.0 | 35.0 | 56.0 |
| East South Central | 87 | 45.6 | 3.6 | 24.0 | 36.0 | 55.0 |
| West South Central | 123 | 44.0 | 2.8 | 24.0 | 35.0 | 54.0 |
| · Texas | 77 | 44.8 | 3.5 | 25.0 | 35.0 | 55.0 |
| · Other | 46 | 42.7 | 4.6 | 21.0 | 35.0 | 44.0 |
| Mountain | 69 | 45.8 | 4.4 | 24.0 | 35.0 | 55.0 |
| Pacific | 180 | 50.9 | 4.0 | 24.0 | 40.0 | 65.0 |
| · California | 129 | 53.9 | 5.3 | 24.0 | 40.0 | 65.0 |
| · Other | 51 | 40.9 | 4.2 | 21.0 | 30.0 | 52.0 |
| *Practice Arrangement* | | | | | | |
| Solo Practice | 568 | 41.3 | 1.5 | 21.0 | 33.0 | 54.0 |
| Two Physician Practice | 137 | 54.2 | 3.8 | 24.0 | 40.0 | 70.0 |
| Three Physician Practice | 105 | 53.8 | 4.9 | 25.0 | 40.0 | 67.0 |
| 4-8 Physician Practice | 223 | 54.3 | 4.0 | 25.0 | 44.0 | 65.0 |
| Over 8 Physician Practice | 90 | 42.7 | 6.2 | 12.0 | 25.0 | 48.0 |

Source: 1995 Socioeconomic Monitoring System survey of nonfederal patient care physicians. See the beginning of this section, the introduction, and appendices for a discussion of the survey sample, definitions, and computation procedures. Statistics are not reported if the number of responses is less than 25.

## Table 59. **Office Expenses per Self-Employed Nonfederal Physician (in thousands of dollars), 1994**

| | Number of Responses | Mean | Standard Error | 25th Percentile | Median | 75th Percentile |
|---|---|---|---|---|---|---|
| All Physicians | 1585 | 47.6 | 1.6 | 16.0 | 30.0 | 52.0 |
| *Specialty* | | | | | | |
| General/Family Practice | 188 | 45.2 | 3.3 | 17.0 | 34.0 | 52.0 |
| Internal Medicine | 292 | 51.3 | 3.8 | 18.0 | 35.0 | 55.0 |
| · General Internal Medicine | 191 | 50.6 | 5.1 | 18.0 | 35.0 | 50.0 |
| · Cardiovascular Diseases | 39 | 58.8 | 10.3 | 20.0 | 36.0 | 90.0 |
| · Other | 62 | 49.1 | 6.0 | 20.0 | 35.0 | 55.0 |
| Surgery | 441 | 67.4 | 3.8 | 25.0 | 40.0 | 80.0 |
| · General Surgery | 104 | 38.3 | 3.7 | 18.0 | 26.0 | 45.0 |
| · Otolaryngology | 43 | 77.6 | 9.9 | 30.0 | 50.0 | 90.0 |
| · Orthopedic Surgery | 90 | 85.4 | 7.9 | 31.0 | 57.0 | 105.0 |
| · Ophthalmology | 88 | 94.8 | 11.8 | 33.0 | 59.0 | 100.0 |
| · Urological Surgery | 53 | 68.5 | 10.8 | 26.0 | 40.0 | 73.0 |
| · Other | 63 | 63.8 | 9.6 | 30.0 | 36.0 | 80.0 |
| Pediatrics | 99 | 38.3 | 3.7 | 18.0 | 28.0 | 48.0 |
| Obstetrics/Gynecology | 111 | 52.6 | 6.4 | 20.0 | 34.0 | 61.0 |
| Radiology | 91 | 33.7 | 6.8 | 0.0 | 10.0 | 37.0 |
| Psychiatry | 131 | 20.1 | 1.5 | 8.0 | 15.0 | 25.0 |
| Anesthesiology | 89 | 19.0 | 4.8 | 2.0 | 6.0 | 20.0 |
| Pathology | 33 | 9.2 | 2.3 | 0.0 | 3.0 | 10.0 |
| Other Specialty | 110 | 35.2 | 4.3 | 4.0 | 24.0 | 41.0 |
| · Emergency Medicine | 28 | 8.1 | 4.1 | 0.0 | 0.0 | 1.0 |
| · Other | 82 | 43.8 | 5.2 | 20.0 | 30.0 | 53.0 |
| *Geographic Area* | | | | | | |
| New England | 78 | 40.8 | 5.5 | 8.0 | 27.0 | 51.0 |
| · Massachusetts | 35 | 34.0 | 6.4 | 10.0 | 30.0 | 48.0 |
| · Other | 43 | 46.5 | 8.6 | 7.0 | 24.0 | 60.0 |
| Middle Atlantic | 248 | 39.9 | 3.6 | 12.0 | 25.0 | 40.0 |
| · New Jersey | 48 | 40.8 | 7.0 | 14.0 | 30.0 | 50.0 |
| · New York | 96 | 40.9 | 6.4 | 10.0 | 25.0 | 40.0 |
| · Pennsylvania | 104 | 38.3 | 5.5 | 10.0 | 22.0 | 40.0 |
| East North Central | 226 | 49.8 | 4.6 | 15.0 | 31.0 | 50.0 |
| · Illinois | 77 | 48.6 | 10.0 | 14.0 | 28.0 | 50.0 |
| · Michigan | 43 | 48.2 | 7.4 | 25.0 | 40.0 | 47.0 |
| · Ohio | 50 | 42.6 | 7.0 | 12.0 | 35.0 | 50.0 |
| · Other | 56 | 59.9 | 9.6 | 18.0 | 36.0 | 82.0 |
| West North Central | 102 | 42.4 | 3.6 | 18.0 | 30.0 | 60.0 |
| South Atlantic | 288 | 49.7 | 3.7 | 16.0 | 35.0 | 59.0 |
| · Florida | 84 | 52.4 | 6.6 | 24.0 | 40.0 | 60.0 |
| · Other | 204 | 48.4 | 4.5 | 16.0 | 33.0 | 56.0 |
| East South Central | 116 | 63.2 | 8.8 | 20.0 | 34.0 | 59.0 |
| West South Central | 164 | 44.0 | 4.2 | 16.0 | 30.0 | 50.0 |
| · Texas | 103 | 44.5 | 5.8 | 16.0 | 30.0 | 50.0 |
| · Other | 61 | 43.2 | 5.8 | 16.0 | 27.0 | 50.0 |
| Mountain | 88 | 43.3 | 4.9 | 10.0 | 30.0 | 55.0 |
| Pacific | 275 | 51.3 | 3.9 | 18.0 | 31.0 | 60.0 |
| · California | 192 | 54.1 | 5.1 | 20.0 | 33.0 | 63.0 |
| · Other | 83 | 42.8 | 5.1 | 15.0 | 25.0 | 50.0 |
| *Practice Arrangement* | | | | | | |
| Solo Practice | 750 | 41.7 | 1.9 | 16.0 | 30.0 | 48.0 |
| Two Physician Practice | 194 | 63.3 | 5.1 | 22.0 | 40.0 | 79.0 |
| Three Physician Practice | 157 | 57.5 | 5.6 | 18.0 | 35.0 | 80.0 |
| 4-8 Physician Practice | 332 | 52.4 | 4.1 | 13.0 | 30.0 | 60.0 |
| Over 8 Physician Practice | 152 | 41.4 | 5.2 | 3.0 | 16.0 | 46.0 |

Source: 1995 Socioeconomic Monitoring System survey of nonfederal patient care physicians. See the beginning of this section, the introduction, and appendices for a discussion of the survey sample, definitions, and computation procedures. Statistics are not reported if the number of responses is less than 25.

Table 60. **Professional Liability Insurance Premiums per Self-Employed Nonfederal Physician (in thousands of dollars), 1994**

| | Number of Responses | Mean | Standard Error | 25th Percentile | Median | 75th Percentile |
|---|---|---|---|---|---|---|
| All Physicians | 1748 | 15.1 | 0.4 | 5.0 | 10.0 | 19.0 |
| *Specialty* | | | | | | |
| General/Family Practice | 209 | 10.2 | 1.2 | 4.0 | 6.0 | 10.0 |
| Internal Medicine | 316 | 8.6 | 0.5 | 4.0 | 7.0 | 10.0 |
| · General Internal Medicine | 204 | 7.9 | 0.5 | 4.0 | 7.0 | 9.0 |
| · Cardiovascular Diseases | 43 | 14.9 | 1.5 | 9.0 | 14.0 | 20.0 |
| · Other | 69 | 6.6 | 0.7 | 3.0 | 6.0 | 10.0 |
| Surgery | 495 | 22.3 | 0.7 | 11.0 | 20.0 | 30.0 |
| · General Surgery | 115 | 21.3 | 1.1 | 15.0 | 21.0 | 27.0 |
| · Otolaryngology | 50 | 17.3 | 0.9 | 10.0 | 16.0 | 22.0 |
| · Orthopedic Surgery | 106 | 31.0 | 1.4 | 20.0 | 30.0 | 40.0 |
| · Ophthalmology | 98 | 10.1 | 0.6 | 6.0 | 9.0 | 12.0 |
| · Urological Surgery | 59 | 15.4 | 0.9 | 8.0 | 16.0 | 21.0 |
| · Other | 67 | 35.5 | 2.9 | 20.0 | 31.0 | 40.0 |
| Pediatrics | 112 | 7.6 | 0.5 | 4.0 | 6.0 | 9.0 |
| Obstetrics/Gynecology | 123 | 37.4 | 2.8 | 17.0 | 30.0 | 46.0 |
| Radiology | 102 | 11.2 | 0.6 | 6.0 | 10.0 | 13.0 |
| Psychiatry | 135 | 9.4 | 2.7 | 2.0 | 3.0 | 6.0 |
| Anesthesiology | 98 | 15.0 | 0.7 | 10.0 | 14.0 | 20.0 |
| Pathology | 36 | 5.9 | 0.4 | 4.0 | 5.0 | 8.0 |
| Other Specialty | 122 | 8.8 | 0.7 | 4.0 | 7.0 | 12.0 |
| · Emergency Medicine | 32 | 13.3 | 1.7 | 7.0 | 12.0 | 15.0 |
| · Other | 90 | 7.4 | 0.6 | 4.0 | 6.0 | 10.0 |
| *Geographic Area* | | | | | | |
| New England | 89 | 16.8 | 2.2 | 5.0 | 8.0 | 21.0 |
| · Massachusetts | 43 | 17.8 | 3.7 | 4.0 | 8.0 | 18.0 |
| · Other | 46 | 15.8 | 2.6 | 5.0 | 8.0 | 21.0 |
| Middle Atlantic | 285 | 19.2 | 1.5 | 5.0 | 10.0 | 21.0 |
| · New Jersey | 53 | 22.6 | 4.4 | 8.0 | 13.0 | 32.0 |
| · New York | 110 | 25.5 | 2.9 | 8.0 | 14.0 | 26.0 |
| · Pennsylvania | 122 | 10.2 | 0.8 | 4.0 | 7.0 | 13.0 |
| East North Central | 249 | 16.4 | 1.0 | 7.0 | 12.0 | 21.0 |
| · Illinois | 84 | 21.5 | 2.4 | 9.0 | 14.0 | 25.0 |
| · Michigan | 45 | 19.0 | 1.8 | 9.0 | 17.0 | 26.0 |
| · Ohio | 58 | 10.8 | 1.2 | 5.0 | 8.0 | 12.0 |
| · Other | 62 | 12.2 | 1.2 | 6.0 | 9.0 | 15.0 |
| West North Central | 121 | 12.9 | 1.2 | 4.0 | 9.0 | 15.0 |
| South Atlantic | 319 | 14.4 | 0.9 | 5.0 | 10.0 | 20.0 |
| · Florida | 92 | 14.8 | 1.6 | 5.0 | 11.0 | 25.0 |
| · Other | 227 | 14.3 | 1.0 | 5.0 | 9.0 | 18.0 |
| East South Central | 124 | 11.3 | 1.1 | 3.0 | 8.0 | 12.0 |
| West South Central | 175 | 14.3 | 0.8 | 6.0 | 11.0 | 20.0 |
| · Texas | 112 | 15.2 | 1.1 | 6.0 | 11.0 | 21.0 |
| · Other | 63 | 12.6 | 1.3 | 4.0 | 10.0 | 17.0 |
| Mountain | 94 | 15.2 | 1.4 | 6.0 | 12.0 | 22.0 |
| Pacific | 292 | 12.9 | 1.3 | 4.0 | 8.0 | 15.0 |
| · California | 208 | 13.4 | 1.8 | 4.0 | 8.0 | 15.0 |
| · Other | 84 | 11.2 | 0.9 | 5.0 | 9.0 | 15.0 |
| *Practice Arrangement* | | | | | | |
| Solo Practice | 807 | 14.4 | 0.7 | 4.0 | 8.0 | 18.0 |
| Two Physician Practice | 211 | 18.2 | 1.6 | 6.0 | 10.0 | 20.0 |
| Three Physician Practice | 169 | 15.4 | 1.1 | 6.0 | 10.0 | 22.0 |
| 4-8 Physician Practice | 378 | 16.1 | 0.8 | 6.0 | 11.0 | 20.0 |
| Over 8 Physician Practice | 183 | 13.1 | 0.9 | 6.0 | 11.0 | 15.0 |

Source: 1995 Socioeconomic Monitoring System survey of nonfederal patient care physicians. See the beginning of this section, the introduction, and appendices for a discussion of the survey sample, definitions, and computation procedures. Statistics are not reported if the number of responses is less than 25.

## Table 61. Total Professional Liability Insurance Coverage Limits per Self-Employed Nonfederal Physician (in millions of dollars), 1994

| | Number of Responses | Mean | Standard Error | 25th Percentile | Median | 75th Percentile |
|---|---|---|---|---|---|---|
| All Physicians | 1651 | 3.0 | 0.1 | 1.0 | 3.0 | 3.0 |
| *Specialty* | | | | | | |
| General/Family Practice | 192 | 2.3 | 0.1 | 0.8 | 3.0 | 3.0 |
| Internal Medicine | 293 | 3.1 | 0.5 | 1.0 | 3.0 | 3.0 |
| · General Internal Medicine | 184 | 2.7 | 0.2 | 1.0 | 3.0 | 3.0 |
| · Cardiovascular Diseases | 37 | 2.8 | 0.4 | 1.0 | 3.0 | 4.0 |
| · Other | 72 | 4.2 | 2.0 | 2.0 | 3.0 | 3.0 |
| Surgery | 477 | 3.3 | 0.4 | 1.0 | 3.0 | 3.0 |
| · General Surgery | 111 | 4.0 | 1.2 | 1.0 | 3.0 | 3.0 |
| · Otolaryngology | 50 | 1.9 | 0.2 | 0.6 | 1.0 | 3.0 |
| · Orthopedic Surgery | 97 | 3.3 | 0.3 | 3.0 | 3.0 | 4.0 |
| · Ophthalmology | 94 | 2.9 | 0.2 | 3.0 | 3.0 | 3.0 |
| · Urological Surgery | 60 | 5.0 | 1.6 | 2.0 | 3.0 | 3.0 |
| · Other | 65 | 2.4 | 0.2 | 0.8 | 3.0 | 3.0 |
| Pediatrics | 101 | 2.7 | 0.2 | 1.0 | 3.0 | 3.0 |
| Obstetrics/Gynecology | 112 | 2.5 | 0.3 | 0.8 | 3.0 | 3.0 |
| Radiology | 102 | 3.5 | 0.2 | 2.0 | 3.0 | 4.0 |
| Psychiatry | 122 | 2.8 | 0.1 | 3.0 | 3.0 | 3.0 |
| Anesthesiology | 94 | 2.8 | 0.2 | 2.0 | 3.0 | 3.0 |
| Pathology | 36 | 3.3 | 0.3 | 3.0 | 3.0 | 5.0 |
| Other Specialty | 122 | 3.1 | 0.3 | 1.0 | 3.0 | 3.0 |
| · Emergency Medicine | 33 | 3.4 | 0.6 | 1.0 | 3.0 | 3.0 |
| · Other | 89 | 2.9 | 0.3 | 2.0 | 3.0 | 3.0 |
| *Geographic Area* | | | | | | |
| New England | 90 | 4.4 | 1.1 | 3.0 | 3.0 | 3.0 |
| · Massachusetts | 45 | 5.2 | 2.3 | 3.0 | 3.0 | 3.0 |
| · Other | 45 | 3.5 | 0.2 | 3.0 | 3.0 | 4.0 |
| Middle Atlantic | 260 | 2.5 | 0.1 | 0.6 | 3.0 | 3.0 |
| · New Jersey | 51 | 3.7 | 0.3 | 3.0 | 3.0 | 4.0 |
| · New York | 102 | 3.0 | 0.2 | 3.0 | 3.0 | 3.0 |
| · Pennsylvania | 107 | 1.2 | 0.1 | 0.6 | 0.6 | 1.0 |
| East North Central | 228 | 2.1 | 0.1 | 0.6 | 3.0 | 3.0 |
| · Illinois | 86 | 2.9 | 0.2 | 3.0 | 3.0 | 3.0 |
| · Michigan | 42 | 0.9 | 0.2 | 0.3 | 0.6 | 0.9 |
| · Ohio | 56 | 2.5 | 0.2 | 1.0 | 3.0 | 3.0 |
| · Other | 44 | 0.9 | 0.1 | 0.3 | 0.3 | 1.0 |
| West North Central | 108 | 2.8 | 0.2 | 1.0 | 3.0 | 3.0 |
| South Atlantic | 302 | 3.5 | 0.6 | 2.0 | 3.0 | 3.0 |
| · Florida | 89 | 3.4 | 1.6 | 0.8 | 2.0 | 3.0 |
| · Other | 213 | 3.5 | 0.5 | 3.0 | 3.0 | 3.0 |
| East South Central | 121 | 4.5 | 0.8 | 3.0 | 3.0 | 4.0 |
| West South Central | 164 | 2.0 | 0.2 | 0.6 | 1.0 | 3.0 |
| · Texas | 108 | 1.8 | 0.2 | 0.6 | 1.0 | 3.0 |
| · Other | 56 | 2.5 | 0.2 | 1.0 | 3.0 | 3.0 |
| Mountain | 91 | 2.9 | 0.1 | 3.0 | 3.0 | 3.0 |
| Pacific | 287 | 3.2 | 0.1 | 3.0 | 3.0 | 3.0 |
| · California | 203 | 3.0 | 0.1 | 3.0 | 3.0 | 3.0 |
| · Other | 84 | 3.6 | 0.2 | 3.0 | 3.0 | 5.0 |
| *Practice Arrangement* | | | | | | |
| Solo Practice | 752 | 2.8 | 0.2 | 1.0 | 3.0 | 3.0 |
| Two Physician Practice | 197 | 2.6 | 0.1 | 1.0 | 3.0 | 3.0 |
| Three Physician Practice | 161 | 3.4 | 0.6 | 2.0 | 3.0 | 3.0 |
| 4-8 Physician Practice | 374 | 3.3 | 0.3 | 1.0 | 3.0 | 3.0 |
| Over 8 Physician Practice | 167 | 3.4 | 0.2 | 2.0 | 3.0 | 4.0 |

Source: 1995 Socioeconomic Monitoring System survey of nonfederal patient care physicians. See the beginning of this section, the introduction, and appendices for a discussion of the survey sample, definitions, and computation procedures. Statistics are not reported if the number of responses is less than 25.

Table 62. **Professional Liability Insurance Coverage Limits per Case per Self-Employed Nonfederal Physician (in millions of dollars), 1994**

| | Number of Responses | Mean | Standard Error | 25th Percentile | Median | 75th Percentile |
|---|---|---|---|---|---|---|
| All Physicians | 1710 | 1.2 | 0.0 | 0.8 | 1.0 | 1.0 |
| *Specialty* | | | | | | |
| General/Family Practice | 200 | 0.9 | 0.1 | 0.3 | 1.0 | 1.0 |
| Internal Medicine | 302 | 1.2 | 0.1 | 1.0 | 1.0 | 1.0 |
| · General Internal Medicine | 190 | 1.2 | 0.1 | 1.0 | 1.0 | 1.0 |
| · Cardiovascular Diseases | 38 | 1.3 | 0.2 | 1.0 | 1.0 | 2.0 |
| · Other | 74 | 1.1 | 0.1 | 1.0 | 1.0 | 1.0 |
| Surgery | 495 | 1.1 | 0.0 | 0.5 | 1.0 | 1.0 |
| · General Surgery | 116 | 1.1 | 0.1 | 0.5 | 1.0 | 1.0 |
| · Otolaryngology | 51 | 0.9 | 0.1 | 0.2 | 1.0 | 1.0 |
| · Orthopedic Surgery | 102 | 1.1 | 0.1 | 1.0 | 1.0 | 1.0 |
| · Ophthalmology | 98 | 1.3 | 0.1 | 1.0 | 1.0 | 1.0 |
| · Urological Surgery | 61 | 1.2 | 0.1 | 1.0 | 1.0 | 1.0 |
| · Other | 67 | 1.0 | 0.1 | 0.3 | 1.0 | 1.0 |
| Pediatrics | 108 | 1.1 | 0.1 | 1.0 | 1.0 | 1.0 |
| Obstetrics/Gynecology | 117 | 0.9 | 0.1 | 0.3 | 1.0 | 1.0 |
| Radiology | 102 | 1.8 | 0.2 | 1.0 | 1.0 | 2.0 |
| Psychiatry | 128 | 1.4 | 0.2 | 1.0 | 1.0 | 1.0 |
| Anesthesiology | 96 | 1.2 | 0.1 | 1.0 | 1.0 | 1.0 |
| Pathology | 37 | 1.6 | 0.2 | 1.0 | 1.0 | 2.0 |
| Other Specialty | 125 | 1.2 | 0.1 | 1.0 | 1.0 | 1.0 |
| · Emergency Medicine | 33 | 1.1 | 0.1 | 1.0 | 1.0 | 1.0 |
| · Other | 92 | 1.2 | 0.1 | 1.0 | 1.0 | 1.0 |
| *Geographic Area* | | | | | | |
| New England | 91 | 1.3 | 0.1 | 1.0 | 1.0 | 1.0 |
| · Massachusetts | 45 | 1.3 | 0.2 | 1.0 | 1.0 | 1.0 |
| · Other | 46 | 1.4 | 0.1 | 1.0 | 1.0 | 1.0 |
| Middle Atlantic | 272 | 1.0 | 0.1 | 0.2 | 1.0 | 1.0 |
| · New Jersey | 53 | 1.8 | 0.3 | 1.0 | 1.0 | 2.0 |
| · New York | 105 | 1.0 | 0.1 | 1.0 | 1.0 | 1.0 |
| · Pennsylvania | 114 | 0.5 | 0.0 | 0.2 | 0.2 | 1.0 |
| East North Central | 239 | 0.9 | 0.1 | 0.2 | 1.0 | 1.0 |
| · Illinois | 88 | 1.0 | 0.1 | 1.0 | 1.0 | 1.0 |
| · Michigan | 43 | 0.3 | 0.1 | 0.1 | 0.2 | 0.3 |
| · Ohio | 57 | 1.5 | 0.1 | 1.0 | 1.0 | 2.0 |
| · Other | 51 | 0.4 | 0.1 | 0.1 | 0.1 | 0.4 |
| West North Central | 115 | 1.3 | 0.1 | 0.5 | 1.0 | 2.0 |
| South Atlantic | 321 | 1.1 | 0.1 | 1.0 | 1.0 | 1.0 |
| · Florida | 91 | 0.7 | 0.0 | 0.3 | 1.0 | 1.0 |
| · Other | 230 | 1.3 | 0.1 | 1.0 | 1.0 | 1.0 |
| East South Central | 123 | 1.6 | 0.2 | 1.0 | 1.0 | 2.0 |
| West South Central | 170 | 1.0 | 0.1 | 0.2 | 1.0 | 1.0 |
| · Texas | 110 | 0.7 | 0.1 | 0.2 | 0.5 | 1.0 |
| · Other | 60 | 1.6 | 0.2 | 0.5 | 1.0 | 3.0 |
| Mountain | 91 | 1.5 | 0.3 | 1.0 | 1.0 | 1.0 |
| Pacific | 288 | 1.2 | 0.0 | 1.0 | 1.0 | 1.0 |
| · California | 205 | 1.2 | 0.1 | 1.0 | 1.0 | 1.0 |
| · Other | 83 | 1.4 | 0.1 | 1.0 | 1.0 | 2.0 |
| *Practice Arrangement* | | | | | | |
| Solo Practice | 783 | 1.1 | 0.0 | 0.5 | 1.0 | 1.0 |
| Two Physician Practice | 205 | 1.1 | 0.1 | 1.0 | 1.0 | 1.0 |
| Three Physician Practice | 165 | 1.2 | 0.1 | 1.0 | 1.0 | 1.0 |
| 4-8 Physician Practice | 383 | 1.3 | 0.1 | 0.5 | 1.0 | 2.0 |
| Over 8 Physician Practice | 174 | 1.4 | 0.1 | 1.0 | 1.0 | 1.0 |

Source: 1995 Socioeconomic Monitoring System survey of nonfederal patient care physicians. See the beginning of this section, the introduction, and appendices for a discussion of the survey sample, definitions, and computation procedures. Statistics are not reported if the number of responses is less than 25.

## Table 63. **Medical Equipment Expense per Self-Employed Nonfederal Physician (in thousands of dollars), 1994**

| | Number of Responses | Mean | Standard Error | 25th Percentile | Median | 75th Percentile |
|---|---|---|---|---|---|---|
| All Physicians | 1516 | 8.5 | 0.6 | 0.0 | 1.0 | 7.0 |
| *Specialty* | | | | | | |
| General/Family Practice | 178 | 12.1 | 2.4 | 0.0 | 3.0 | 10.0 |
| Internal Medicine | 277 | 7.6 | 1.3 | 0.0 | 2.0 | 6.0 |
| · General Internal Medicine | 180 | 6.0 | 1.2 | 0.0 | 2.0 | 5.0 |
| · Cardiovascular Diseases | 35 | 19.0 | 6.8 | 3.0 | 10.0 | 19.0 |
| · Other | 62 | 5.5 | 1.9 | 0.0 | 2.0 | 5.0 |
| Surgery | 411 | 10.8 | 1.4 | 0.0 | 4.0 | 10.0 |
| · General Surgery | 101 | 6.1 | 1.6 | 0.0 | 1.0 | 5.0 |
| · Otolaryngology | 38 | 9.0 | 1.8 | 0.0 | 6.0 | 12.0 |
| · Orthopedic Surgery | 84 | 10.1 | 2.4 | 0.0 | 5.0 | 7.0 |
| · Ophthalmology | 83 | 23.7 | 5.8 | 2.0 | 10.0 | 21.0 |
| · Urological Surgery | 45 | 13.2 | 2.5 | 1.0 | 7.0 | 15.0 |
| · Other | 60 | 5.1 | 1.1 | 0.0 | 1.0 | 7.0 |
| Pediatrics | 95 | 5.6 | 1.6 | 0.0 | 1.0 | 6.0 |
| Obstetrics/Gynecology | 100 | 13.6 | 3.1 | 0.0 | 4.0 | 10.0 |
| Radiology | 95 | 19.9 | 4.2 | 0.0 | 0.0 | 15.0 |
| Psychiatry | 133 | 0.5 | 0.2 | 0.0 | 0.0 | 0.0 |
| Anesthesiology | 88 | 0.3 | 0.2 | 0.0 | 0.0 | 0.0 |
| Pathology | 32 | 3.6 | 1.3 | 0.0 | 0.0 | 2.0 |
| Other Specialty | 107 | 3.3 | 0.6 | 0.0 | 0.0 | 4.0 |
| · Emergency Medicine | 29 | 0.4 | 0.3 | 0.0 | 0.0 | 0.0 |
| · Other | 78 | 4.3 | 0.8 | 0.0 | 1.0 | 6.0 |
| *Geographic Area* | | | | | | |
| New England | 76 | 4.2 | 1.2 | 0.0 | 0.0 | 4.0 |
| · Massachusetts | 34 | 4.7 | 1.8 | 0.0 | 1.0 | 4.0 |
| · Other | 42 | 3.8 | 1.5 | 0.0 | 0.0 | 3.0 |
| Middle Atlantic | 240 | 11.2 | 2.3 | 0.0 | 0.0 | 5.0 |
| · New Jersey | 44 | 15.5 | 9.2 | 0.0 | 0.0 | 8.0 |
| · New York | 95 | 14.0 | 3.7 | 0.0 | 0.0 | 10.0 |
| · Pennsylvania | 101 | 5.3 | 1.5 | 0.0 | 0.0 | 3.0 |
| East North Central | 220 | 7.3 | 1.3 | 0.0 | 2.0 | 6.0 |
| · Illinois | 74 | 4.7 | 1.6 | 0.0 | 1.0 | 5.0 |
| · Michigan | 42 | 8.3 | 3.1 | 0.0 | 2.0 | 10.0 |
| · Ohio | 51 | 6.0 | 1.4 | 0.0 | 3.0 | 8.0 |
| · Other | 53 | 12.1 | 3.8 | 0.0 | 3.0 | 10.0 |
| West North Central | 96 | 11.9 | 4.7 | 0.0 | 3.0 | 9.0 |
| South Atlantic | 277 | 8.6 | 1.3 | 0.0 | 2.0 | 8.0 |
| · Florida | 78 | 12.3 | 3.1 | 0.0 | 3.0 | 13.0 |
| · Other | 199 | 6.9 | 1.3 | 0.0 | 1.0 | 7.0 |
| East South Central | 111 | 10.4 | 2.7 | 0.0 | 1.0 | 8.0 |
| West South Central | 153 | 8.7 | 1.3 | 0.0 | 2.0 | 10.0 |
| · Texas | 94 | 7.5 | 1.2 | 0.0 | 2.0 | 7.0 |
| · Other | 59 | 10.8 | 2.8 | 0.0 | 1.0 | 10.0 |
| Mountain | 83 | 8.3 | 1.8 | 0.0 | 2.0 | 9.0 |
| Pacific | 260 | 6.5 | 1.1 | 0.0 | 1.0 | 6.0 |
| · California | 183 | 6.2 | 1.2 | 0.0 | 2.0 | 6.0 |
| · Other | 77 | 7.3 | 2.3 | 0.0 | 0.0 | 6.0 |
| *Practice Arrangement* | | | | | | |
| Solo Practice | 715 | 6.4 | 0.8 | 0.0 | 1.0 | 5.0 |
| Two Physician Practice | 186 | 13.6 | 2.5 | 0.0 | 3.0 | 10.0 |
| Three Physician Practice | 148 | 7.3 | 1.6 | 0.0 | 3.0 | 7.0 |
| 4-8 Physician Practice | 314 | 10.4 | 1.4 | 0.0 | 1.0 | 7.0 |
| Over 8 Physician Practice | 153 | 11.8 | 2.3 | 0.0 | 0.0 | 12.0 |

Source: 1995 Socioeconomic Monitoring System survey of nonfederal patient care physicians. See the beginning of this section, the introduction, and appendices for a discussion of the survey sample, definitions, and computation procedures. Statistics are not reported if the number of responses is less than 25.

## Table 64. **Medical Supply Expenses per Self-Employed Nonfederal Physician (in thousands of dollars), 1994**

| | Number of Responses | Mean | Standard Error | 25th Percentile | Median | 75th Percentile |
|---|---|---|---|---|---|---|
| All Physicians | 1550 | 19.3 | 1.2 | 1.0 | 6.0 | 20.0 |
| *Specialty* | | | | | | |
| General/Family Practice | 183 | 21.6 | 1.8 | 7.0 | 14.0 | 26.0 |
| Internal Medicine | 283 | 25.6 | 4.8 | 4.0 | 10.0 | 18.0 |
| · General Internal Medicine | 186 | 34.2 | 7.2 | 4.0 | 10.0 | 24.0 |
| · Cardiovascular Diseases | 37 | 12.3 | 3.3 | 3.0 | 8.0 | 11.0 |
| · Other | 60 | 9.3 | 1.5 | 3.0 | 7.0 | 10.0 |
| Surgery | 430 | 22.9 | 2.0 | 3.0 | 9.0 | 25.0 |
| · General Surgery | 103 | 5.4 | 0.7 | 1.0 | 4.0 | 6.0 |
| · Otolaryngology | 39 | 17.2 | 2.9 | 6.0 | 10.0 | 15.0 |
| · Orthopedic Surgery | 87 | 30.8 | 4.3 | 10.0 | 18.0 | 31.0 |
| · Ophthalmology | 89 | 28.2 | 6.3 | 4.0 | 10.0 | 20.0 |
| · Urological Surgery | 48 | 63.3 | 6.9 | 20.0 | 60.0 | 92.0 |
| · Other | 64 | 17.2 | 3.4 | 2.0 | 5.0 | 28.0 |
| Pediatrics | 97 | 30.2 | 3.9 | 8.0 | 20.0 | 37.0 |
| Obstetrics/Gynecology | 100 | 16.6 | 2.4 | 4.0 | 10.0 | 20.0 |
| Radiology | 94 | 18.8 | 5.2 | 0.0 | 0.0 | 10.0 |
| Psychiatry | 132 | 0.8 | 0.2 | 0.0 | 0.0 | 0.0 |
| Anesthesiology | 88 | 0.6 | 0.4 | 0.0 | 0.0 | 0.0 |
| Pathology | 33 | 11.3 | 3.7 | 0.0 | 1.0 | 6.0 |
| Other Specialty | 110 | 10.7 | 2.1 | 0.0 | 2.0 | 12.0 |
| · Emergency Medicine | 29 | 4.3 | 3.3 | 0.0 | 0.0 | 0.0 |
| · Other | 81 | 12.8 | 2.6 | 1.0 | 5.0 | 15.0 |
| *Geographic Area* | | | | | | |
| New England | 76 | 8.9 | 1.5 | 1.0 | 5.0 | 12.0 |
| · Massachusetts | 34 | 6.0 | 1.1 | 0.0 | 5.0 | 10.0 |
| · Other | 42 | 11.3 | 2.4 | 2.0 | 5.0 | 16.0 |
| Middle Atlantic | 244 | 19.7 | 2.3 | 2.0 | 8.0 | 20.0 |
| · New Jersey | 45 | 24.9 | 5.4 | 5.0 | 15.0 | 28.0 |
| · New York | 93 | 18.9 | 4.3 | 2.0 | 5.0 | 17.0 |
| · Pennsylvania | 106 | 17.1 | 3.0 | 0.0 | 5.0 | 20.0 |
| East North Central | 222 | 13.6 | 2.1 | 2.0 | 5.0 | 15.0 |
| · Illinois | 75 | 13.5 | 2.9 | 2.0 | 5.0 | 15.0 |
| · Michigan | 41 | 11.2 | 2.5 | 4.0 | 6.0 | 10.0 |
| · Ohio | 52 | 9.0 | 2.1 | 1.0 | 5.0 | 12.0 |
| · Other | 54 | 20.3 | 7.0 | 1.0 | 9.0 | 23.0 |
| West North Central | 99 | 14.0 | 1.8 | 2.0 | 8.0 | 20.0 |
| South Atlantic | 278 | 18.1 | 2.3 | 2.0 | 7.0 | 18.0 |
| · Florida | 80 | 21.9 | 4.7 | 3.0 | 10.0 | 20.0 |
| · Other | 198 | 16.3 | 2.6 | 1.0 | 5.0 | 16.0 |
| East South Central | 112 | 30.7 | 9.0 | 2.0 | 10.0 | 25.0 |
| West South Central | 161 | 25.4 | 4.0 | 1.0 | 9.0 | 24.0 |
| · Texas | 100 | 29.3 | 6.0 | 1.0 | 10.0 | 25.0 |
| · Other | 61 | 18.5 | 3.7 | 1.0 | 6.0 | 24.0 |
| Mountain | 88 | 13.1 | 2.3 | 2.0 | 8.0 | 13.0 |
| Pacific | 270 | 24.1 | 3.3 | 0.0 | 5.0 | 25.0 |
| · California | 190 | 27.7 | 4.6 | 1.0 | 5.0 | 30.0 |
| · Other | 80 | 13.2 | 2.2 | 0.0 | 4.0 | 20.0 |
| *Practice Arrangement* | | | | | | |
| Solo Practice | 730 | 14.1 | 0.9 | 1.0 | 6.0 | 16.0 |
| Two Physician Practice | 187 | 31.9 | 5.7 | 5.0 | 13.0 | 32.0 |
| Three Physician Practice | 153 | 29.3 | 5.1 | 2.0 | 9.0 | 20.0 |
| 4-8 Physician Practice | 329 | 22.0 | 2.6 | 1.0 | 6.0 | 20.0 |
| Over 8 Physician Practice | 151 | 17.6 | 3.7 | 0.0 | 2.0 | 12.0 |

Source: 1995 Socioeconomic Monitoring System survey of nonfederal patient care physicians. See the beginning of this section, the introduction, and appendices for a discussion of the survey sample, definitions, and computation procedures. Statistics are not reported if the number of responses is less than 25.

**Table 65. Total Professional Expenses per Self-Employed Nonfederal Physician (in thousands of dollars), 1994 – General/Family Practice**

| | Number of Responses | Mean | Standard Error | 25th Percentile | Median | 75th Percentile |
|---|---|---|---|---|---|---|
| All Physicians | 195 | 190.5 | 10.3 | 100 | 150 | 243 |
| *Geographic Area* | | | | | | |
| New England | 12 | . | . | . | . | . |
| Middle Atlantic | 23 | . | . | . | . | . |
| East North Central | 40 | 178.0 | 22.1 | 80 | 126 | 251 |
| West North Central | 19 | . | . | . | . | . |
| South Atlantic | 28 | 161.2 | 16.5 | 100 | 138 | 242 |
| East South Central | 13 | . | . | . | . | . |
| West South Central | 9 | . | . | . | . | . |
| Mountain | 15 | . | . | . | . | . |
| Pacific | 36 | 235.8 | 29.0 | 115 | 173 | 338 |
| *Practice Arrangement* | | | | | | |
| · Solo Practice | 111 | 158.1 | 9.4 | 92 | 135 | 199 |
| · Two Physician Practice | 28 | 318.1 | 44.0 | 151 | 253 | 383 |
| · Three Physician Practice | 13 | . | . | . | . | . |
| · 4-8 Physician Practice | 32 | 184.3 | 16.7 | 122 | 175 | 251 |
| · Over 8 Physician Practice | 11 | . | . | . | . | . |

Source: 1995 Socioeconomic Monitoring System survey of nonfederal patient care physicians. See the beginning of this section, the introduction, and appendices for a discussion of the survey sample, definitions, and computation procedures. Statistics are not reported if the number of responses is less than 25.

**Table 66. Total Professional Expenses per Self-Employed Nonfederal Physician (in thousands of dollars), 1994 – Internal Medicine**

| | Number of Responses | Mean | Standard Error | 25th Percentile | Median | 75th Percentile |
|---|---|---|---|---|---|---|
| All Physicians | 294 | 186.4 | 10.9 | 83 | 144 | 226 |
| *Geographic Area* | | | | | | |
| New England | 18 | . | . | . | . | . |
| Middle Atlantic | 60 | 186.4 | 28.5 | 82 | 132 | 218 |
| East North Central | 46 | 151.8 | 19.4 | 96 | 125 | 174 |
| West North Central | 13 | . | . | . | . | . |
| South Atlantic | 55 | 159.6 | 15.9 | 76 | 140 | 224 |
| East South Central | 24 | . | . | . | . | . |
| West South Central | 27 | 239.4 | 45.4 | 120 | 221 | 290 |
| Mountain | 9 | . | . | . | . | . |
| Pacific | 42 | 241.6 | 36.3 | 115 | 152 | 290 |
| *Practice Arrangement* | | | | | | |
| · Solo Practice | 143 | 151.2 | 12.1 | 76 | 118 | 171 |
| · Two Physician Practice | 27 | 225.8 | 36.0 | 114 | 205 | 238 |
| · Three Physician Practice | 31 | 233.4 | 35.9 | 98 | 160 | 282 |
| · 4-8 Physician Practice | 64 | 212.9 | 21.6 | 127 | 190 | 240 |
| · Over 8 Physician Practice | 29 | 254.1 | 56.9 | 79 | 225 | 270 |

Source: 1995 Socioeconomic Monitoring System survey of nonfederal patient care physicians. See the beginning of this section, the introduction, and appendices for a discussion of the survey sample, definitions, and computation procedures. Statistics are not reported if the number of responses is less than 25.

Table 67. **Total Professional Expenses per Self-Employed Nonfederal Physician (in thousands of dollars), 1994 – Surgery**

| | Number of Responses | Mean | Standard Error | 25th Percentile | Median | 75th Percentile |
|---|---|---|---|---|---|---|
| All Physicians | 444 | 249.9 | 9.4 | 134 | 199 | 304 |
| *Geographic Area* | | | | | | |
| New England | 17 | . | . | . | . | . |
| Middle Atlantic | 65 | 220.7 | 16.4 | 126 | 216 | 254 |
| East North Central | 50 | 235.9 | 24.9 | 103 | 196 | 262 |
| West North Central | 36 | 263.5 | 41.6 | 130 | 205 | 357 |
| South Atlantic | 100 | 265.2 | 24.5 | 134 | 218 | 327 |
| East South Central | 32 | 329.1 | 43.3 | 155 | 227 | 392 |
| West South Central | 53 | 257.5 | 28.0 | 104 | 187 | 348 |
| Mountain | 22 | . | . | . | . | . |
| Pacific | 69 | 243.0 | 20.3 | 130 | 187 | 300 |
| *Practice Arrangement* | | | | | | |
| · Solo Practice | 203 | 209.6 | 12.3 | 120 | 171 | 250 |
| · Two Physician Practice | 71 | 299.3 | 23.2 | 140 | 227 | 392 |
| · Three Physician Practice | 62 | 259.6 | 22.1 | 112 | 224 | 333 |
| · 4-8 Physician Practice | 87 | 308.5 | 27.2 | 162 | 238 | 368 |
| · Over 8 Physician Practice | 21 | . | . | . | . | . |

Source: 1995 Socioeconomic Monitoring System survey of nonfederal patient care physicians. See the beginning of this section, the introduction, and appendices for a discussion of the survey sample, definitions, and computation procedures. Statistics are not reported if the number of responses is less than 25.

Table 68. **Total Professional Expenses per Self-Employed Nonfederal Physician (in thousands of dollars), 1994 – Pediatrics**

| | Number of Responses | Mean | Standard Error | 25th Percentile | Median | 75th Percentile |
|---|---|---|---|---|---|---|
| All Physicians | 104 | 157.8 | 11.4 | 85 | 142 | 200 |
| *Geographic Area* | | | | | | |
| New England | 4 | . | . | . | . | . |
| Middle Atlantic | 19 | . | . | . | . | . |
| East North Central | 9 | . | . | . | . | . |
| West North Central | 9 | . | . | . | . | . |
| South Atlantic | 20 | . | . | . | . | . |
| East South Central | 9 | . | . | . | . | . |
| West South Central | 12 | . | . | . | . | . |
| Mountain | 6 | . | . | . | . | . |
| Pacific | 16 | . | . | . | . | . |
| *Practice Arrangement* | | | | | | |
| · Solo Practice | 51 | 129.9 | 10.5 | 62 | 137 | 187 |
| · Two Physician Practice | 17 | . | . | . | . | . |
| · Three Physician Practice | 11 | . | . | . | . | . |
| · 4-8 Physician Practice | 20 | . | . | . | . | . |
| · Over 8 Physician Practice | 4 | . | . | . | . | . |

Source: 1995 Socioeconomic Monitoring System survey of nonfederal patient care physicians. See the beginning of this section, the introduction, and appendices for a discussion of the survey sample, definitions, and computation procedures. Statistics are not reported if the number of responses is less than 25.

Table 69. **Total Professional Expenses per Self-Employed Nonfederal Physician (in thousands of dollars), 1994 – Obstetrics/Gynecology**

| | Number of Responses | Mean | Standard Error | 25th Percentile | Median | 75th Percentile |
|---|---|---|---|---|---|---|
| All Physicians | 100 | 196.8 | 12.1 | 120 | 178 | 247 |
| *Geographic Area* | | | | | | |
| New England | 5 | . | . | . | . | . |
| Middle Atlantic | 12 | . | . | . | . | . |
| East North Central | 17 | . | . | . | . | . |
| West North Central | 4 | . | . | . | . | . |
| South Atlantic | 14 | . | . | . | . | . |
| East South Central | 7 | . | . | . | . | . |
| West South Central | 15 | . | . | . | . | . |
| Mountain | 9 | . | . | . | . | . |
| Pacific | 17 | . | . | . | . | . |
| *Practice Arrangement* | | | | | | |
| · Solo Practice | 50 | 172.4 | 16.9 | 106 | 144 | 225 |
| · Two Physician Practice | 11 | . | . | . | . | . |
| · Three Physician Practice | 10 | . | . | . | . | . |
| · 4-8 Physician Practice | 20 | . | . | . | . | . |
| · Over 8 Physician Practice | 9 | . | . | . | . | . |

Source: 1995 Socioeconomic Monitoring System survey of nonfederal patient care physicians. See the beginning of this section, the introduction, and appendices for a discussion of the survey sample, definitions, and computation procedures. Statistics are not reported if the number of responses is less than 25.

Table 70. **Total Professional Expenses per Self-Employed Nonederal Physician (in thousands of dollars), 1994 – Radiology**

| | Number of Responses | Mean | Standard Error | 25th Percentile | Median | 75th Percentile |
|---|---|---|---|---|---|---|
| All Physicians | 95 | 174.0 | 20.2 | 50 | 94 | 221 |
| *Geographic Area* | | | | | | |
| New England | 4 | . | . | . | . | . |
| Middle Atlantic | 15 | . | . | . | . | . |
| East North Central | 20 | . | . | . | . | . |
| West North Central | 5 | . | . | . | . | . |
| South Atlantic | 15 | . | . | . | . | . |
| East South Central | 11 | . | . | . | . | . |
| West South Central | 7 | . | . | . | . | . |
| Mountain | 3 | . | . | . | . | . |
| Pacific | 15 | . | . | . | . | . |
| *Practice Arrangement* | | | | | | |
| · Solo Practice | 5 | . | . | . | . | . |
| · Two Physician Practice | 11 | . | . | . | . | . |
| · Three Physician Practice | 6 | . | . | . | . | . |
| · 4-8 Physician Practice | 41 | 167.7 | 28.6 | 43 | 108 | 221 |
| · Over 8 Physician Practice | 32 | 199.3 | 34.8 | 70 | 94 | 184 |

Source: 1995 Socioeconomic Monitoring System survey of nonfederal patient care physicians. See the beginning of this section, the introduction, and appendices for a discussion of the survey sample, definitions, and computation procedures. Statistics are not reported if the number of responses is less than 25.

Table 71. **Total Professional Expenses per Self-Employed Nonfederal Physician (in thousands of dollars), 1994 – Psychiatry**

| | Number of Responses | Mean | Standard Error | 25th Percentile | Median | 75th Percentile |
|---|---|---|---|---|---|---|
| All Physicians | 132 | 62.3 | 5.8 | 25 | 41 | 75 |
| *Geographic Area* | | | | | | |
| New England | 10 | . | . | . | . | . |
| Middle Atlantic | 29 | 39.1 | 6.4 | 19 | 27 | 44 |
| East North Central | 10 | . | . | . | . | . |
| West North Central | 9 | . | . | . | . | . |
| South Atlantic | 23 | . | . | . | . | . |
| East South Central | 2 | . | . | . | . | . |
| West South Central | 9 | . | . | . | . | . |
| Mountain | 10 | . | . | . | . | . |
| Pacific | 30 | 77.9 | 14.0 | 30 | 41 | 81 |
| *Practice Arrangement* | | | | | | |
| · Solo Practice | 115 | 58.4 | 6.2 | 23 | 39 | 60 |
| · Two Physician Practice | 11 | . | . | . | . | . |
| · Three Physician Practice | 1 | . | . | . | . | . |
| · 4-8 Physician Practice | 4 | . | . | . | . | . |
| · Over 8 Physician Practice | 1 | . | . | . | . | . |

Source: 1995 Socioeconomic Monitoring System survey of nonfederal patient care physicians. See the beginning of this section, the introduction, and appendices for a discussion of the survey sample, definitions, and computation procedures. Statistics are not reported if the number of responses is less than 25.

Table 72. **Total Professional Expenses per Self-Employed Nonfederal Physician (in thousands of dollars), 1994 – Anesthesiology**

| | Number of Responses | Mean | Standard Error | 25th Percentile | Median | 75th Percentile |
|---|---|---|---|---|---|---|
| All Physicians | 93 | 86.6 | 9.9 | 34 | 63 | 94 |
| *Geographic Area* | | | | | | |
| New England | 4 | . | . | . | . | . |
| Middle Atlantic | 13 | . | . | . | . | . |
| East North Central | 13 | . | . | . | . | . |
| West North Central | 5 | . | . | . | . | . |
| South Atlantic | 13 | . | . | . | . | . |
| East South Central | 5 | . | . | . | . | . |
| West South Central | 13 | . | . | . | . | . |
| Mountain | 5 | . | . | . | . | . |
| Pacific | 22 | . | . | . | . | . |
| *Practice Arrangement* | | | | | | |
| · Solo Practice | 20 | . | . | . | . | . |
| · Two Physician Practice | 1 | . | . | . | . | . |
| · Three Physician Practice | 8 | . | . | . | . | . |
| · 4-8 Physician Practice | 25 | 98.2 | 19.4 | 34 | 55 | 123 |
| · Over 8 Physician Practice | 39 | 96.0 | 17.3 | 33 | 58 | 85 |

Source: 1995 Socioeconomic Monitoring System survey of nonfederal patient care physicians. See the beginning of this section, the introduction, and appendices for a discussion of the survey sample, definitions, and computation procedures. Statistics are not reported if the number of responses is less than 25.

Table 73. **Total Professional Expenses per Self-Employed Nonfederal Physician (in thousands of dollars), 1994 – Pathology**

| | Number of Responses | Mean | Standard Error | 25th Percentile | Median | 75th Percentile |
|---|---|---|---|---|---|---|
| All Physicians | 34 | 124.7 | 21.1 | 28 | 59 | 111 |
| *Geographic Area* | | | | | | |
| New England | 1 | . | . | . | . | . |
| Middle Atlantic | 3 | . | . | . | . | . |
| East North Central | 5 | . | . | . | . | . |
| West North Central | 4 | . | . | . | . | . |
| South Atlantic | 6 | . | . | . | . | . |
| East South Central | 3 | . | . | . | . | . |
| West South Central | 5 | . | . | . | . | . |
| Mountain | 3 | . | . | . | . | . |
| Pacific | 4 | . | . | . | . | . |
| *Practice Arrangement* | | | | | | |
| · Solo Practice | 3 | . | . | . | . | . |
| · Two Physician Practice | 6 | . | . | . | . | . |
| · Three Physician Practice | 3 | . | . | . | . | . |
| · 4-8 Physician Practice | 18 | . | . | . | . | . |
| · Over 8 Physician Practice | 4 | . | . | . | . | . |

Source: 1995 Socioeconomic Monitoring System survey of nonfederal patient care physicians. See the beginning of this section, the introduction, and appendices for a discussion of the survey sample, definitions, and computation procedures. Statistics are not reported if the number of responses is less than 25.

Table 74. **Total Professional Expenses per Self-Employed Nonfederal Physician (in thousands of dollars), 1994 – Other Specialty**

| | Number of Responses | Mean | Standard Error | 25th Percentile | Median | 75th Percentile |
|---|---|---|---|---|---|---|
| All Physicians | 110 | 135.2 | 12.0 | 51 | 100 | 165 |
| *Geographic Area* | | | | | | |
| New England | 3 | . | . | . | . | . |
| Middle Atlantic | 17 | . | . | . | . | . |
| East North Central | 17 | . | . | . | . | . |
| West North Central | 9 | . | . | . | . | . |
| South Atlantic | 18 | . | . | . | . | . |
| East South Central | 7 | . | . | . | . | . |
| West South Central | 8 | . | . | . | . | . |
| Mountain | 3 | . | . | . | . | . |
| Pacific | 28 | 132.9 | 21.7 | 57 | 106 | 158 |
| *Practice Arrangement* | | | | | | |
| · Solo Practice | 45 | 150.2 | 19.3 | 64 | 118 | 165 |
| · Two Physician Practice | 7 | . | . | . | . | . |
| · Three Physician Practice | 10 | . | . | . | . | . |
| · 4-8 Physician Practice | 30 | 108.6 | 16.4 | 16 | 97 | 160 |
| · Over 8 Physician Practice | 18 | . | . | . | . | . |

Source: 1995 Socioeconomic Monitoring System survey of nonfederal patient care physicians. See the beginning of this section, the introduction, and appendices for a discussion of the survey sample, definitions, and computation procedures. Statistics are not reported if the number of responses is less than 25.

# Compensation of Nonfederal Physicians

Trends in Net Income, 1984-1994

Net Income after Expenses before Taxes

Total Practice Revenue

# Compensation of Nonfederal Physicians

One measure of physician compensation is net income from medical practice. Physician net income is defined to include all earnings from medical practice after expenses before taxes, including contributions into deferred compensation plans. The following questions were used to obtain information on physician's net income from medical practice:

1a. Did you have income in 1994 from investments in medical-related enterprises that are independent from your medical practice?

This investment income includes dividends and other returns from investments in medical-related enterprises, such as medical labs or imaging centers.

[IF NO GO TO QUESTION 2]

1b. What was your investment income from these independent medical related enterprises?

2. During 1994, what was your own net income from medical practice to the nearest $1000, after expenses but before taxes? Please include all income from fees, salaries, retainers, bonuses, deferred compensation, and other forms of monetary compensation but not the investment income you reported in Question 1b.

*If physician is an employee*

3a. In 1994, did you receive any medical, dental, life, or disability insurance benefits through your employer?

[IF NO GO TO QUESTION 5a]

3b. What was the dollar value of these insurance benefits, to the nearest $1000?

3c. Did you add in the dollar value of these insurance benefits when reporting your net income of (response to Question 2)?

*If physician is self-employed*

4a. In 1994, did you have medical, dental, life, or disability insurance either personally, or through your practice?

[IF NO GO TO QUESTION 5a]

4b. What was the cost of this insurance to the nearest $1000?

4c. How much of this cost did you pay out of your own net income of (response to Question 2) to the nearest $1000?

*All physicians*

5a. Did you receive any income in bonuses in 1994?

Do not include any income from salaries, retainers or consulting fees or other forms of compensation.

[IF NO GO TO QUESTION 6a]

5b. To the nearest $1000, how much of your 1994 income was paid in bonuses?

6a. Did you receive any income from salaries in 1994?

Do not include any income from retainers or consulting fees as salaries.

6b. To the nearest $1000, what was your income from salaries in 1994?

Question 1a was asked to ensure that only cash compensation from medical practice was included in the physician's net income response (Question 2). The bonus and salary information was used to adjust the final net income figure if there was a discrepancy in the physician's responses to these questions (e.g., if total bonus and salary amount was greater than the original net income figure given by the physician).

Employee physicians were asked Questions 3a-3c. Employee physicians who received noncash benefits such as health and life insurance were asked for the dollar value of these benefits. These physicians were then asked if they included the dollar value of noncash benefits in their net income response. In cases where they did, the amount was subtracted from the net income figure. The intent was to ensure that noncash benefits were not included in net income.

Self-employed physicians were asked Questions 4a-4c. The purpose of these questions was to ensure that physicians reported all of their income, even if some of that income went towards purchasing insurance through the practice. If it was reported that none of the physician's net income went towards purchasing the insurance (i.e., it was paid for through the practice) then the cost of the insurance was added to the physician's net income (the response to Question 2). Because the physician is self-employed, any purchases for standard benefit-type items that would not be considered practice expenses (e.g., the physicians own life or health insurance) should be considered net income.

Net income information is presented in Figures 23-27. Figure 23 presents annual real (inflation-adjusted) and nominal (unadjusted) percentage changes in net income during the period 1984-1994. Figure 24 shows the average annual percentage change in net income during the period 1984-1994 for selected specialties. The amount of the change in net income that is due to economy-wide price inflation over this period is also shown on the chart. The All Items index of the Consumer Price Index (CPI) was used to construct the inflation-adjusted figures. The CPI data are from the Bureau of Labor Statistics.

Net income figures are reported for all physicians, employee physicians and self-employed physicians in Tables 75, 76 and 77, respectively. Total revenue from medical practice in Table 78 is calculated based on responses from self-employed physicians who reported both total professional expense and net income information. Specialty-specific net income figures are presented in Tables 79-88. State level data are not presented in any of the physician compensation tables (i.e., net income and practice revenue). Because of wide variation in the earnings of physicians, imprecision caused by small samples is magnified. In order to ensure precision, census division is the most detailed break-out presented in the physician compensation tables.

As noted above, physicians were asked to include deferred compensation in their response to Question 2. However, previous SMS surveys asked more specific questions that were designed to ensure that deferred compensation was included in net income. In 1994 (and previous surveys) physicians were asked the following questions:

- How much was contributed for or by you into pension, profit-sharing or other deferred compensation plans during 1993 to the nearest $1,000?

- Did you include this amount in your net income figure for 1993?

Deferred compensation was added to net income if it was not included in the initial response to the net income question.

It is not clear how the new question wording will affect the calculation of 1994 net income compared with previous years. However, in general, responses to a single question (e.g., what is your net income) tend to be smaller than the sum of responses to multiple questions (e.g., what is your net income, how much is your deferred compensation). This is because the respondents are thinking more about each component apart from the total. By putting deferred compensation in a long list of items that the physician should include in net income (rather then asking questions specifically about deferred compensation), deferred compensation may be a less prominent part of the final net income figure. Because deferred income questions were not asked on the 1995 survey, tables showing deferred compensation per physician and net income minus deferred compensation are not included in this edition of *Physician Marketplace Statistics*.

Figure 23. **Annual Percentage Change in Median Net Income after Expenses before Taxes, for Nonfederal Physicians, 1984-1994.**

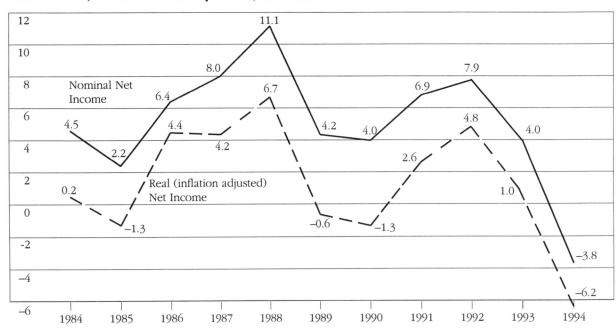

Figure 24. **Average Annual Percentage Change in Median Net Income after Expenses before Taxes, for Nonfederal Physicians, for Selected Specialties, 1984-1994.**

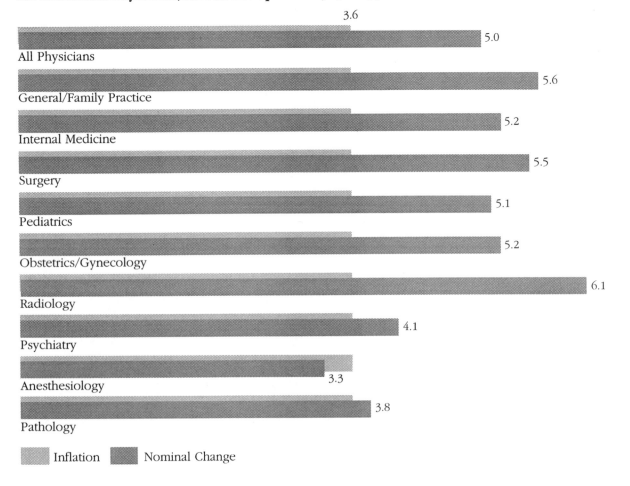

Figure 25. **Median Net Income (in thousands of dollars) after Expenses before Taxes, for Nonfederal Physicians, for Selected Specialties, 1994**

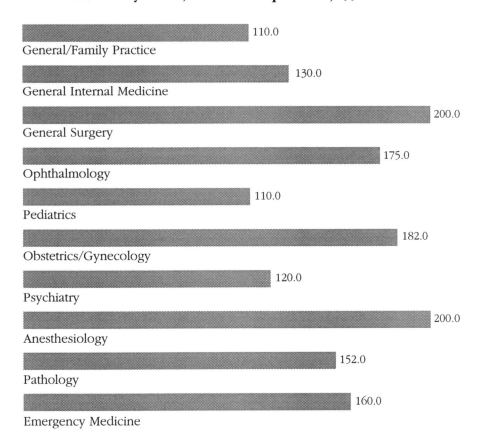

110.0
General/Family Practice

130.0
General Internal Medicine

200.0
General Surgery

175.0
Ophthalmology

110.0
Pediatrics

182.0
Obstetrics/Gynecology

120.0
Psychiatry

200.0
Anesthesiology

152.0
Pathology

160.0
Emergency Medicine

Figure 26. **Median Net Income (in thousands of dollars) after Expenses before Taxes for Nonfederal Physicians, by Census Division, 1994**

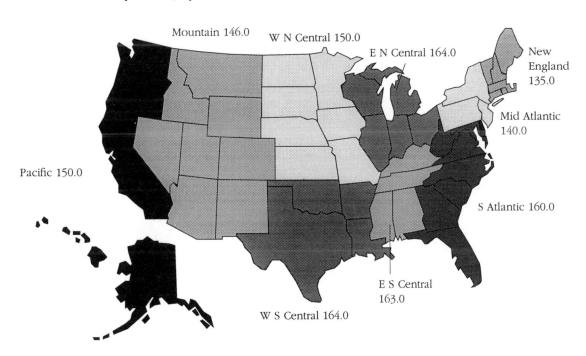

Mountain 146.0      W N Central 150.0
E N Central 164.0
New England 135.0
Mid Atlantic 140.0
Pacific 150.0
S Atlantic 160.0
E S Central 163.0
W S Central 164.0

Figure 27. **Median Net Income (in thousands of dollars) after Expenses before Taxes per Self-Employed Nonfederal Physician, by Size of Practice, 1994**

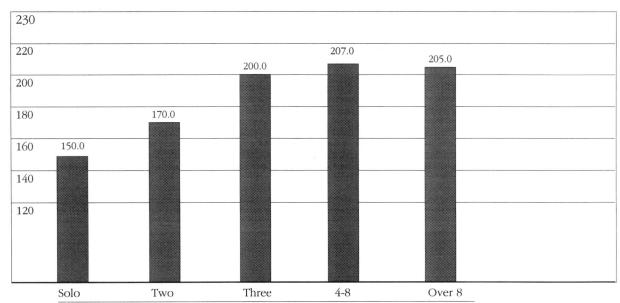

Number of Physicians in Practice

### Table 75. Net Income after Expenses before Taxes per Nonfederal Physician (in thousands of dollars), 1994

| | Number of Responses | Mean | Standard Error | 25th Percentile | Median | 75th Percentile |
|---|---|---|---|---|---|---|
| All Physicians | 3106 | 182.4 | 2.2 | 105.0 | 150.0 | 220.0 |
| *Specialty* | | | | | | |
| General/Family Practice | 414 | 121.2 | 2.9 | 85.0 | 110.0 | 144.0 |
| Internal Medicine | 578 | 174.9 | 5.4 | 100.0 | 150.0 | 199.0 |
| · General Internal Medicine | 411 | 148.0 | 4.5 | 98.0 | 130.0 | 175.0 |
| · Cardiovascular Diseases | 65 | 278.7 | 25.0 | 150.0 | 220.0 | 400.0 |
| · Other | 102 | 221.2 | 15.0 | 130.0 | 182.0 | 280.0 |
| Surgery | 668 | 255.2 | 6.3 | 150.0 | 219.0 | 300.0 |
| · General Surgery | 172 | 240.0 | 11.1 | 140.0 | 200.0 | 275.0 |
| · Otolaryngology | 55 | 245.5 | 14.0 | 175.0 | 225.0 | 300.0 |
| · Orthopedic Surgery | 138 | 310.7 | 16.6 | 190.0 | 272.0 | 375.0 |
| · Ophthalmology | 138 | 225.0 | 13.9 | 125.0 | 175.0 | 250.0 |
| · Urological Surgery | 77 | 223.1 | 11.3 | 150.0 | 204.0 | 277.0 |
| · Other | 88 | 279.5 | 20.0 | 150.0 | 228.0 | 350.0 |
| Pediatrics | 236 | 126.2 | 4.7 | 85.0 | 110.0 | 150.0 |
| Obstetrics/Gynecology | 183 | 200.4 | 8.9 | 130.0 | 182.0 | 248.0 |
| Radiology | 193 | 237.4 | 7.1 | 165.0 | 220.0 | 302.0 |
| Psychiatry | 236 | 128.5 | 4.0 | 90.0 | 120.0 | 150.0 |
| Anesthesiology | 196 | 218.1 | 5.8 | 168.0 | 200.0 | 262.0 |
| Pathology | 103 | 182.5 | 8.9 | 120.0 | 152.0 | 210.0 |
| Other Specialty | 299 | 158.2 | 4.4 | 105.0 | 150.0 | 190.0 |
| · Emergency Medicine | 122 | 166.6 | 5.9 | 120.0 | 160.0 | 200.0 |
| · Other | 177 | 152.9 | 6.3 | 96.0 | 140.0 | 175.0 |
| *Geographic Area* | | | | | | |
| New England | 197 | 156.1 | 7.2 | 98.0 | 135.0 | 180.0 |
| Middle Atlantic | 467 | 177.8 | 6.5 | 100.0 | 140.0 | 220.0 |
| East North Central | 454 | 191.9 | 6.0 | 117.0 | 164.0 | 237.0 |
| West North Central | 239 | 183.8 | 7.9 | 110.0 | 150.0 | 225.0 |
| South Atlantic | 533 | 189.3 | 5.4 | 106.0 | 160.0 | 248.0 |
| East South Central | 189 | 199.2 | 9.1 | 120.0 | 163.0 | 230.0 |
| West South Central | 286 | 195.5 | 7.5 | 110.0 | 164.0 | 234.0 |
| Mountain | 185 | 175.4 | 8.3 | 100.0 | 146.0 | 209.0 |
| Pacific | 556 | 171.8 | 4.4 | 105.0 | 150.0 | 210.0 |
| *Practice Arrangement* | | | | | | |
| Self-Employed | 1698 | 210.2 | 3.4 | 121.0 | 176.0 | 260.0 |
| · Solo Practice | 744 | 179.3 | 4.8 | 98.0 | 150.0 | 222.0 |
| · Two Physician Practice | 195 | 235.2 | 13.9 | 120.0 | 170.0 | 285.0 |
| · Three Physician Practice | 167 | 231.2 | 10.1 | 148.0 | 200.0 | 300.0 |
| · 4-8 Physician Practice | 386 | 242.5 | 6.4 | 150.0 | 207.0 | 300.0 |
| · Over 8 Physician Practice | 204 | 238.7 | 7.6 | 155.0 | 205.0 | 300.0 |
| Employee | 1204 | 148.2 | 2.5 | 98.0 | 130.0 | 180.0 |
| Independent Contractor | 204 | 168.5 | 7.3 | 100.0 | 140.0 | 230.0 |

Source: 1995 Socioeconomic Monitoring System survey of nonfederal patient care physicians. See the beginning of this section, the introduction, and appendices for a discussion of the survey sample, definitions, and computation procedures. Statistics are not reported if the number of responses is less than 25.

Table 76. **Net Income after Expenses before Taxes per Employee Nonfederal Physician (in thousands of dollars), 1994**

| | Number of Responses | Mean | Standard Error | 25th Percentile | Median | 75th Percentile |
|---|---|---|---|---|---|---|
| All Physicians | 1204 | 148.2 | 2.5 | 98.0 | 130.0 | 180.0 |
| *Specialty* | | | | | | |
| General/Family Practice | 182 | 108.7 | 3.3 | 85.0 | 100.0 | 125.0 |
| Internal Medicine | 236 | 132.8 | 4.2 | 97.0 | 125.0 | 160.0 |
| · General Internal Medicine | 186 | 126.3 | 4.1 | 96.0 | 120.0 | 150.0 |
| · Cardiovascular Diseases | 23 | · | · | · | · | · |
| · Other | 27 | 158.5 | 12.8 | 120.0 | 139.0 | 202.0 |
| Surgery | 180 | 212.2 | 10.1 | 135.0 | 180.0 | 250.0 |
| · General Surgery | 50 | 224.0 | 18.7 | 130.0 | 183.0 | 250.0 |
| · Otolaryngology | 11 | · | · | · | · | · |
| · Orthopedic Surgery | 38 | 209.5 | 16.7 | 150.0 | 200.0 | 240.0 |
| · Ophthalmology | 41 | 157.9 | 10.8 | 115.0 | 150.0 | 190.0 |
| · Urological Surgery | 19 | · | · | · | · | · |
| · Other | 21 | · | · | · | · | · |
| Pediatrics | 113 | 116.2 | 5.8 | 75.0 | 105.0 | 148.0 |
| Obstetrics/Gynecology | 57 | 188.6 | 13.4 | 122.0 | 175.0 | 235.0 |
| Radiology | 86 | 198.1 | 8.8 | 145.0 | 185.0 | 230.0 |
| Psychiatry | 97 | 117.8 | 3.9 | 90.0 | 120.0 | 140.0 |
| Anesthesiology | 66 | 184.9 | 8.5 | 136.0 | 180.0 | 218.0 |
| Pathology | 54 | 142.3 | 7.0 | 101.0 | 147.0 | 175.0 |
| Other Specialty | 133 | 143.1 | 5.0 | 100.0 | 140.0 | 174.0 |
| · Emergency Medicine | 48 | 152.2 | 7.4 | 116.0 | 150.0 | 175.0 |
| · Other | 85 | 138.4 | 6.5 | 96.0 | 140.0 | 174.0 |
| *Geographic Area* | | | | | | |
| New England | 99 | 127.6 | 5.7 | 90.0 | 115.0 | 150.0 |
| Middle Atlantic | 180 | 134.7 | 5.2 | 90.0 | 120.0 | 150.0 |
| East North Central | 184 | 164.8 | 7.2 | 106.0 | 148.0 | 195.0 |
| West North Central | 104 | 172.1 | 13.2 | 112.0 | 150.0 | 190.0 |
| South Atlantic | 198 | 139.1 | 5.3 | 88.0 | 120.0 | 173.0 |
| East South Central | 50 | 146.5 | 8.1 | 112.0 | 140.0 | 181.0 |
| West South Central | 106 | 155.2 | 9.7 | 97.0 | 132.0 | 180.0 |
| Mountain | 78 | 134.4 | 9.4 | 90.0 | 120.0 | 150.0 |
| Pacific | 205 | 156.4 | 4.8 | 105.0 | 140.0 | 190.0 |

Source: 1995 Socioeconomic Monitoring System survey of nonfederal patient care physicians. See the beginning of this section, the introduction, and appendices for a discussion of the survey sample, definitions, and computation procedures. Statistics are not reported if the number of responses is less than 25.

Table 77. **Net Income after Expenses before Taxes per Self-Employed Nonfederal Physician (in thousands of dollars), 1994**

| | Number of Responses | Mean | Standard Error | 25th Percentile | Median | 75th Percentile |
|---|---|---|---|---|---|---|
| All Physicians | 1698 | 210.2 | 3.4 | 121.0 | 176.0 | 260.0 |
| *Specialty* | | | | | | |
| General/Family Practice | 206 | 133.5 | 4.9 | 89.0 | 122.0 | 162.0 |
| Internal Medicine | 322 | 210.1 | 8.6 | 125.0 | 170.0 | 246.0 |
| · General Internal Medicine | 210 | 171.7 | 7.6 | 110.0 | 150.0 | 197.0 |
| · Cardiovascular Diseases | 40 | 343.5 | 33.5 | 200.0 | 295.0 | 480.0 |
| · Other | 72 | 242.2 | 19.7 | 155.0 | 200.0 | 301.0 |
| Surgery | 466 | 274.5 | 7.9 | 160.0 | 250.0 | 326.0 |
| · General Surgery | 116 | 250.6 | 14.1 | 150.0 | 242.0 | 300.0 |
| · Otolaryngology | 43 | 236.9 | 16.9 | 165.0 | 207.0 | 300.0 |
| · Orthopedic Surgery | 96 | 357.7 | 21.5 | 240.0 | 304.0 | 408.0 |
| · Ophthalmology | 90 | 262.4 | 19.6 | 130.0 | 215.0 | 300.0 |
| · Urological Surgery | 58 | 238.1 | 13.0 | 164.0 | 213.0 | 278.0 |
| · Other | 63 | 278.6 | 20.5 | 128.0 | 250.0 | 350.0 |
| Pediatrics | 114 | 135.3 | 7.5 | 100.0 | 113.0 | 155.0 |
| Obstetrics/Gynecology | 121 | 209.9 | 11.7 | 143.0 | 200.0 | 260.0 |
| Radiology | 89 | 291.5 | 9.7 | 208.0 | 282.0 | 350.0 |
| Psychiatry | 128 | 144.1 | 6.5 | 90.0 | 137.0 | 170.0 |
| Anesthesiology | 100 | 237.0 | 7.3 | 180.0 | 220.0 | 298.0 |
| Pathology | 33 | 256.4 | 15.4 | 185.0 | 215.0 | 343.0 |
| Other Specialty | 119 | 171.8 | 8.6 | 120.0 | 158.0 | 220.0 |
| · Emergency Medicine | 32 | 190.0 | 12.6 | 150.0 | 185.0 | 226.0 |
| · Other | 87 | 165.7 | 10.7 | 96.0 | 142.0 | 210.0 |
| *Geographic Area* | | | | | | |
| New England | 85 | 200.9 | 13.9 | 120.0 | 170.0 | 250.0 |
| Middle Atlantic | 268 | 206.7 | 10.2 | 115.0 | 166.0 | 250.0 |
| East North Central | 242 | 221.6 | 9.1 | 128.0 | 190.0 | 283.0 |
| West North Central | 125 | 190.3 | 9.8 | 110.0 | 160.0 | 250.0 |
| South Atlantic | 300 | 217.9 | 8.1 | 129.0 | 180.0 | 280.0 |
| East South Central | 125 | 227.5 | 12.5 | 130.0 | 182.0 | 285.0 |
| West South Central | 166 | 225.4 | 10.6 | 150.0 | 188.0 | 280.0 |
| Mountain | 91 | 214.8 | 13.1 | 120.0 | 183.0 | 265.0 |
| Pacific | 296 | 190.4 | 7.1 | 110.0 | 160.0 | 240.0 |
| *Practice Arrangement* | | | | | | |
| Self-Employed | | | | | | |
| · Solo Practice | 744 | 179.3 | 4.8 | 98.0 | 150.0 | 222.0 |
| · Two Physician Practice | 195 | 235.2 | 13.9 | 120.0 | 170.0 | 285.0 |
| · Three Physician Practice | 167 | 231.2 | 10.1 | 148.0 | 200.0 | 300.0 |
| · 4-8 Physician Practice | 386 | 242.5 | 6.4 | 150.0 | 207.0 | 300.0 |
| · Over 8 Physician Practice | 204 | 238.7 | 7.6 | 155.0 | 205.0 | 300.0 |

Source: 1995 Socioeconomic Monitoring System survey of nonfederal patient care physicians. See the beginning of this section, the introduction, and appendices for a discussion of the survey sample, definitions, and computation procedures. Statistics are not reported if the number of responses is less than 25.

## Table 78. **Total Practice Revenue per Self-Employed Nonfederal Physician (in thousands of dollars), 1994**

| | Number of Responses | Mean | Standard Error | 25th Percentile | Median | 75th Percentile |
|---|---|---|---|---|---|---|
| All Physicians | 1416 | 396.4 | 6.8 | 231.0 | 343.0 | 478.0 |
| *Specialty* | | | | | | |
| General/Family Practice | 175 | 334.6 | 14.4 | 210.0 | 288.0 | 409.0 |
| Internal Medicine | 263 | 399.5 | 17.3 | 232.0 | 324.0 | 475.0 |
| · General Internal Medicine | 168 | 353.2 | 19.3 | 193.0 | 304.0 | 406.0 |
| · Cardiovascular Diseases | 36 | 581.9 | 58.0 | 320.0 | 476.0 | 720.0 |
| · Other | 59 | 413.5 | 34.8 | 234.0 | 324.0 | 519.0 |
| Surgery | 389 | 525.0 | 15.4 | 343.0 | 457.0 | 618.0 |
| · General Surgery | 99 | 406.8 | 22.4 | 283.0 | 384.0 | 498.0 |
| · Otolaryngology | 36 | 499.6 | 25.1 | 399.0 | 482.0 | 591.0 |
| · Orthopedic Surgery | 74 | 682.4 | 36.8 | 472.0 | 597.0 | 923.0 |
| · Ophthalmology | 81 | 583.5 | 46.2 | 331.0 | 459.0 | 665.0 |
| · Urological Surgery | 44 | 513.4 | 32.7 | 372.0 | 446.0 | 625.0 |
| · Other | 55 | 524.2 | 35.6 | 344.0 | 462.0 | 638.0 |
| Pediatrics | 92 | 297.5 | 16.7 | 192.0 | 267.0 | 382.0 |
| Obstetrics/Gynecology | 92 | 416.1 | 23.0 | 287.0 | 366.0 | 500.0 |
| Radiology | 76 | 448.9 | 23.7 | 314.0 | 412.0 | 486.0 |
| Psychiatry | 119 | 210.6 | 10.6 | 125.0 | 176.0 | 272.0 |
| Anesthesiology | 86 | 323.8 | 14.6 | 232.0 | 282.0 | 379.0 |
| Pathology | 29 | 392.4 | 24.1 | 245.0 | 375.0 | 472.0 |
| Other Specialty | 95 | 313.7 | 17.6 | 201.0 | 261.0 | 383.0 |
| · Emergency Medicine | 26 | 270.2 | 30.2 | 205.0 | 217.0 | 305.0 |
| · Other | 69 | 329.0 | 21.2 | 201.0 | 278.0 | 406.0 |
| *Geographic Area* | | | | | | |
| New England | 71 | 348.0 | 24.6 | 196.0 | 307.0 | 415.0 |
| Middle Atlantic | 224 | 372.7 | 18.8 | 203.0 | 309.0 | 440.0 |
| East North Central | 195 | 392.4 | 16.9 | 230.0 | 348.0 | 473.0 |
| West North Central | 104 | 397.6 | 26.7 | 230.0 | 340.0 | 470.0 |
| South Atlantic | 247 | 419.1 | 17.1 | 254.0 | 381.0 | 502.0 |
| East South Central | 104 | 442.6 | 26.5 | 234.0 | 352.0 | 609.0 |
| West South Central | 140 | 415.4 | 20.9 | 257.0 | 351.0 | 470.0 |
| Mountain | 79 | 389.9 | 22.2 | 234.0 | 351.0 | 513.0 |
| Pacific | 252 | 385.9 | 15.2 | 232.0 | 314.0 | 462.0 |
| *Practice Arrangement* | | | | | | |
| Self-Employed | | | | | | |
| · Solo Practice | 659 | 337.4 | 8.8 | 189.0 | 284.0 | 416.0 |
| · Two Physician Practice | 167 | 487.0 | 24.3 | 271.0 | 388.0 | 589.0 |
| · Three Physician Practice | 141 | 447.4 | 20.2 | 279.0 | 384.0 | 520.0 |
| · 4-8 Physician Practice | 300 | 452.8 | 14.6 | 298.0 | 397.0 | 518.0 |
| · Over 8 Physician Practice | 148 | 438.8 | 20.7 | 263.0 | 370.0 | 501.0 |

Source: 1995 Socioeconomic Monitoring System survey of nonfederal patient care physicians. See the beginning of this section, the introduction, and appendices for a discussion of the survey sample, definitions, and computation procedures. Statistics are not reported if the number of responses is less than 25.

Table 79. **Net Income after Expenses before Taxes per Nonfederal Physician (in thousands of dollars), 1994 – General/Family Practice**

| | Number of Responses | Mean | Standard Error | 25th Percentile | Median | 75th Percentile |
|---|---|---|---|---|---|---|
| All Physicians | 414 | 121.2 | 2.9 | 85 | 110 | 144 |
| *Geographic Area* | | | | | | |
| New England | 21 | . | . | . | . | . |
| Middle Atlantic | 46 | 110.3 | 9.6 | 75 | 103 | 125 |
| East North Central | 70 | 121.0 | 7.0 | 90 | 120 | 144 |
| West North Central | 53 | 117.2 | 6.2 | 88 | 120 | 150 |
| South Atlantic | 59 | 122.8 | 10.0 | 79 | 97 | 147 |
| East South Central | 27 | 152.5 | 13.9 | 97 | 134 | 190 |
| West South Central | 36 | 126.6 | 7.8 | 94 | 111 | 140 |
| Mountain | 36 | 108.6 | 6.5 | 87 | 100 | 140 |
| Pacific | 66 | 127.7 | 8.2 | 80 | 120 | 150 |
| *Practice Arrangement* | | | | | | |
| Self Employed | 206 | 133.5 | 4.9 | 89 | 122 | 162 |
| · Solo Practice | 114 | 124.2 | 6.5 | 75 | 111 | 156 |
| · Two Physician Practice | 28 | 177.4 | 19.1 | 91 | 162 | 240 |
| · Three Physician Practice | 16 | . | . | . | . | . |
| · 4-8 Physician Practice | 35 | 133.5 | 5.6 | 106 | 125 | 164 |
| · Over 8 Physician Practice | 13 | . | . | . | . | . |
| Employee | 182 | 108.7 | 3.3 | 85 | 100 | 125 |
| Independent Contractor | 26 | 115.1 | 9.9 | 95 | 111 | 144 |

Source: 1995 Socioeconomic Monitoring System survey of nonfederal patient care physicians. See the beginning of this section, the introduction, and appendices for a discussion of the survey sample, definitions, and computation procedures. Statistics are not reported if the number of responses is less than 25.

Table 80. **Net Income after Expenses before Taxes per Nonfederal Physician (in thousands of dollars), 1994 – Internal Medicine**

| | Number of Responses | Mean | Standard Error | 25th Percentile | Median | 75th Percentile |
|---|---|---|---|---|---|---|
| All Physicians | 578 | 174.9 | 5.4 | 100 | 150 | 199 |
| *Geographic Area* | | | | | | |
| New England | 55 | 129.4 | 8.2 | 95 | 115 | 160 |
| Middle Atlantic | 97 | 170.2 | 11.2 | 110 | 135 | 205 |
| East North Central | 79 | 172.7 | 15.2 | 100 | 150 | 195 |
| West North Central | 31 | 191.0 | 22.1 | 120 | 160 | 208 |
| South Atlantic | 103 | 177.0 | 13.9 | 100 | 140 | 200 |
| East South Central | 38 | 204.7 | 27.6 | 112 | 155 | 227 |
| West South Central | 47 | 177.5 | 14.0 | 120 | 165 | 205 |
| Mountain | 27 | 188.2 | 29.2 | 110 | 145 | 200 |
| Pacific | 101 | 180.4 | 15.0 | 106 | 150 | 197 |
| *Practice Arrangement* | | | | | | |
| Self Employed | 322 | 210.1 | 8.6 | 125 | 170 | 246 |
| · Solo Practice | 145 | 177.4 | 11.6 | 96 | 153 | 200 |
| · Two Physician Practice | 26 | 277.8 | 46.7 | 150 | 170 | 350 |
| · Three Physician Practice | 40 | 230.1 | 17.7 | 152 | 206 | 301 |
| · 4-8 Physician Practice | 69 | 241.9 | 17.7 | 137 | 186 | 295 |
| · Over 8 Physician Practice | 42 | 237.0 | 23.1 | 148 | 165 | 300 |
| Employee | 236 | 132.8 | 4.2 | 97 | 125 | 160 |
| Independent Contractor | 20 | . | . | . | . | . |

Source: 1995 Socioeconomic Monitoring System survey of nonfederal patient care physicians. See the beginning of this section, the introduction, and appendices for a discussion of the survey sample, definitions, and computation procedures. Statistics are not reported if the number of responses is less than 25.

Table 81. **Net Income after Expenses before Taxes per Nonfederal Physician (in thousands of dollars), 1994 – Surgery**

| | Number of Responses | Mean | Standard Error | 25th Percentile | Median | 75th Percentile |
|---|---|---|---|---|---|---|
| All Physicians | 668 | 255.2 | 6.3 | 150 | 219 | 300 |
| *Geographic Area* | | | | | | |
| New England | 34 | 220.4 | 25.0 | 134 | 160 | 300 |
| Middle Atlantic | 99 | 265.0 | 22.3 | 128 | 200 | 308 |
| East North Central | 91 | 283.3 | 18.0 | 180 | 237 | 301 |
| West North Central | 57 | 263.5 | 22.8 | 170 | 247 | 319 |
| South Atlantic | 127 | 256.7 | 13.2 | 168 | 230 | 301 |
| East South Central | 40 | 265.6 | 18.6 | 150 | 240 | 316 |
| West South Central | 70 | 261.7 | 22.0 | 125 | 200 | 300 |
| Mountain | 34 | 254.0 | 21.1 | 150 | 230 | 336 |
| Pacific | 116 | 219.8 | 9.7 | 140 | 210 | 280 |
| *Practice Arrangement* | | | | | | |
| Self Employed | 466 | 274.5 | 7.9 | 160 | 250 | 326 |
| · Solo Practice | 194 | 247.8 | 11.9 | 128 | 206 | 295 |
| · Two Physician Practice | 78 | 325.8 | 26.2 | 184 | 264 | 376 |
| · Three Physician Practice | 63 | 263.4 | 16.8 | 178 | 250 | 308 |
| · 4-8 Physician Practice | 109 | 298.5 | 13.7 | 204 | 262 | 350 |
| · Over 8 Physician Practice | 21 | . | . | . | . | . |
| Employee | 180 | 212.2 | 10.1 | 135 | 180 | 250 |
| Independent Contractor | 22 | . | . | . | . | . |

Source: 1995 Socioeconomic Monitoring System survey of nonfederal patient care physicians. See the beginning of this section, the introduction, and appendices for a discussion of the survey sample, definitions, and computation procedures. Statistics are not reported if the number of responses is less than 25.

Table 82. **Net Income after Expenses before Taxes per Nonfederal Physician (in thousands of dollars), 1994 – Pediatrics**

| | Number of Responses | Mean | Standard Error | 25th Percentile | Median | 75th Percentile |
|---|---|---|---|---|---|---|
| All Physicians | 236 | 126.2 | 4.7 | 85 | 110 | 150 |
| *Geographic Area* | | | | | | |
| New England | 14 | . | . | . | . | . |
| Middle Atlantic | 39 | 120.3 | 11.1 | 72 | 100 | 150 |
| East North Central | 26 | 126.3 | 8.2 | 90 | 120 | 162 |
| West North Central | 15 | . | . | . | . | . |
| South Atlantic | 52 | 131.7 | 12.3 | 79 | 120 | 150 |
| East South Central | 13 | . | . | . | . | . |
| West South Central | 26 | 110.6 | 7.9 | 80 | 110 | 120 |
| Mountain | 16 | . | . | . | . | . |
| Pacific | 35 | 125.7 | 12.6 | 90 | 113 | 150 |
| *Practice Arrangement* | | | | | | |
| Self Employed | 114 | 135.3 | 7.5 | 100 | 113 | 155 |
| · Solo Practice | 49 | 116.9 | 8.6 | 80 | 110 | 147 |
| · Two Physician Practice | 15 | . | . | . | . | . |
| · Three Physician Practice | 12 | . | . | . | . | . |
| · 4-8 Physician Practice | 28 | 164.9 | 13.1 | 110 | 155 | 193 |
| · Over 8 Physician Practice | 9 | . | . | . | . | . |
| Employee | 113 | 116.2 | 5.8 | 75 | 105 | 148 |
| Independent Contractor | 9 | . | . | . | . | . |

Source: 1995 Socioeconomic Monitoring System survey of nonfederal patient care physicians. See the beginning of this section, the introduction, and appendices for a discussion of the survey sample, definitions, and computation procedures. Statistics are not reported if the number of responses is less than 25.

Table 83. **Net Income after Expenses before Taxes per Nonfederal Physician (in thousands of dollars), 1994 – Obstetrics/Gynecology**

| | Number of Responses | Mean | Standard Error | 25th Percentile | Median | 75th Percentile |
|---|---|---|---|---|---|---|
| All Physicians | 183 | 200.4 | 8.9 | 130 | 182 | 248 |
| *Geographic Area* | | | | | | |
| New England | 9 | . | . | . | . | . |
| Middle Atlantic | 27 | 182.7 | 28.1 | 120 | 152 | 237 |
| East North Central | 31 | 219.0 | 16.1 | 165 | 220 | 265 |
| West North Central | 11 | . | . | . | . | . |
| South Atlantic | 25 | 196.7 | 18.0 | 135 | 200 | 217 |
| East South Central | 14 | . | . | . | . | . |
| West South Central | 21 | . | . | . | . | . |
| Mountain | 17 | . | . | . | . | . |
| Pacific | 28 | 137.7 | 13.5 | 80 | 125 | 180 |
| *Practice Arrangement* | | | | | | |
| Self Employed | 121 | 209.9 | 11.7 | 143 | 200 | 260 |
| · Solo Practice | 55 | 189.9 | 17.6 | 114 | 150 | 260 |
| · Two Physician Practice | 13 | . | . | . | . | . |
| · Three Physician Practice | 11 | . | . | . | . | . |
| · 4-8 Physician Practice | 31 | 251.6 | 23.2 | 176 | 211 | 250 |
| · Over 8 Physician Practice | 11 | . | . | . | . | . |
| Employee | 57 | 188.6 | 13.4 | 122 | 175 | 235 |
| Independent Contractor | 5 | . | . | . | . | . |

Source: 1995 Socioeconomic Monitoring System survey of nonfederal patient care physicians. See the beginning of this section, the introduction, and appendices for a discussion of the survey sample, definitions, and computation procedures. Statistics are not reported if the number of responses is less than 25.

Table 84. **Net Income after Expenses before Taxes per Nonfederal Physician (in thousands of dollars), 1994 – Radiology**

| | Number of Responses | Mean | Standard Error | 25th Percentile | Median | 75th Percentile |
|---|---|---|---|---|---|---|
| All Physicians | 193 | 237.4 | 7.1 | 165 | 220 | 302 |
| *Geographic Area* | | | | | | |
| New England | 12 | . | . | . | . | . |
| Middle Atlantic | 30 | 202.2 | 20.5 | 90 | 180 | 240 |
| East North Central | 38 | 292.4 | 16.5 | 198 | 266 | 322 |
| West North Central | 14 | . | . | . | . | . |
| South Atlantic | 30 | 243.7 | 11.3 | 200 | 250 | 300 |
| East South Central | 13 | . | . | . | . | . |
| West South Central | 15 | . | . | . | . | . |
| Mountain | 5 | . | . | . | . | . |
| Pacific | 36 | 195.5 | 15.6 | 130 | 200 | 256 |
| *Practice Arrangement* | | | | | | |
| Self Employed | 89 | 291.5 | 9.7 | 208 | 282 | 350 |
| · Solo Practice | 4 | . | . | . | . | . |
| · Two Physician Practice | 13 | . | . | . | . | . |
| · Three Physician Practice | 6 | . | . | . | . | . |
| · 4-8 Physician Practice | 35 | 276.7 | 12.7 | 212 | 270 | 317 |
| · Over 8 Physician Practice | 31 | 303.7 | 17.1 | 215 | 300 | 400 |
| Employee | 86 | 198.1 | 8.8 | 145 | 185 | 230 |
| Independent Contractor | 18 | . | . | . | . | . |

Source: 1995 Socioeconomic Monitoring System survey of nonfederal patient care physicians. See the beginning of this section, the introduction, and appendices for a discussion of the survey sample, definitions, and computation procedures. Statistics are not reported if the number of responses is less than 25.

Table 85. **Net Income after Expenses before Taxes per Nonfederal Physician (in thousands of dollars), 1994 – Psychiatry**

| | Number of Responses | Mean | Standard Error | 25th Percentile | Median | 75th Percentile |
|---|---|---|---|---|---|---|
| All Physicians | 236 | 128.5 | 4.0 | 90 | 120 | 150 |
| *Geographic Area* | | | | | | |
| New England | 18 | · | · | · | · | · |
| Middle Atlantic | 48 | 124.8 | 7.2 | 90 | 123 | 150 |
| East North Central | 32 | 111.6 | 7.2 | 85 | 120 | 140 |
| West North Central | 21 | · | · | · | · | · |
| South Atlantic | 36 | 171.0 | 13.2 | 100 | 143 | 232 |
| East South Central | 7 | · | · | · | · | · |
| West South Central | 13 | · | · | · | · | · |
| Mountain | 12 | · | · | · | · | · |
| Pacific | 49 | 118.6 | 7.4 | 85 | 105 | 148 |
| *Practice Arrangement* | | | | | | |
| Self Employed | 128 | 144.1 | 6.5 | 90 | 137 | 170 |
| · Solo Practice | 112 | 131.8 | 5.6 | 85 | 125 | 160 |
| · Two Physician Practice | 8 | · | · | · | · | · |
| · Three Physician Practice | 1 | · | · | · | · | · |
| · 4-8 Physician Practice | 5 | · | · | · | · | · |
| · Over 8 Physician Practice | 2 | · | · | · | · | · |
| Employee | 97 | 117.8 | 3.9 | 90 | 120 | 140 |
| Independent Contractor | 11 | · | · | · | · | · |

Source: 1995 Socioeconomic Monitoring System survey of nonfederal patient care physicians. See the beginning of this section, the introduction, and appendices for a discussion of the survey sample, definitions, and computation procedures. Statistics are not reported if the number of responses is less than 25.

Table 86. **Net Income after Expenses before Taxes per Nonfederal Physician (in thousands of dollars), 1994 – Anesthesiology**

| | Number of Responses | Mean | Standard Error | 25th Percentile | Median | 75th Percentile |
|---|---|---|---|---|---|---|
| All Physicians | 196 | 218.1 | 5.8 | 168 | 200 | 262 |
| *Geographic Area* | | | | | | |
| New England | 14 | · | · | · | · | · |
| Middle Atlantic | 26 | 209.4 | 20.2 | 160 | 190 | 250 |
| East North Central | 30 | 247.0 | 15.1 | 180 | 252 | 304 |
| West North Central | 9 | · | · | · | · | · |
| South Atlantic | 29 | 244.1 | 13.7 | 188 | 227 | 301 |
| East South Central | 10 | · | · | · | · | · |
| West South Central | 23 | · | · | · | · | · |
| Mountain | 12 | · | · | · | · | · |
| Pacific | 43 | 209.7 | 9.6 | 150 | 200 | 250 |
| *Practice Arrangement* | | | | | | |
| Self Employed | 100 | 237.0 | 7.3 | 180 | 220 | 298 |
| · Solo Practice | 20 | · | · | · | · | · |
| · Two Physician Practice | 1 | · | · | · | · | · |
| · Three Physician Practice | 7 | · | · | · | · | · |
| · 4-8 Physician Practice | 25 | 257.7 | 14.7 | 193 | 240 | 301 |
| · Over 8 Physician Practice | 47 | 249.4 | 8.5 | 200 | 247 | 290 |
| Employee | 66 | 184.9 | 8.5 | 136 | 180 | 218 |
| Independent Contractor | 30 | 230.1 | 19.7 | 140 | 225 | 280 |

Source: 1995 Socioeconomic Monitoring System survey of nonfederal patient care physicians. See the beginning of this section, the introduction, and appendices for a discussion of the survey sample, definitions, and computation procedures. Statistics are not reported if the number of responses is less than 25.

Table 87. **Net Income after Expenses before Taxes per Nonfederal Physician (in thousands of dollars), 1994 – Pathology**

|  | Number of Responses | Mean | Standard Error | 25th Percentile | Median | 75th Percentile |
|---|---|---|---|---|---|---|
| All Physicians | 103 | 182.5 | 8.9 | 120 | 152 | 210 |
| *Geographic Area* |  |  |  |  |  |  |
| New England | 6 | . | . | . | . | . |
| Middle Atlantic | 16 | . | . | . | . | . . |
| East North Central | 12 | . | . | . | . | . |
| West North Central | 6 | . | . | . | . | . |
| South Atlantic | 19 | . | . | . | . | . |
| East South Central | 9 | . | . | . | . | . |
| West South Central | 11 | . | . | . | . | . |
| Mountain | 7 | . | . | . | . | . |
| Pacific | 17 | . | . | . | . | . |
| *Practice Arrangement* |  |  |  |  |  |  |
| Self Employed | 33 | 256.4 | 15.4 | 185 | 215 | 343 |
| · Solo Practice | 3 | . | . | . | . | . |
| · Two Physician Practice | 4 | . | . | . | . | . |
| · Three Physician Practice | 3 | . | . | . | . | . |
| · 4-8 Physician Practice | 18 | . | . | . | . | . |
| · Over 8 Physician Practice | 5 | . | . | . | . | . |
| Employee | 54 | 142.3 | 7.0 | 101 | 147 | 175 |
| Independent Contractor | 16 | . | . | . | . | . |

Source: 1995 Socioeconomic Monitoring System survey of nonfederal patient care physicians. See the beginning of this section, the introduction, and appendices for a discussion of the survey sample, definitions, and computation procedures. Statistics are not reported if the number of responses is less than 25.

Table 88. **Net Income after Expenses before Taxes per Nonfederal Physician (in thousands of dollars), 1994 – Other Specialty**

|  | Number of Responses | Mean | Standard Error | 25th Percentile | Median | 75th Percentile |
|---|---|---|---|---|---|---|
| All Physicians | 299 | 158.2 | 4.4 | 105 | 150 | 190 |
| *Geographic Area* |  |  |  |  |  |  |
| New England | 14 | . | . | . | . | . |
| Middle Atlantic | 39 | 168.4 | 10.8 | 110 | 150 | 220 |
| East North Central | 45 | 155.8 | 9.8 | 100 | 144 | 200 |
| West North Central | 22 | . | . | . | . | . |
| South Atlantic | 53 | 147.6 | 12.7 | 96 | 140 | 175 |
| East South Central | 18 | . | . | . | . | . |
| West South Central | 24 | . | . | . | . | . |
| Mountain | 19 | . | . | . | . | . |
| Pacific | 65 | 177.0 | 10.1 | 120 | 150 | 221 |
| *Practice Arrangement* |  |  |  |  |  |  |
| Self Employed | 119 | 171.8 | 8.6 | 120 | 158 | 220 |
| · Solo Practice | 48 | 139.6 | 12.4 | 87 | 137 | 170 |
| · Two Physician Practice | 9 | . | . | . | . | . |
| · Three Physician Practice | 8 | . | . | . | . | . |
| · 4-8 Physician Practice | 31 | 187.1 | 16.6 | 120 | 156 | 221 |
| · Over 8 Physician Practice | 23 | . | . | . | . | . |
| Employee | 133 | 143.1 | 5.0 | 100 | 140 | 174 |
| Independent Contractor | 47 | 167.7 | 10.3 | 115 | 150 | 208 |

Source: 1995 Socioeconomic Monitoring System survey of nonfederal patient care physicians. See the beginning of this section, the introduction, and appendices for a discussion of the survey sample, definitions, and computation procedures. Statistics are not reported if the number of responses is less than 25.

# Distribution of Nonfederal Physician Revenue by Source of Payer

Percent of Revenue from Medicare

Percent of Revenue from Medicaid

Percent of Revenue from Private Insurance Plans

Percent of Revenue from Patients

# Distribution of Physician Revenue by Source of Payer

Physicians receive reimbursement for their services from several sources. Physicians were asked what percentage of their revenue were received from several payers including Medicare, Medicaid, and private insurance plans. Physicians were also asked what percentage of their revenue was received directly from their patients.

Questions 1-3 were used to collect the information that is reported in Tables 89-92. Physicians indicating that they were independent contractors were not asked Questions 1-3.

1. What percentage of your practice revenue is received from Medicare?

2. What percentage of your practice revenue is received from Medicaid?

In previous years, physicians were asked to indicate the percentage of revenue they received from Blue Cross and Blue Shield and the percentage they received from other private insurance plans. In 1995, they were asked for the percentage of revenue they received from all private insurance plans (including Blue Cross and Blue Shield).

3. What percentage of your practice revenue is received from private medical plans? (Include all revenue received from commercial plans. That includes payments made directly to you by these plans and reimbursements to your patients for services they had previously paid for. However, do not include patient payments that are not reimbursed by any third-party plan.)

Responses from questions 1-3 were summed and the physician was asked if the remaining percent (i.e, the difference between.the sum of questions 1-3 and 100) was received from patient payments that are not reimbursed by any third-party plan. The physician's response to each of the questions was reviewed if the remaining percent did not equal the amount that the physician received from patients without any third-party plan. A review of the questions was also made if the responses did not sum to 100%.

Responses to questions 1-3 are summarized, respectively, in Tables 89-91. Information on the percentage of revenues received directly from patients is summarized in Table 92. The sum of the average percent of revenues from each source may not equal 100% because of rounding.

Responses to the questions on the percentage of revenues by payer are also summarized in Figure 5 of the overview section (page 9 of this volume). Figures 28-30 show the percentage of physicians revenue that is derived from Medicare.

Figure 28. **Mean and Median Percentage of Revenue from Medicare per Nonfederal Physician, for Selected Specialties, 1995**

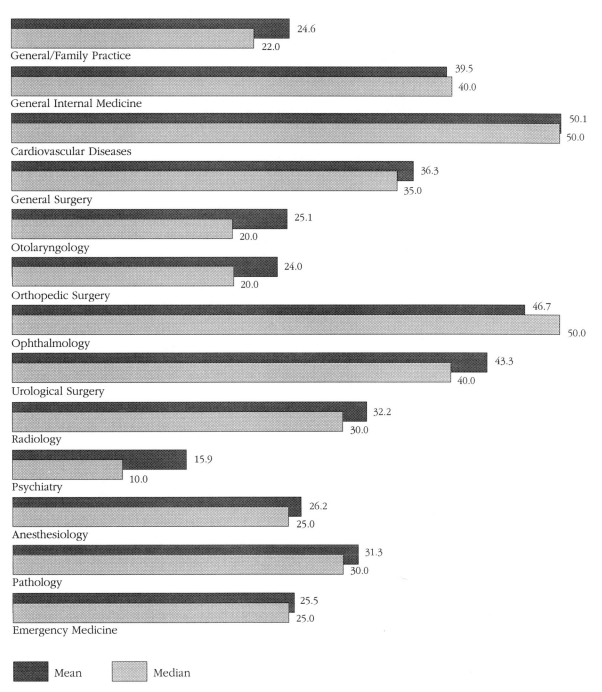

General/Family Practice — 24.6, 22.0

General Internal Medicine — 39.5, 40.0

Cardiovascular Diseases — 50.1, 50.0

General Surgery — 36.3, 35.0

Otolaryngology — 25.1, 20.0

Orthopedic Surgery — 24.0, 20.0

Ophthalmology — 46.7, 50.0

Urological Surgery — 43.3, 40.0

Radiology — 32.2, 30.0

Psychiatry — 15.9, 10.0

Anesthesiology — 26.2, 25.0

Pathology — 31.3, 30.0

Emergency Medicine — 25.5, 25.0

Mean    Median

Figure 29. **Mean and Median Percentage of Revenue from Medicare per Nonfederal Physician, for Selected States, 1995**

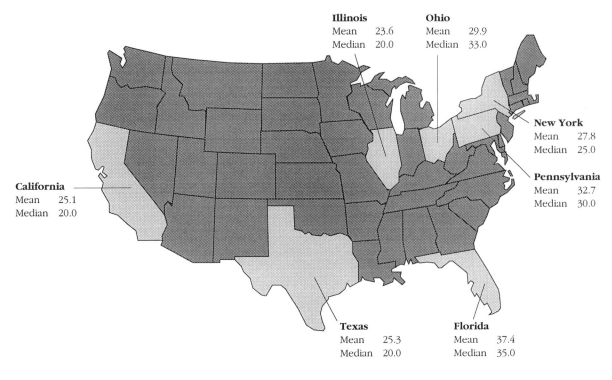

**Illinois**
Mean    23.6
Median    20.0

**Ohio**
Mean    29.9
Median    33.0

**New York**
Mean    27.8
Median    25.0

**Pennsylvania**
Mean    32.7
Median    30.0

**California**
Mean    25.1
Median    20.0

**Texas**
Mean    25.3
Median    20.0

**Florida**
Mean    37.4
Median    35.0

Figure 30. **Mean and Median Percentage of Revenue from Medicare per Self-Employed Nonfederal Physician, by Size of Practice, 1995**

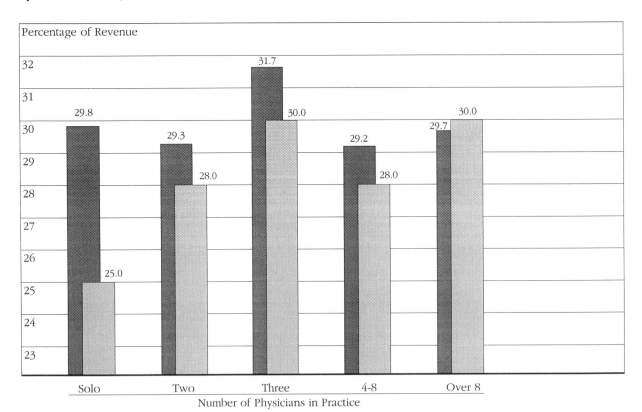

Percentage of Revenue

| | Solo | Two | Three | 4-8 | Over 8 |
|---|---|---|---|---|---|
| Mean | 29.8 | 29.3 | 31.7 | 29.2 | 29.7 |
| Median | 25.0 | 28.0 | 30.0 | 28.0 | 30.0 |

Number of Physicians in Practice

Mean    Median

## Table 89. **Percentage of Revenue from Medicare per Nonfederal Physician, 1995**

| | Number of Responses | Mean | Standard Error | 25th Percentile | Median | 75th Percentile |
|---|---|---|---|---|---|---|
| All Physicians | 3271 | 27.5 | 0.4 | 7.0 | 25.0 | 40.0 |
| *Specialty* | | | | | | |
| General/Family Practice | 420 | 24.6 | 0.9 | 10.0 | 22.0 | 33.0 |
| Internal Medicine | 650 | 40.5 | 0.9 | 25.0 | 40.0 | 55.0 |
| · General Internal Medicine | 441 | 39.5 | 1.2 | 20.0 | 40.0 | 60.0 |
| · Cardiovascular Diseases | 82 | 50.1 | 1.9 | 45.0 | 50.0 | 60.0 |
| · Other | 127 | 38.3 | 2.1 | 20.0 | 40.0 | 50.0 |
| Surgery | 774 | 34.3 | 0.7 | 20.0 | 30.0 | 50.0 |
| · General Surgery | 184 | 36.3 | 1.4 | 25.0 | 35.0 | 50.0 |
| · Otolaryngology | 64 | 25.1 | 1.9 | 15.0 | 20.0 | 30.0 |
| · Orthopedic Surgery | 168 | 24.0 | 1.3 | 10.0 | 20.0 | 34.0 |
| · Ophthalmology | 166 | 46.7 | 1.7 | 33.0 | 50.0 | 61.0 |
| · Urological Surgery | 94 | 43.3 | 2.0 | 30.0 | 40.0 | 60.0 |
| · Other | 98 | 25.5 | 1.8 | 10.0 | 21.0 | 35.0 |
| Pediatrics | 270 | 1.9 | 0.5 | 0.0 | 0.0 | 0.0 |
| Obstetrics/Gynecology | 214 | 9.9 | 0.8 | 2.0 | 5.0 | 12.0 |
| Radiology | 214 | 32.2 | 1.0 | 21.0 | 30.0 | 40.0 |
| Psychiatry | 223 | 15.9 | 1.3 | 1.0 | 10.0 | 25.0 |
| Anesthesiology | 168 | 26.2 | 1.3 | 15.0 | 25.0 | 35.0 |
| Pathology | 73 | 31.3 | 1.7 | 23.0 | 30.0 | 40.0 |
| Other Specialty | 265 | 24.3 | 1.3 | 5.0 | 25.0 | 35.0 |
| · Emergency Medicine | 66 | 25.5 | 1.5 | 15.0 | 25.0 | 30.0 |
| · Other | 199 | 24.0 | 1.6 | 1.0 | 20.0 | 40.0 |
| *Geographic Area* | | | | | | |
| New England | 192 | 29.2 | 1.7 | 10.0 | 30.0 | 45.0 |
| · Massachusetts | 89 | 30.7 | 2.6 | 10.0 | 30.0 | 50.0 |
| · Other | 103 | 27.7 | 2.2 | 8.0 | 23.0 | 45.0 |
| Middle Atlantic | 527 | 28.6 | 1.1 | 5.0 | 25.0 | 45.0 |
| · New Jersey | 98 | 25.2 | 2.8 | 0.0 | 20.0 | 40.0 |
| · New York | 207 | 26.4 | 1.8 | 2.0 | 20.0 | 40.0 |
| · Pennsylvania | 222 | 33.1 | 1.6 | 10.0 | 30.0 | 50.0 |
| East North Central | 493 | 28.9 | 1.0 | 10.0 | 30.0 | 45.0 |
| · Illinois | 160 | 25.3 | 1.8 | 3.0 | 25.0 | 40.0 |
| · Michigan | 87 | 32.0 | 2.2 | 20.0 | 30.0 | 50.0 |
| · Ohio | 108 | 30.5 | 2.0 | 12.0 | 34.0 | 40.0 |
| · Other | 138 | 30.1 | 1.7 | 12.0 | 30.0 | 45.0 |
| West North Central | 246 | 28.7 | 1.3 | 10.0 | 30.0 | 40.0 |
| South Atlantic | 607 | 28.9 | 1.0 | 7.0 | 26.0 | 45.0 |
| · Florida | 170 | 39.0 | 2.1 | 15.0 | 40.0 | 60.0 |
| · Other | 437 | 24.9 | 1.0 | 5.0 | 25.0 | 35.0 |
| East South Central | 194 | 30.8 | 1.4 | 15.0 | 30.0 | 45.0 |
| West South Central | 311 | 25.2 | 1.3 | 2.0 | 20.0 | 40.0 |
| · Texas | 202 | 24.4 | 1.6 | 0.0 | 20.0 | 40.0 |
| · Other | 109 | 26.8 | 2.1 | 6.0 | 20.0 | 40.0 |
| Mountain | 181 | 22.8 | 1.5 | 5.0 | 20.0 | 33.0 |
| Pacific | 520 | 23.9 | 0.9 | 6.0 | 20.0 | 38.0 |
| · California | 356 | 24.2 | 1.1 | 5.0 | 20.0 | 40.0 |
| · Other | 164 | 23.0 | 1.5 | 6.0 | 20.0 | 35.0 |
| *Practice Arrangement* | | | | | | |
| Self-Employed | 2087 | 29.6 | 0.5 | 10.0 | 30.0 | 45.0 |
| · Solo Practice | 934 | 30.2 | 0.8 | 10.0 | 30.0 | 50.0 |
| · Two Physician Practice | 254 | 28.3 | 1.4 | 5.0 | 25.0 | 40.0 |
| · Three Physician Practice | 200 | 31.1 | 1.5 | 13.0 | 30.0 | 45.0 |
| · 4-8 Physician Practice | 465 | 28.4 | 0.9 | 10.0 | 25.0 | 40.0 |
| · Over 8 Physician Practice | 233 | 29.5 | 1.2 | 15.0 | 30.0 | 40.0 |
| Employee | 1181 | 24.1 | 0.7 | 2.0 | 20.0 | 40.0 |
| Independent Contractor | 3 | . | . | . | . | . |

Source: 1995 Socioeconomic Monitoring System survey of nonfederal patient care physicians. See the beginning of this section, the introduction, and appendices for a discussion of the survey sample, definitions, and computation procedures. Statistics are not reported if the number of responses is less than 25.

Table 90. **Percentage of Revenue from Medicaid per Nonfederal Physician, 1995**

| | Number of Responses | Mean | Standard Error | 25th Percentile | Median | 75th Percentile |
|---|---|---|---|---|---|---|
| All Physicians | 3271 | 11.2 | 0.3 | 1.0 | 5.0 | 15.0 |
| *Specialty* | | | | | | |
| General/Family Practice | 420 | 10.8 | 0.7 | 1.0 | 6.0 | 15.0 |
| Internal Medicine | 650 | 7.6 | 0.4 | 1.0 | 5.0 | 10.0 |
| · General Internal Medicine | 441 | 7.8 | 0.5 | 1.0 | 5.0 | 10.0 |
| · Cardiovascular Diseases | 82 | 5.9 | 0.8 | 2.0 | 5.0 | 5.0 |
| · Other | 127 | 7.8 | 0.7 | 2.0 | 5.0 | 10.0 |
| Surgery | 774 | 7.8 | 0.3 | 1.0 | 5.0 | 10.0 |
| · General Surgery | 184 | 10.2 | 0.8 | 3.0 | 5.0 | 15.0 |
| · Otolaryngology | 64 | 8.2 | 0.9 | 1.0 | 5.0 | 10.0 |
| · Orthopedic Surgery | 168 | 7.5 | 0.7 | 1.0 | 5.0 | 10.0 |
| · Ophthalmology | 166 | 7.1 | 0.7 | 1.0 | 5.0 | 10.0 |
| · Urological Surgery | 94 | 5.9 | 0.6 | 2.0 | 5.0 | 5.0 |
| · Other | 98 | 6.4 | 0.9 | 0.0 | 2.0 | 10.0 |
| Pediatrics | 270 | 24.5 | 1.6 | 1.0 | 17.0 | 40.0 |
| Obstetrics/Gynecology | 214 | 15.8 | 1.5 | 1.0 | 5.0 | 25.0 |
| Radiology | 214 | 9.2 | 0.5 | 4.0 | 8.0 | 12.0 |
| Psychiatry | 223 | 14.8 | 1.5 | 0.0 | 2.0 | 20.0 |
| Anesthesiology | 168 | 11.4 | 0.8 | 5.0 | 10.0 | 15.0 |
| Pathology | 73 | 10.4 | 1.2 | 3.0 | 5.0 | 15.0 |
| Other Specialty | 265 | 12.6 | 1.0 | 0.0 | 5.0 | 20.0 |
| · Emergency Medicine | 66 | 16.4 | 1.6 | 5.0 | 15.0 | 25.0 |
| · Other | 199 | 11.4 | 1.3 | 0.0 | 5.0 | 15.0 |
| *Geographic Area* | | | | | | |
| New England | 192 | 11.9 | 0.9 | 2.0 | 8.0 | 20.0 |
| · Massachusetts | 89 | 13.2 | 1.3 | 5.0 | 10.0 | 20.0 |
| · Other | 103 | 10.4 | 1.3 | 1.0 | 5.0 | 12.0 |
| Middle Atlantic | 527 | 9.9 | 0.8 | 0.0 | 3.0 | 10.0 |
| · New Jersey | 98 | 9.3 | 2.0 | 0.0 | 2.0 | 10.0 |
| · New York | 207 | 11.0 | 1.5 | 0.0 | 1.0 | 10.0 |
| · Pennsylvania | 222 | 9.0 | 0.9 | 1.0 | 5.0 | 10.0 |
| East North Central | 493 | 10.3 | 0.6 | 2.0 | 5.0 | 12.0 |
| · Illinois | 160 | 9.5 | 1.2 | 1.0 | 5.0 | 12.0 |
| · Michigan | 87 | 10.9 | 1.5 | 3.0 | 5.0 | 15.0 |
| · Ohio | 108 | 11.9 | 1.6 | 2.0 | 6.0 | 15.0 |
| · Other | 138 | 9.5 | 0.9 | 3.0 | 5.0 | 15.0 |
| West North Central | 246 | 10.8 | 0.8 | 2.0 | 5.0 | 15.0 |
| South Atlantic | 607 | 12.0 | 0.6 | 1.0 | 5.0 | 17.0 |
| · Florida | 170 | 10.5 | 1.3 | 1.0 | 5.0 | 10.0 |
| · Other | 437 | 12.6 | 0.7 | 2.0 | 6.0 | 20.0 |
| East South Central | 194 | 14.4 | 1.2 | 3.0 | 10.0 | 20.0 |
| West South Central | 311 | 11.9 | 0.9 | 1.0 | 5.0 | 15.0 |
| · Texas | 202 | 11.5 | 1.2 | 1.0 | 5.0 | 15.0 |
| · Other | 109 | 12.7 | 1.4 | 1.0 | 5.0 | 20.0 |
| Mountain | 181 | 11.8 | 1.1 | 1.0 | 5.0 | 15.0 |
| Pacific | 520 | 11.0 | 0.7 | 1.0 | 5.0 | 15.0 |
| · California | 356 | 10.6 | 1.0 | 0.0 | 3.0 | 12.0 |
| · Other | 164 | 11.9 | 0.9 | 2.0 | 8.0 | 20.0 |
| *Practice Arrangement* | | | | | | |
| Self-Employed | 2087 | 9.6 | 0.3 | 1.0 | 5.0 | 10.0 |
| · Solo Practice | 934 | 10.1 | 0.5 | 1.0 | 5.0 | 12.0 |
| · Two Physician Practice | 254 | 10.2 | 0.9 | 1.0 | 5.0 | 10.0 |
| · Three Physician Practice | 200 | 9.8 | 1.0 | 1.0 | 5.0 | 10.0 |
| · 4-8 Physician Practice | 465 | 8.1 | 0.5 | 1.0 | 5.0 | 10.0 |
| · Over 8 Physician Practice | 233 | 9.5 | 0.7 | 2.0 | 5.0 | 12.0 |
| Employee | 1181 | 13.9 | 0.5 | 1.0 | 7.0 | 20.0 |
| Independent Contractor | 3 | . | . | . | . | . |

Source: 1995 Socioeconomic Monitoring System survey of nonfederal patient care physicians. See the beginning of this section, the introduction, and appendices for a discussion of the survey sample, definitions, and computation procedures. Statistics are not reported if the number of responses is less than 25.

## Table 91. **Percentage of Revenue from Private Insurance Plans per Nonfederal Physician, 1995**

| | Number of Responses | Mean | Standard Error | 25th Percentile | Median | 75th Percentile |
|---|---|---|---|---|---|---|
| All Physicians | 3271 | 43.2 | 0.4 | 25.0 | 44.0 | 60.0 |
| *Specialty* | | | | | | |
| General/Family Practice | 420 | 42.7 | 1.2 | 25.0 | 45.0 | 62.0 |
| Internal Medicine | 650 | 39.1 | 1.0 | 20.0 | 40.0 | 55.0 |
| · General Internal Medicine | 441 | 39.2 | 1.3 | 20.0 | 40.0 | 56.0 |
| · Cardiovascular Diseases | 82 | 33.5 | 1.9 | 20.0 | 30.0 | 45.0 |
| · Other | 127 | 42.3 | 2.1 | 30.0 | 40.0 | 60.0 |
| Surgery | 774 | 42.9 | 0.8 | 25.0 | 45.0 | 60.0 |
| · General Surgery | 184 | 44.5 | 1.5 | 30.0 | 45.0 | 60.0 |
| · Otolaryngology | 64 | 55.7 | 2.3 | 45.0 | 58.0 | 73.0 |
| · Orthopedic Surgery | 168 | 51.7 | 1.8 | 38.0 | 55.0 | 70.0 |
| · Ophthalmology | 166 | 27.9 | 1.4 | 15.0 | 25.0 | 40.0 |
| · Urological Surgery | 94 | 40.0 | 1.9 | 25.0 | 40.0 | 55.0 |
| · Other | 98 | 44.8 | 2.4 | 29.0 | 50.0 | 60.0 |
| Pediatrics | 270 | 49.4 | 1.8 | 25.0 | 50.0 | 75.0 |
| Obstetrics/Gynecology | 214 | 59.8 | 1.8 | 45.0 | 62.0 | 80.0 |
| Radiology | 214 | 40.9 | 1.3 | 30.0 | 40.0 | 58.0 |
| Psychiatry | 223 | 35.7 | 1.8 | 10.0 | 33.0 | 60.0 |
| Anesthesiology | 168 | 48.7 | 1.6 | 37.0 | 50.0 | 65.0 |
| Pathology | 73 | 39.9 | 2.1 | 25.0 | 40.0 | 55.0 |
| Other Specialty | 265 | 39.8 | 1.6 | 20.0 | 40.0 | 59.0 |
| · Emergency Medicine | 66 | 40.0 | 2.6 | 20.0 | 40.0 | 57.0 |
| · Other | 199 | 39.8 | 1.9 | 20.0 | 40.0 | 60.0 |
| *Geographic Area* | | | | | | |
| New England | 192 | 44.4 | 1.8 | 25.0 | 45.0 | 63.0 |
| · Massachusetts | 89 | 44.0 | 2.6 | 25.0 | 45.0 | 60.0 |
| · Other | 103 | 44.8 | 2.5 | 24.0 | 45.0 | 65.0 |
| Middle Atlantic | 527 | 40.1 | 1.2 | 20.0 | 40.0 | 60.0 |
| · New Jersey | 98 | 39.1 | 3.0 | 15.0 | 40.0 | 60.0 |
| · New York | 207 | 40.4 | 2.1 | 15.0 | 40.0 | 60.0 |
| · Pennsylvania | 222 | 40.5 | 1.5 | 20.0 | 40.0 | 60.0 |
| East North Central | 493 | 43.0 | 1.1 | 25.0 | 42.0 | 60.0 |
| · Illinois | 160 | 40.5 | 2.0 | 23.0 | 40.0 | 55.0 |
| · Michigan | 87 | 48.0 | 2.5 | 30.0 | 42.0 | 65.0 |
| · Ohio | 108 | 40.3 | 2.4 | 25.0 | 45.0 | 55.0 |
| · Other | 138 | 45.3 | 2.0 | 25.0 | 45.0 | 65.0 |
| West North Central | 246 | 44.2 | 1.4 | 30.0 | 45.0 | 60.0 |
| South Atlantic | 607 | 41.0 | 1.0 | 25.0 | 40.0 | 58.0 |
| · Florida | 170 | 34.3 | 1.7 | 19.0 | 34.0 | 50.0 |
| · Other | 437 | 43.7 | 1.2 | 25.0 | 45.0 | 60.0 |
| East South Central | 194 | 42.0 | 1.4 | 29.0 | 40.0 | 56.0 |
| West South Central | 311 | 42.0 | 1.4 | 20.0 | 44.0 | 60.0 |
| · Texas | 202 | 41.8 | 1.8 | 20.0 | 45.0 | 60.0 |
| · Other | 109 | 42.3 | 2.2 | 20.0 | 41.0 | 60.0 |
| Mountain | 181 | 49.2 | 1.7 | 35.0 | 50.0 | 65.0 |
| Pacific | 520 | 47.4 | 1.2 | 30.0 | 50.0 | 70.0 |
| · California | 356 | 46.8 | 1.5 | 25.0 | 48.0 | 70.0 |
| · Other | 164 | 48.9 | 1.8 | 30.0 | 50.0 | 70.0 |
| *Practice Arrangement* | | | | | | |
| Self-Employed | 2087 | 44.2 | 0.5 | 25.0 | 45.0 | 60.0 |
| · Solo Practice | 934 | 41.1 | 0.8 | 25.0 | 40.0 | 60.0 |
| · Two Physician Practice | 254 | 44.7 | 1.4 | 24.0 | 48.0 | 60.0 |
| · Three Physician Practice | 200 | 44.9 | 1.5 | 29.0 | 45.0 | 61.0 |
| · 4-8 Physician Practice | 465 | 48.3 | 1.0 | 31.0 | 50.0 | 65.0 |
| · Over 8 Physician Practice | 233 | 48.8 | 1.4 | 35.0 | 50.0 | 62.0 |
| Employee | 1181 | 41.6 | 0.8 | 20.0 | 40.0 | 60.0 |
| Independent Contractor | 3 | . | . | . | . | . |

Source: 1995 Socioeconomic Monitoring System survey of nonfederal patient care physicians. See the beginning of this section, the introduction, and appendices for a discussion of the survey sample, definitions, and computation procedures. Statistics are not reported if the number of responses is less than 25.

Table 92. **Percentage of Revenue from Patients per Nonfederal Physician, 1995**

| | Number of Responses | Mean | Standard Error | 25th Percentile | Median | 75th Percentile |
|---|---|---|---|---|---|---|
| All Physicians | 3271 | 18.0 | 0.4 | 5.0 | 10.0 | 20.0 |
| *Specialty* | | | | | | |
| General/Family Practice | 420 | 21.9 | 1.2 | 5.0 | 12.0 | 26.0 |
| Internal Medicine | 650 | 12.8 | 0.9 | 2.0 | 5.0 | 15.0 |
| · General Internal Medicine | 441 | 13.6 | 1.2 | 2.0 | 5.0 | 15.0 |
| · Cardiovascular Diseases | 82 | 10.5 | 1.5 | 2.0 | 6.0 | 15.0 |
| · Other | 127 | 11.5 | 1.8 | 3.0 | 7.0 | 10.0 |
| Surgery | 774 | 14.9 | 0.7 | 3.0 | 10.0 | 15.0 |
| · General Surgery | 184 | 9.1 | 0.9 | 2.0 | 5.0 | 11.0 |
| · Otolaryngology | 64 | 10.9 | 1.6 | 4.0 | 5.0 | 15.0 |
| · Orthopedic Surgery | 168 | 16.7 | 1.7 | 4.0 | 10.0 | 15.0 |
| · Ophthalmology | 166 | 18.3 | 1.7 | 5.0 | 10.0 | 20.0 |
| · Urological Surgery | 94 | 10.8 | 1.7 | 1.0 | 5.0 | 14.0 |
| · Other | 98 | 23.3 | 3.0 | 4.0 | 10.0 | 35.0 |
| Pediatrics | 270 | 24.2 | 1.7 | 5.0 | 15.0 | 35.0 |
| Obstetrics/Gynecology | 214 | 14.6 | 1.4 | 3.0 | 10.0 | 17.0 |
| Radiology | 214 | 17.8 | 1.6 | 5.0 | 10.0 | 15.0 |
| Psychiatry | 223 | 33.6 | 2.1 | 5.0 | 20.0 | 55.0 |
| Anesthesiology | 168 | 13.7 | 1.7 | 2.0 | 6.0 | 12.0 |
| Pathology | 73 | 18.4 | 2.4 | 5.0 | 10.0 | 20.0 |
| Other Specialty | 265 | 23.3 | 1.8 | 5.0 | 10.0 | 29.0 |
| · Emergency Medicine | 66 | 18.1 | 2.3 | 6.0 | 10.0 | 25.0 |
| · Other | 199 | 24.8 | 2.3 | 4.0 | 10.0 | 35.0 |
| *Geographic Area* | | | | | | |
| New England | 192 | 14.5 | 1.5 | 5.0 | 10.0 | 15.0 |
| · Massachusetts | 89 | 12.1 | 2.0 | 5.0 | 10.0 | 10.0 |
| · Other | 103 | 17.1 | 2.1 | 5.0 | 10.0 | 20.0 |
| Middle Atlantic | 527 | 21.4 | 1.3 | 4.0 | 10.0 | 25.0 |
| · New Jersey | 98 | 26.4 | 3.7 | 4.0 | 10.0 | 40.0 |
| · New York | 207 | 22.3 | 2.1 | 3.0 | 10.0 | 25.0 |
| · Pennsylvania | 222 | 17.5 | 1.6 | 3.0 | 10.0 | 20.0 |
| East North Central | 493 | 17.8 | 1.1 | 4.0 | 10.0 | 20.0 |
| · Illinois | 160 | 24.8 | 2.3 | 5.0 | 14.0 | 32.0 |
| · Michigan | 87 | 9.1 | 1.4 | 2.0 | 5.0 | 10.0 |
| · Ohio | 108 | 17.3 | 2.7 | 4.0 | 6.0 | 15.0 |
| · Other | 138 | 15.1 | 1.7 | 4.0 | 7.0 | 17.0 |
| West North Central | 246 | 16.2 | 1.1 | 5.0 | 10.0 | 20.0 |
| South Atlantic | 607 | 18.0 | 1.0 | 5.0 | 10.0 | 20.0 |
| · Florida | 170 | 16.2 | 1.8 | 3.0 | 9.0 | 20.0 |
| · Other | 437 | 18.8 | 1.2 | 5.0 | 10.0 | 20.0 |
| East South Central | 194 | 12.8 | 1.1 | 5.0 | 10.0 | 15.0 |
| West South Central | 311 | 21.0 | 1.5 | 5.0 | 10.0 | 24.0 |
| · Texas | 202 | 22.3 | 2.1 | 5.0 | 10.0 | 22.0 |
| · Other | 109 | 18.2 | 1.9 | 5.0 | 10.0 | 25.0 |
| Mountain | 181 | 16.2 | 1.5 | 5.0 | 10.0 | 18.0 |
| Pacific | 520 | 17.7 | 1.2 | 3.0 | 8.0 | 18.0 |
| · California | 356 | 18.4 | 1.5 | 2.0 | 6.0 | 15.0 |
| · Other | 164 | 16.1 | 1.7 | 5.0 | 10.0 | 20.0 |
| *Practice Arrangement* | | | | | | |
| Self-Employed | 2087 | 16.6 | 0.5 | 5.0 | 10.0 | 20.0 |
| · Solo Practice | 934 | 18.6 | 0.8 | 5.0 | 10.0 | 20.0 |
| · Two Physician Practice | 254 | 16.8 | 1.3 | 5.0 | 10.0 | 20.0 |
| · Three Physician Practice | 200 | 14.2 | 1.2 | 4.0 | 10.0 | 16.0 |
| · 4-8 Physician Practice | 465 | 15.2 | 0.9 | 5.0 | 10.0 | 19.0 |
| · Over 8 Physician Practice | 233 | 12.3 | 1.1 | 3.0 | 10.0 | 13.0 |
| Employee | 1181 | 20.4 | 0.9 | 4.0 | 10.0 | 20.0 |
| Independent Contractor | 3 | . | . | . | . | . |

Source: 1995 Socioeconomic Monitoring System survey of nonfederal patient care physicians. See the beginning of this section, the introduction, and appendices for a discussion of the survey sample, definitions, and computation procedures. Statistics are not reported if the number of responses is less than 25.

# Special Topics on the Nonfederal Physician Marketplace

Percentage of Time Spent in Primary Care Activities

Revenue from Outpatient Hospital Care

Revenue from Inpatient Hospital Care

Appointment Delays

Waiting Time

## Special Topics on the Nonfederal Physician Marketplace

### Time Spent in Primary Care Activities

Primary care services include routine comprehensive physical exams not related to a specific complaint or symptom, coordinating the patient's general medical care and treating common ailments. Physicians were asked the following questions regarding their primary care activities:

1. Do you provide primary care services such as preventive care, routine physical exams or treatment of common ailments as part of your practice? Primary care services include routine comprehensive physical exams not related to a specific complaint or symptom, coordinating your patients general medical care and treating common ailments.

[IF NO GOT TO QUESTION 3]

2. About what percentage of your time in your last complete week of practice was spent providing primary care services? Primary care services include routine comprehensive physical exams not related to a specific complaint or symptom, coordinating your patient's general medical care and treating common ailments.

The percentage of time physicians spend in primary care activities was derived from responses to Questions 2 and 3. Table 93 shows the percentage of time spent in primary care activities for all physicians. Table 94 shows the percentage of time spent in primary care activities only for physicians who engage in primary care activities.

### Revenue from Outpatient and Inpatient Hospital Care

Revenue from outpatient (Table 95) and inpatient (Table 96) hospital care was obtained from the following questions:

3. What proportion of your medical practice revenue in 1994 was generated by services provided in hospital inpatient settings? For example, if your 1994 revenue was $100,000 and $50,000 was revenue from services provided in hospital inpatient settings, the answer would be 50%.

4. What proportion of your medical practice revenue in 1994 was generated by services provided in hospital outpatient settings. If you charge a global fee which includes office visits before or after surgery, estimate the proportion which applies to hospital services.

### Appointment Delays and Waiting Times

Appointment delays (Table 97) and waiting time (Table 98) statistics were derived from responses to the following questions:

5. How many days does a new patient wishing to see you typically have to wait for an appointment?

6. How many minutes does a patient typically have to wait to see you after arriving for a scheduled appointment?

Figure 31. **Mean and Median Total Percentage of Time Spent in Primary Care Activities by Nonfederal Physicians, for Selected Specialties, 1995**

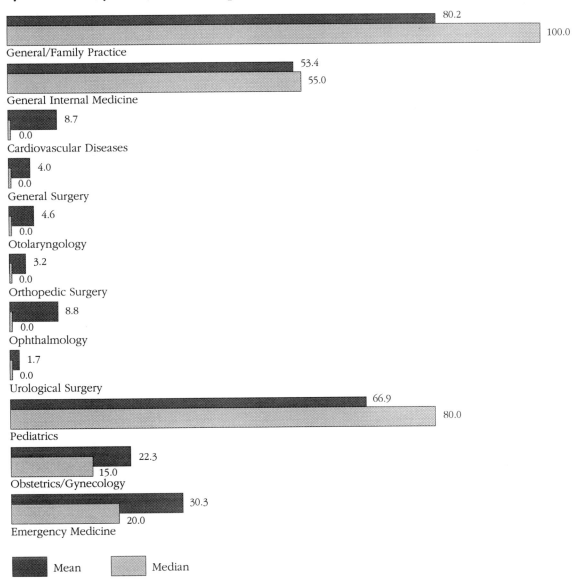

Mean        Median

Figure 32. **Mean and Median Total Percentage of Time Spent in Primary Care Activities by Nonfederal Physicians, for Selected States, 1994**

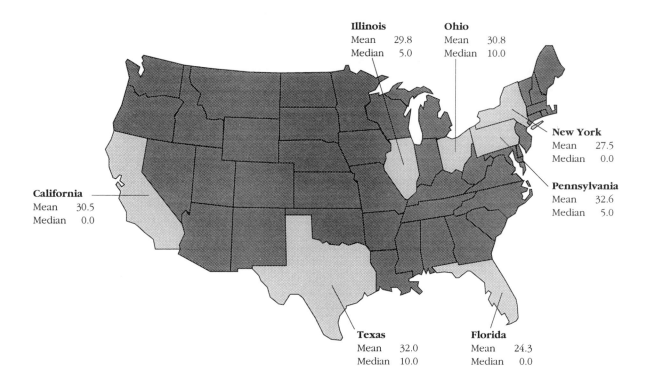

**Illinois**
Mean    29.8
Median   5.0

**Ohio**
Mean    30.8
Median  10.0

**New York**
Mean    27.5
Median   0.0

**Pennsylvania**
Mean    32.6
Median   5.0

**California**
Mean    30.5
Median   0.0

**Texas**
Mean    32.0
Median  10.0

**Florida**
Mean    24.3
Median   0.0

Figure 33. **Mean and Median Percentage of Time Spent in Primary Care Activities by Nonfederal Physicians, by Size of Practice, 1995**

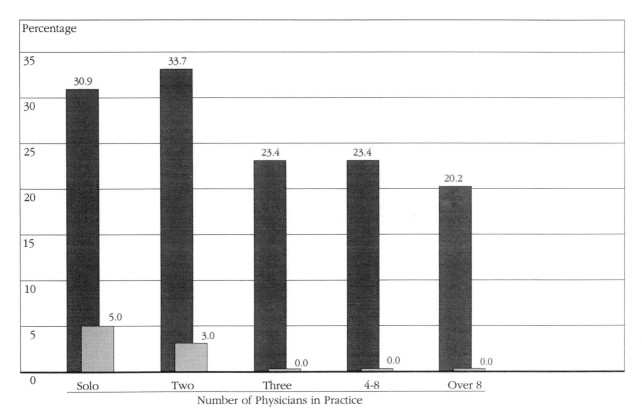

## Table 93. **Percentage of Time Spent in Primary Care Activities by Nonfederal Physicians, 1995**

| | Number of Responses | Mean | Standard Error | 25th Percentile | Median | 75th Percentile |
|---|---|---|---|---|---|---|
| All Physicians | 3706 | 30.9 | 0.7 | 0.0 | 1.0 | 70.0 |
| *Specialty* | | | | | | |
| General/Family Practice | 507 | 80.2 | 1.3 | 75.0 | 100.0 | 100.0 |
| Internal Medicine | 753 | 39.5 | 1.6 | 0.0 | 25.0 | 80.0 |
| · General Internal Medicine | 514 | 53.4 | 2.0 | 10.0 | 55.0 | 99.0 |
| · Cardiovascular Diseases | 100 | 8.7 | 2.1 | 0.0 | 0.0 | 5.0 |
| · Other | 139 | 7.2 | 1.3 | 0.0 | 0.0 | 5.0 |
| Surgery | 882 | 4.4 | 0.5 | 0.0 | 0.0 | 0.0 |
| · General Surgery | 219 | 4.0 | 0.9 | 0.0 | 0.0 | 0.0 |
| · Otolaryngology | 76 | 4.6 | 1.3 | 0.0 | 0.0 | 0.0 |
| · Orthopedic Surgery | 188 | 3.2 | 0.8 | 0.0 | 0.0 | 0.0 |
| · Ophthalmology | 184 | 8.8 | 1.5 | 0.0 | 0.0 | 0.0 |
| · Urological Surgery | 97 | 1.7 | 0.6 | 0.0 | 0.0 | 0.0 |
| · Other | 118 | 2.9 | 1.3 | 0.0 | 0.0 | 0.0 |
| Pediatrics | 302 | 66.9 | 2.2 | 40.0 | 80.0 | 100.0 |
| Obstetrics/Gynecology | 247 | 22.3 | 1.6 | 2.0 | 15.0 | 40.0 |
| Radiology | 166 | 4.0 | 1.3 | 0.0 | 0.0 | 0.0 |
| Psychiatry | 274 | 3.3 | 0.7 | 0.0 | 0.0 | 0.0 |
| Anesthesiology | 145 | 0.0 | 0.0 | 0.0 | 0.0 | 0.0 |
| Pathology | 63 | 1.4 | 1.2 | 0.0 | 0.0 | 0.0 |
| Other Specialty | 367 | 22.3 | 1.8 | 0.0 | 0.0 | 40.0 |
| · Emergency Medicine | 133 | 30.3 | 2.8 | 0.0 | 20.0 | 50.0 |
| · Other | 234 | 18.0 | 2.2 | 0.0 | 0.0 | 10.0 |
| *Geographic Area* | | | | | | |
| New England | 239 | 31.0 | 2.7 | 0.0 | 2.0 | 75.0 |
| · Massachusetts | 111 | 33.1 | 4.3 | 0.0 | 2.0 | 75.0 |
| · Other | 128 | 29.0 | 3.5 | 0.0 | 0.0 | 67.0 |
| Middle Atlantic | 585 | 31.2 | 1.7 | 0.0 | 0.0 | 70.0 |
| · New Jersey | 103 | 36.4 | 4.4 | 0.0 | 10.0 | 75.0 |
| · New York | 239 | 27.5 | 2.7 | 0.0 | 0.0 | 50.0 |
| · Pennsylvania | 243 | 32.6 | 2.5 | 0.0 | 5.0 | 80.0 |
| East North Central | 552 | 29.0 | 1.7 | 0.0 | 0.0 | 60.0 |
| · Illinois | 170 | 29.8 | 3.1 | 0.0 | 5.0 | 70.0 |
| · Michigan | 103 | 24.6 | 3.8 | 0.0 | 0.0 | 50.0 |
| · Ohio | 128 | 30.8 | 3.5 | 0.0 | 10.0 | 60.0 |
| · Other | 151 | 29.7 | 3.2 | 0.0 | 0.0 | 60.0 |
| West North Central | 278 | 33.6 | 2.4 | 0.0 | 2.0 | 80.0 |
| South Atlantic | 669 | 27.8 | 1.5 | 0.0 | 0.0 | 50.0 |
| · Florida | 187 | 24.3 | 2.9 | 0.0 | 0.0 | 40.0 |
| · Other | 482 | 29.3 | 1.8 | 0.0 | 0.0 | 60.0 |
| East South Central | 215 | 32.5 | 2.7 | 0.0 | 5.0 | 80.0 |
| West South Central | 343 | 31.3 | 2.1 | 0.0 | 2.0 | 70.0 |
| · Texas | 225 | 32.0 | 2.6 | 0.0 | 10.0 | 70.0 |
| · Other | 118 | 29.9 | 3.4 | 0.0 | 0.0 | 70.0 |
| Mountain | 216 | 36.5 | 2.7 | 0.0 | 20.0 | 80.0 |
| Pacific | 609 | 32.0 | 1.6 | 0.0 | 0.0 | 75.0 |
| · California | 425 | 30.5 | 2.0 | 0.0 | 0.0 | 65.0 |
| · Other | 184 | 36.3 | 2.9 | 0.0 | 5.0 | 80.0 |
| *Practice Arrangement* | | | | | | |
| Self-Employed | 2137 | 28.0 | 0.8 | 0.0 | 0.0 | 55.0 |
| · Solo Practice | 995 | 30.9 | 1.3 | 0.0 | 5.0 | 65.0 |
| · Two Physician Practice | 257 | 33.7 | 2.5 | 0.0 | 3.0 | 75.0 |
| · Three Physician Practice | 207 | 23.4 | 2.5 | 0.0 | 0.0 | 33.0 |
| · 4-8 Physician Practice | 448 | 23.4 | 1.6 | 0.0 | 0.0 | 40.0 |
| · Over 8 Physician Practice | 228 | 20.2 | 2.2 | 0.0 | 0.0 | 30.0 |
| Employee | 1356 | 34.7 | 1.1 | 0.0 | 10.0 | 80.0 |
| Independent Contractor | 213 | 33.4 | 2.9 | 0.0 | 10.0 | 75.0 |

Source: 1995 Socioeconomic Monitoring System survey of nonfederal patient care physicians. See the beginning of this section, the introduction, and appendices for a discussion of the survey sample, definitions, and computation procedures. Statistics are not reported if the number of responses is less than 25.

Table 94. **Percentage of Time Spent in Primary Care Activities, by Nonfederal Physicians Who Perform Primary Care Activities, 1995**

| | Number of Responses | Mean | Standard Error | 25th Percentile | Median | 75th Percentile |
|---|---|---|---|---|---|---|
| All Physicians | 1771 | 61.0 | 0.9 | 25.0 | 70.0 | 100.0 |
| *Specialty* | | | | | | |
| General/Family Practice | 502 | 80.9 | 1.3 | 75.0 | 100.0 | 100.0 |
| Internal Medicine | 507 | 59.3 | 1.7 | 25.0 | 60.0 | 100.0 |
| · General Internal Medicine | 430 | 65.4 | 1.8 | 30.0 | 75.0 | 100.0 |
| · Cardiovascular Diseases | 30 | 29.9 | 5.0 | 10.0 | 20.0 | 50.0 |
| · Other | 47 | 20.7 | 2.6 | 5.0 | 20.0 | 30.0 |
| Surgery | 119 | 31.5 | 2.4 | 10.0 | 25.0 | 50.0 |
| · General Surgery | 25 | 26.6 | 4.9 | 10.0 | 25.0 | 50.0 |
| · Otolaryngology | 15 | · | · | · | · | · |
| · Orthopedic Surgery | 20 | · | · | · | · | · |
| · Ophthalmology | 39 | 45.0 | 4.3 | 20.0 | 40.0 | 70.0 |
| · Urological Surgery | 11 | · | · | · | · | · |
| · Other | 9 | · | · | · | · | · |
| Pediatrics | 257 | 78.1 | 1.7 | 60.0 | 90.0 | 100.0 |
| Obstetrics/Gynecology | 193 | 29.1 | 1.7 | 10.0 | 25.0 | 50.0 |
| Radiology | 7 | · | · | · | · | · |
| Psychiatry | 31 | 26.1 | 4.8 | 10.0 | 15.0 | 40.0 |
| Anesthesiology | 1 | · | · | · | · | · |
| Pathology | 2 | · | · | · | · | · |
| Other Specialty | 152 | 50.8 | 2.9 | 20.0 | 50.0 | 80.0 |
| · Emergency Medicine | 88 | 45.2 | 3.2 | 20.0 | 40.0 | 70.0 |
| · Other | 64 | 57.3 | 5.1 | 15.0 | 70.0 | 100.0 |
| *Geographic Area* | | | | | | |
| New England | 121 | 59.1 | 3.7 | 20.0 | 70.0 | 100.0 |
| · Massachusetts | 57 | 61.6 | 5.7 | 20.0 | 70.0 | 100.0 |
| · Other | 64 | 56.4 | 4.8 | 15.0 | 67.0 | 100.0 |
| Middle Atlantic | 272 | 62.7 | 2.3 | 25.0 | 70.0 | 100.0 |
| · New Jersey | 48 | 69.6 | 4.8 | 50.0 | 70.0 | 100.0 |
| · New York | 98 | 62.0 | 4.0 | 30.0 | 70.0 | 100.0 |
| · Pennsylvania | 126 | 59.6 | 3.4 | 20.0 | 75.0 | 100.0 |
| East North Central | 269 | 56.6 | 2.4 | 20.0 | 50.0 | 99.0 |
| · Illinois | 86 | 58.1 | 4.1 | 20.0 | 65.0 | 95.0 |
| · Michigan | 45 | 51.8 | 6.3 | 10.0 | 50.0 | 100.0 |
| · Ohio | 65 | 55.8 | 4.8 | 20.0 | 50.0 | 100.0 |
| · Other | 73 | 58.7 | 4.4 | 25.0 | 60.0 | 100.0 |
| West North Central | 134 | 66.4 | 2.9 | 30.0 | 80.0 | 100.0 |
| South Atlantic | 298 | 58.0 | 2.3 | 20.0 | 50.0 | 100.0 |
| · Florida | 74 | 56.6 | 4.8 | 25.0 | 50.0 | 100.0 |
| · Other | 224 | 58.6 | 2.6 | 20.0 | 60.0 | 100.0 |
| East South Central | 116 | 58.5 | 3.5 | 20.0 | 60.0 | 100.0 |
| West South Central | 162 | 62.3 | 2.6 | 30.0 | 70.0 | 96.0 |
| · Texas | 109 | 61.1 | 3.3 | 30.0 | 60.0 | 100.0 |
| · Other | 53 | 65.2 | 4.2 | 30.0 | 75.0 | 95.0 |
| Mountain | 122 | 63.6 | 3.1 | 30.0 | 75.0 | 100.0 |
| Pacific | 277 | 64.4 | 2.2 | 30.0 | 75.0 | 100.0 |
| · California | 187 | 62.8 | 2.7 | 30.0 | 65.0 | 100.0 |
| · Other | 90 | 68.4 | 3.5 | 50.0 | 80.0 | 100.0 |
| *Practice Arrangement* | | | | | | |
| Self-Employed | 962 | 59.3 | 1.2 | 25.0 | 60.0 | 100.0 |
| · Solo Practice | 495 | 59.8 | 1.6 | 25.0 | 60.0 | 100.0 |
| · Two Physician Practice | 124 | 64.8 | 3.1 | 40.0 | 70.0 | 100.0 |
| · Three Physician Practice | 86 | 55.6 | 3.9 | 20.0 | 70.0 | 100.0 |
| · 4-8 Physician Practice | 175 | 57.9 | 2.7 | 20.0 | 60.0 | 100.0 |
| · Over 8 Physician Practice | 81 | 53.9 | 4.1 | 20.0 | 50.0 | 90.0 |
| Employee | 710 | 63.2 | 1.4 | 25.0 | 75.0 | 100.0 |
| Independent Contractor | 99 | 60.3 | 4.2 | 25.0 | 65.0 | 100.0 |

Source: 1995 Socioeconomic Monitoring System survey of nonfederal patient care physicians. See the beginning of this section, the introduction, and appendices for a discussion of the survey sample, definitions, and computation procedures. Statistics are not reported if the number of responses is less than 25.

## Table 95. **Percentage of Revenue from Outpatient Hospital Care, for Nonfederal Physicians, 1994**

| | Number of Responses | Mean | Standard Error | 25th Percentile | Median | 75th Percentile |
|---|---|---|---|---|---|---|
| All Physicians | 3207 | 29.2 | 0.6 | 0.0 | 10.0 | 50.0 |
| *Specialty* | | | | | | |
| General/Family Practice | 432 | 16.2 | 1.5 | 0.0 | 0.0 | 5.0 |
| Internal Medicine | 610 | 23.6 | 1.4 | 0.0 | 5.0 | 40.0 |
| · General Internal Medicine | 424 | 21.8 | 1.8 | 0.0 | 1.0 | 35.0 |
| · Cardiovascular Diseases | 70 | 17.0 | 2.3 | 5.0 | 10.0 | 25.0 |
| · Other | 116 | 33.8 | 3.1 | 5.0 | 30.0 | 50.0 |
| Surgery | 747 | 33.9 | 1.0 | 10.0 | 30.0 | 50.0 |
| · General Surgery | 177 | 35.9 | 1.9 | 10.0 | 40.0 | 60.0 |
| · Otolaryngology | 66 | 46.1 | 3.2 | 20.0 | 50.0 | 65.0 |
| · Orthopedic Surgery | 156 | 30.4 | 1.8 | 10.0 | 30.0 | 40.0 |
| · Ophthalmology | 171 | 36.0 | 2.3 | 6.0 | 30.0 | 50.0 |
| · Urological Surgery | 82 | 26.8 | 2.3 | 10.0 | 23.0 | 32.0 |
| · Other | 95 | 30.1 | 3.2 | 4.0 | 15.0 | 60.0 |
| Pediatrics | 227 | 15.9 | 2.0 | 0.0 | 0.0 | 10.0 |
| Obstetrics/Gynecology | 190 | 21.8 | 1.7 | 5.0 | 15.0 | 30.0 |
| Radiology | 217 | 49.2 | 1.7 | 25.0 | 50.0 | 70.0 |
| Psychiatry | 241 | 23.8 | 2.3 | 0.0 | 0.0 | 50.0 |
| Anesthesiology | 163 | 53.4 | 1.9 | 40.0 | 55.0 | 70.0 |
| Pathology | 76 | 32.6 | 2.4 | 10.0 | 33.0 | 55.0 |
| Other Specialty | 304 | 44.4 | 2.6 | 0.0 | 20.0 | 100.0 |
| · Emergency Medicine | 113 | 86.2 | 3.0 | 98.0 | 100.0 | 100.0 |
| · Other | 191 | 20.1 | 2.3 | 0.0 | 0.0 | 35.0 |
| *Geographic Area* | | | | | | |
| New England | 194 | 27.6 | 2.5 | 0.0 | 10.0 | 50.0 |
| · Massachusetts | 90 | 29.7 | 3.7 | 0.0 | 20.0 | 50.0 |
| · Other | 104 | 25.8 | 3.3 | 0.0 | 10.0 | 50.0 |
| Middle Atlantic | 495 | 29.0 | 1.5 | 0.0 | 10.0 | 60.0 |
| · New Jersey | 86 | 29.3 | 4.2 | 0.0 | 10.0 | 60.0 |
| · New York | 199 | 28.1 | 2.5 | 0.0 | 7.0 | 60.0 |
| · Pennsylvania | 210 | 29.9 | 2.2 | 0.0 | 15.0 | 55.0 |
| East North Central | 475 | 33.4 | 1.7 | 0.0 | 20.0 | 60.0 |
| · Illinois | 151 | 32.2 | 3.2 | 0.0 | 15.0 | 70.0 |
| · Michigan | 84 | 40.6 | 4.2 | 1.0 | 35.0 | 75.0 |
| · Ohio | 105 | 32.2 | 3.6 | 0.0 | 20.0 | 60.0 |
| · Other | 135 | 31.3 | 2.7 | 1.0 | 20.0 | 60.0 |
| West North Central | 241 | 29.3 | 2.0 | 1.0 | 15.0 | 50.0 |
| South Atlantic | 581 | 28.8 | 1.3 | 0.0 | 15.0 | 50.0 |
| · Florida | 168 | 28.3 | 2.5 | 0.0 | 20.0 | 50.0 |
| · Other | 413 | 29.0 | 1.6 | 0.0 | 15.0 | 50.0 |
| East South Central | 188 | 27.7 | 2.1 | 0.0 | 15.0 | 50.0 |
| West South Central | 293 | 27.0 | 1.8 | 0.0 | 15.0 | 50.0 |
| · Texas | 195 | 27.0 | 2.3 | 0.0 | 10.0 | 50.0 |
| · Other | 98 | 27.0 | 2.7 | 1.0 | 20.0 | 40.0 |
| Mountain | 197 | 31.0 | 2.5 | 0.0 | 12.0 | 60.0 |
| Pacific | 543 | 27.3 | 1.5 | 0.0 | 10.0 | 50.0 |
| · California | 385 | 27.1 | 1.8 | 0.0 | 6.0 | 50.0 |
| · Other | 158 | 27.7 | 2.5 | 0.0 | 10.0 | 50.0 |
| *Practice Arrangement* | | | | | | |
| Self-Employed | 1935 | 23.8 | 0.6 | 0.0 | 10.0 | 40.0 |
| · Solo Practice | 887 | 19.7 | 0.9 | 0.0 | 5.0 | 30.0 |
| · Two Physician Practice | 234 | 22.9 | 1.8 | 0.0 | 10.0 | 40.0 |
| · Three Physician Practice | 178 | 23.9 | 2.1 | 1.0 | 10.0 | 40.0 |
| · 4-8 Physician Practice | 422 | 28.3 | 1.4 | 1.0 | 20.0 | 50.0 |
| · Over 8 Physician Practice | 214 | 35.0 | 2.1 | 5.0 | 30.0 | 60.0 |
| Employee | 1086 | 34.4 | 1.1 | 0.0 | 20.0 | 70.0 |
| Independent Contractor | 186 | 49.4 | 3.1 | 0.0 | 50.0 | 99.0 |

Source: 1995 Socioeconomic Monitoring System survey of nonfederal patient care physicians. See the beginning of this section, the introduction, and appendices for a discussion of the survey sample, definitions, and computation procedures. Statistics are not reported if the number of responses is less than 25.

Table 96. **Percentage of Revenue from Inpatient Hospital Care, for Nonfederal Physicians, 1994**

| | Number of Responses | Mean | Standard Error | 25th Percentile | Median | 75th Percentile |
|---|---|---|---|---|---|---|
| All Physicians | 3305 | 28.9 | 0.5 | 3.0 | 20.0 | 50.0 |
| *Specialty* | | | | | | |
| General/Family Practice | 427 | 11.5 | 0.7 | 0.0 | 10.0 | 15.0 |
| Internal Medicine | 612 | 29.4 | 1.2 | 10.0 | 20.0 | 50.0 |
| · General Internal Medicine | 428 | 25.1 | 1.3 | 5.0 | 20.0 | 35.0 |
| · Cardiovascular Diseases | 70 | 53.8 | 3.3 | 40.0 | 60.0 | 70.0 |
| · Other | 114 | 31.7 | 2.6 | 10.0 | 30.0 | 50.0 |
| Surgery | 755 | 33.2 | 1.1 | 5.0 | 30.0 | 60.0 |
| · General Surgery | 179 | 50.8 | 2.0 | 30.0 | 50.0 | 75.0 |
| · Otolaryngology | 64 | 17.0 | 2.2 | 2.0 | 8.0 | 30.0 |
| · Orthopedic Surgery | 156 | 38.5 | 1.9 | 20.0 | 33.0 | 60.0 |
| · Ophthalmology | 176 | 3.7 | 0.7 | 0.0 | 1.0 | 3.0 |
| · Urological Surgery | 81 | 36.7 | 2.2 | 20.0 | 30.0 | 50.0 |
| · Other | 99 | 45.0 | 3.7 | 5.0 | 40.0 | 80.0 |
| Pediatrics | 235 | 21.5 | 1.7 | 5.0 | 12.0 | 25.0 |
| Obstetrics/Gynecology | 191 | 37.9 | 1.7 | 20.0 | 40.0 | 50.0 |
| Radiology | 222 | 36.6 | 1.4 | 20.0 | 35.0 | 50.0 |
| Psychiatry | 249 | 23.6 | 2.0 | 0.0 | 2.0 | 45.0 |
| Anesthesiology | 207 | 53.1 | 2.1 | 30.0 | 50.0 | 80.0 |
| Pathology | 80 | 57.9 | 2.7 | 40.0 | 60.0 | 80.0 |
| Other Specialty | 327 | 20.1 | 1.8 | 0.0 | 1.0 | 30.0 |
| · Emergency Medicine | 127 | 14.2 | 3.0 | 0.0 | 0.0 | 1.0 |
| · Other | 200 | 23.8 | 2.2 | 0.0 | 8.0 | 40.0 |
| *Geographic Area* | | | | | | |
| New England | 203 | 29.3 | 2.2 | 5.0 | 20.0 | 50.0 |
| · Massachusetts | 95 | 33.3 | 3.6 | 5.0 | 25.0 | 50.0 |
| · Other | 108 | 25.5 | 2.7 | 4.0 | 15.0 | 40.0 |
| Middle Atlantic | 510 | 31.4 | 1.4 | 2.0 | 25.0 | 50.0 |
| · New Jersey | 89 | 27.8 | 3.5 | 2.0 | 20.0 | 40.0 |
| · New York | 203 | 28.2 | 2.1 | 1.0 | 20.0 | 50.0 |
| · Pennsylvania | 218 | 36.8 | 2.0 | 10.0 | 33.0 | 60.0 |
| East North Central | 481 | 29.5 | 1.4 | 3.0 | 20.0 | 50.0 |
| · Illinois | 149 | 29.6 | 2.5 | 3.0 | 20.0 | 50.0 |
| · Michigan | 87 | 28.3 | 3.4 | 2.0 | 20.0 | 50.0 |
| · Ohio | 104 | 26.5 | 2.7 | 2.0 | 15.0 | 50.0 |
| · Other | 141 | 32.9 | 2.4 | 8.0 | 30.0 | 50.0 |
| West North Central | 245 | 27.9 | 1.6 | 5.0 | 20.0 | 45.0 |
| South Atlantic | 594 | 27.9 | 1.2 | 2.0 | 20.0 | 45.0 |
| · Florida | 167 | 31.5 | 2.3 | 2.0 | 25.0 | 50.0 |
| · Other | 427 | 26.5 | 1.3 | 1.0 | 20.0 | 40.0 |
| East South Central | 198 | 36.0 | 2.1 | 10.0 | 30.0 | 50.0 |
| West South Central | 311 | 28.7 | 1.6 | 5.0 | 20.0 | 50.0 |
| · Texas | 209 | 27.7 | 2.0 | 5.0 | 20.0 | 50.0 |
| · Other | 102 | 31.1 | 2.6 | 5.0 | 30.0 | 50.0 |
| Mountain | 199 | 26.9 | 1.9 | 5.0 | 20.0 | 40.0 |
| Pacific | 564 | 25.8 | 1.2 | 1.0 | 15.0 | 40.0 |
| · California | 399 | 25.3 | 1.5 | 0.0 | 10.0 | 40.0 |
| · Other | 165 | 27.2 | 2.1 | 3.0 | 20.0 | 40.0 |
| *Practice Arrangement* | | | | | | |
| Self-Employed | 1959 | 27.8 | 0.6 | 5.0 | 20.0 | 45.0 |
| · Solo Practice | 884 | 24.2 | 0.9 | 2.0 | 15.0 | 40.0 |
| · Two Physician Practice | 233 | 23.2 | 1.4 | 5.0 | 20.0 | 35.0 |
| · Three Physician Practice | 185 | 32.5 | 1.9 | 10.0 | 25.0 | 50.0 |
| · 4-8 Physician Practice | 433 | 32.3 | 1.2 | 10.0 | 30.0 | 50.0 |
| · Over 8 Physician Practice | 224 | 36.0 | 1.9 | 10.0 | 30.0 | 55.0 |
| Employee | 1142 | 31.2 | 1.0 | 1.0 | 20.0 | 50.0 |
| Independent Contractor | 204 | 26.7 | 2.4 | 0.0 | 10.0 | 50.0 |

Source: 1995 Socioeconomic Monitoring System survey of nonfederal patient care physicians. See the beginning of this section, the introduction, and appendices for a discussion of the survey sample, definitions, and computation procedures. Statistics are not reported if the number of responses is less than 25.

Table 97. **Average Days of Wait for an Appointment by New Patients, for Nonfederal Physicians (excluding Physicians in Radiology, Psychiatry, Anesthesiology, and Pathology), 1995**

| | Number of Responses | Mean | Standard Error | 25th Percentile | Median | 75th Percentile |
|---|---|---|---|---|---|---|
| All Physicians | 2825 | 9.5 | 0.3 | 1.0 | 4.0 | 10.0 |
| *Specialty* | | | | | | |
| General/Family Practice | 470 | 6.3 | 0.6 | 0.0 | 2.0 | 7.0 |
| Internal Medicine | 727 | 11.0 | 0.7 | 2.0 | 5.0 | 14.0 |
| · General Internal Medicine | 491 | 12.1 | 0.9 | 2.0 | 7.0 | 14.0 |
| · Cardiovascular Diseases | 100 | 9.4 | 1.6 | 2.0 | 5.0 | 10.0 |
| · Other | 136 | 8.0 | 0.9 | 2.0 | 5.0 | 10.0 |
| Surgery | 872 | 8.5 | 0.4 | 2.0 | 5.0 | 10.0 |
| · General Surgery | 215 | 4.3 | 0.4 | 1.0 | 2.0 | 7.0 |
| · Otolaryngology | 76 | 7.4 | 1.3 | 1.0 | 4.0 | 7.0 |
| · Orthopedic Surgery | 186 | 9.3 | 0.9 | 2.0 | 5.0 | 12.0 |
| · Ophthalmology | 184 | 14.2 | 1.4 | 2.0 | 7.0 | 15.0 |
| · Urological Surgery | 96 | 8.7 | 0.9 | 2.0 | 7.0 | 14.0 |
| · Other | 115 | 8.0 | 0.9 | 2.0 | 5.0 | 10.0 |
| Pediatrics | 289 | 7.1 | 0.7 | 0.0 | 1.0 | 7.0 |
| Obstetrics/Gynecology | 240 | 15.4 | 1.4 | 2.0 | 7.0 | 18.0 |
| Other Specialty | 227 | 9.8 | 0.8 | 1.0 | 5.0 | 14.0 |
| · Emergency Medicine | 0 | . | . | . | . | . |
| · Other | 227 | 9.8 | 0.8 | 1.0 | 5.0 | 14.0 |
| *Geographic Area* | | | | | | |
| New England | 173 | 11.5 | 1.2 | 2.0 | 7.0 | 14.0 |
| · Massachusetts | 80 | 10.9 | 1.9 | 1.0 | 5.0 | 14.0 |
| · Other | 93 | 12.0 | 1.6 | 2.0 | 7.0 | 14.0 |
| Middle Atlantic | 442 | 10.0 | 0.8 | 1.0 | 5.0 | 14.0 |
| · New Jersey | 84 | 5.4 | 1.2 | 1.0 | 3.0 | 7.0 |
| · New York | 172 | 11.7 | 1.5 | 2.0 | 5.0 | 14.0 |
| · Pennsylvania | 186 | 11.0 | 1.1 | 2.0 | 7.0 | 14.0 |
| East North Central | 416 | 11.5 | 0.9 | 2.0 | 5.0 | 14.0 |
| · Illinois | 140 | 8.6 | 1.1 | 1.0 | 3.0 | 10.0 |
| · Michigan | 75 | 17.1 | 3.1 | 2.0 | 7.0 | 21.0 |
| · Ohio | 94 | 10.7 | 1.4 | 3.0 | 7.0 | 14.0 |
| · Other | 107 | 12.5 | 1.8 | 3.0 | 5.0 | 14.0 |
| West North Central | 210 | 10.9 | 1.2 | 1.0 | 4.0 | 14.0 |
| South Atlantic | 522 | 8.6 | 0.6 | 1.0 | 3.0 | 10.0 |
| · Florida | 148 | 7.5 | 0.9 | 1.0 | 3.0 | 8.0 |
| · Other | 374 | 9.1 | 0.8 | 1.0 | 3.0 | 14.0 |
| East South Central | 173 | 7.7 | 1.0 | 1.0 | 3.0 | 7.0 |
| West South Central | 267 | 8.9 | 0.8 | 2.0 | 5.0 | 10.0 |
| · Texas | 177 | 9.1 | 0.9 | 2.0 | 5.0 | 10.0 |
| · Other | 90 | 8.6 | 1.5 | 1.0 | 4.0 | 8.0 |
| Mountain | 164 | 8.9 | 0.9 | 1.0 | 4.0 | 14.0 |
| Pacific | 458 | 8.1 | 0.7 | 1.0 | 3.0 | 10.0 |
| · California | 319 | 8.1 | 0.9 | 1.0 | 3.0 | 10.0 |
| · Other | 139 | 8.0 | 1.0 | 1.0 | 4.0 | 10.0 |
| *Practice Arrangement* | | | | | | |
| Self-Employed | 1725 | 8.9 | 0.3 | 1.0 | 4.0 | 10.0 |
| · Solo Practice | 826 | 6.6 | 0.4 | 1.0 | 3.0 | 7.0 |
| · Two Physician Practice | 228 | 9.2 | 0.9 | 1.0 | 5.0 | 14.0 |
| · Three Physician Practice | 183 | 12.0 | 1.2 | 2.0 | 5.0 | 14.0 |
| · 4-8 Physician Practice | 360 | 11.6 | 0.9 | 2.0 | 7.0 | 14.0 |
| · Over 8 Physician Practice | 126 | 12.7 | 1.5 | 3.0 | 7.0 | 14.0 |
| Employee | 1008 | 10.9 | 0.5 | 1.0 | 5.0 | 14.0 |
| Independent Contractor | 92 | 6.2 | 0.9 | 0.0 | 3.0 | 10.0 |

Source: 1995 Socioeconomic Monitoring System survey of nonfederal patient care physicians. See the beginning of this section, the introduction, and appendices for a discussion of the survey sample, definitions, and computation procedures. Statistics are not reported if the number of responses is less than 25.

**Table 98. Average Minutes Waiting by Patients upon Arriving for a Scheduled Appointment, for Nonfederal Physicians (excluding Physicians in Radiology, Psychiatry, Anesthesiology, and Pathology), 1995**

| | Number of Responses | Mean | Standard Error | 25th Percentile | Median | 75th Percentile |
|---|---|---|---|---|---|---|
| All Physicians | 2882 | 19.8 | 0.3 | 10.0 | 15.0 | 30.0 |
| *Specialty* | | | | | | |
| General/Family Practice | 497 | 20.2 | 0.6 | 10.0 | 15.0 | 30.0 |
| Internal Medicine | 750 | 19.6 | 0.7 | 10.0 | 15.0 | 30.0 |
| · General Internal Medicine | 512 | 20.1 | 1.0 | 10.0 | 15.0 | 30.0 |
| · Cardiovascular Diseases | 100 | 17.5 | 1.2 | 10.0 | 15.0 | 20.0 |
| · Other | 138 | 19.1 | 1.2 | 10.0 | 15.0 | 30.0 |
| Surgery | 868 | 21.1 | 0.6 | 10.0 | 15.0 | 30.0 |
| · General Surgery | 212 | 20.2 | 1.0 | 10.0 | 15.0 | 30.0 |
| · Otolaryngology | 74 | 18.0 | 1.3 | 15.0 | 15.0 | 20.0 |
| · Orthopedic Surgery | 182 | 24.2 | 1.3 | 15.0 | 15.0 | 30.0 |
| · Ophthalmology | 186 | 21.3 | 1.2 | 10.0 | 15.0 | 30.0 |
| · Urological Surgery | 96 | 19.8 | 1.2 | 10.0 | 15.0 | 30.0 |
| · Other | 118 | 21.1 | 2.1 | 10.0 | 15.0 | 30.0 |
| Pediatrics | 298 | 18.5 | 0.7 | 10.0 | 15.0 | 30.0 |
| Obstetrics/Gynecology | 241 | 20.0 | 1.0 | 10.0 | 15.0 | 30.0 |
| Other Specialty | 228 | 16.5 | 0.9 | 10.0 | 15.0 | 20.0 |
| · Emergency Medicine | 0 | . | . | . | . | . |
| · Other | 228 | 16.5 | 0.9 | 10.0 | 15.0 | 20.0 |
| *Geographic Area* | | | | | | |
| New England | 181 | 15.6 | 0.9 | 10.0 | 15.0 | 20.0 |
| · Massachusetts | 83 | 14.7 | 1.1 | 10.0 | 15.0 | 20.0 |
| · Other | 98 | 16.5 | 1.3 | 10.0 | 15.0 | 20.0 |
| Middle Atlantic | 448 | 20.0 | 0.8 | 10.0 | 15.0 | 30.0 |
| · New Jersey | 85 | 17.7 | 1.2 | 10.0 | 15.0 | 30.0 |
| · New York | 172 | 22.8 | 1.8 | 10.0 | 15.0 | 30.0 |
| · Pennsylvania | 191 | 18.2 | 1.0 | 10.0 | 15.0 | 20.0 |
| East North Central | 426 | 19.6 | 0.8 | 10.0 | 15.0 | 25.0 |
| · Illinois | 141 | 20.9 | 1.6 | 10.0 | 15.0 | 25.0 |
| · Michigan | 79 | 20.4 | 1.8 | 10.0 | 15.0 | 30.0 |
| · Ohio | 97 | 16.9 | 1.1 | 10.0 | 15.0 | 20.0 |
| · Other | 109 | 19.8 | 1.3 | 10.0 | 15.0 | 30.0 |
| West North Central | 216 | 19.8 | 1.1 | 10.0 | 15.0 | 20.0 |
| South Atlantic | 524 | 19.8 | 0.6 | 10.0 | 15.0 | 30.0 |
| · Florida | 149 | 21.1 | 1.4 | 15.0 | 15.0 | 30.0 |
| · Other | 375 | 19.3 | 0.7 | 10.0 | 15.0 | 30.0 |
| East South Central | 176 | 26.0 | 1.5 | 15.0 | 20.0 | 30.0 |
| West South Central | 270 | 23.5 | 1.4 | 15.0 | 20.0 | 30.0 |
| · Texas | 177 | 22.0 | 1.3 | 15.0 | 15.0 | 30.0 |
| · Other | 93 | 26.7 | 3.1 | 15.0 | 20.0 | 30.0 |
| Mountain | 170 | 18.8 | 1.2 | 10.0 | 15.0 | 20.0 |
| Pacific | 471 | 17.6 | 0.7 | 10.0 | 15.0 | 20.0 |
| · California | 326 | 18.4 | 0.9 | 10.0 | 15.0 | 30.0 |
| · Other | 145 | 15.3 | 0.7 | 10.0 | 15.0 | 20.0 |
| *Practice Arrangement* | | | | | | |
| Self-Employed | 1757 | 19.4 | 0.3 | 10.0 | 15.0 | 30.0 |
| · Solo Practice | 833 | 18.3 | 0.5 | 10.0 | 15.0 | 20.0 |
| · Two Physician Practice | 234 | 21.2 | 0.9 | 15.0 | 15.0 | 30.0 |
| · Three Physician Practice | 186 | 20.3 | 0.9 | 15.0 | 15.0 | 25.0 |
| · 4-8 Physician Practice | 372 | 19.0 | 0.6 | 10.0 | 15.0 | 30.0 |
| · Over 8 Physician Practice | 130 | 23.5 | 1.6 | 15.0 | 20.0 | 30.0 |
| Employee | 1028 | 20.3 | 0.6 | 10.0 | 15.0 | 30.0 |
| Independent Contractor | 97 | 21.0 | 2.2 | 15.0 | 15.0 | 30.0 |

Source: 1995 Socioeconomic Monitoring System survey of nonfederal patient care physicians. See the beginning of this section, the introduction, and appendices for a discussion of the survey sample, definitions, and computation procedures. Statistics are not reported if the number of responses is less than 25.

# Nonfederal Physicians and Nonphysician Employees in Medical Practices

Distribution of Nonfederal Physicians by Employment Status

Distribution of Employee Nonfederal Physicians by Employer Type

Distribution of Nonfederal Physicians by Practice Size

Number of Nonfederal Physicians in Medical Practices

Number of Nonphysician Personnel in Medical Practices

## Nonfederal Physicians and Nonphysician Employees in Medical Practices

Information on physician employment status, practice size, numbers of physicians in medical practices, numbers of self-employed and employee physicians in medical practices, and the employers of physicians are presented in this section of *Physician Marketplace Statistics 1995*. Information on the employment of nonphysician personnel by medical practices is also presented in this section.

Physician employment status is based on responses from the following question:

1. Are you a full or part owner of your main practice?

Physicians responding affirmatively to Question 1 were classified as self-employed; those responding in the negative were classified as employees. If the physician described himself or herself as an independent contractor, the physician was classified in a separate employment status category for independent contractors. Note that no special question or prompt was used to elicit this type of response, so this category is essentially self-defined by individual physician respondents who deem themselves to better fit this description than as being a whole or part owner of their practice. Physicians indicating they were unsure whether they were independent contractors or employees, were classified as employees.

The number of physicians in physicians' main practices was based on responses in the survey to the following question:

2. Including yourself, how many physicians are in your main practice?

The number of physicians that were either self-employed or employees in a practice was derived from the following question:

3. How many of the physicians in your practice are full or part owners?

Employee physicians were asked the following questions about their employer:

4a. In your main practice, are you employed by a hospital?

4aa. Is this a private hospital or is this hospital governed by a medical school, university or college, state or local government, or some other type of organization?

4b. In your main practice, are you employed by a [Health Maintenance Organization] HMO, a free-standing ambulatory care, surgical or emergency care center, another physician or group of physicians, a medical school, a university or college, state or local government, or some other type of employer?

Responses to Question 1 were used to derive the information presented in Figure 6 of the section Overview of the Nonfederal Physician Marketplace and Table 99 of this section. Responses to Questions 1 and 2 were used to derive the information in Figures 34-36 and Tables 101-107. Responses to Questions 4a-4b were used to derive the information presented in Figure 7 of the overview section and Table 100 of this section.

Responses to Questions 1 and 2 were also used to derive the practice arrangement classification that are included in most of the tables in this volume. This practice arrangement classification is based on the employment status of the physician and, if the physician is self-employed, the total number of physicians in the physician's main practice.

Responses from all physicians were used to derive the information presented in Figure 6 and Table 99. Only responses from self-employed physicians and physicians employed by group practices or free-standing ambulatory or emergency care centers were used to derive the information presented in Figure 34 and Tables 104-107. Table 104 shows the number of nonfederal physicians (both self-employed and employees) in medical practices. In the 1994 edition of *Physician Marketplace Statistics*, information on the number of physicians per medical practice was derived from responses from self-employed physicians only. Responses from self-employed physicians only were used to derive information presented in Figure 35, and Table 102. Responses from all employee physicians were used to derive the information presented in Figure 7 and Table 100. Only responses from physicians employed by group practices or free-standing centers were used to derive information in Figure 36 and Table 103.

The employment classification used in Figure 7 of the overview section and in Table 100 of this section is derived from Questions 4a-4b and includes:

- HMOs;
- Group Practices (also includes free-standing ambulatory care or emergency care centers);
- Private hospitals;
- Medical Schools, Universities, or Colleges; and
- State or local government and other types of employers (not identified in the survey).

For classification purposes, a physician employed by a hospital that is governed or owned by a medical school, university or college, state or local government, or other organization, is considered to be employed by the owner of the hospital rather than the hospital. For example, if a physician is employed by a hospital owned by a medical school then the physician is considered an employee of a medical school.

Responses from self-employed physicians regarding their practices' use of nonphysician personnel were obtained with the following questions:

5a. Altogether, during 1994 how many nonphysician personnel were employed in the practice? Include both full-time and part-time employees in your answer.

5b. How many of these nonphysician personnel were full-time employees. (Full-time would be the number of hours you consider full-time in your practice).

5c. How many of these nonphysician personnel (both full-time and part-time) were employed primarily in administrative, secretarial, or clerical activities?

For each self-employed physician, the responses to Questions 5a-5b were divided by the response to Question 2. The resulting information on nonphysician personnel per physician in each self-employed physician's practice provided the basis for statistics reported in Tables 108-110. It should

be noted that physicians were asked how many nonphysician personnel their practice employed in 1994. Therefore information in Tables 108-110 are for 1994 rather than 1995.

Figure 34. **Distribution of Nonfederal Physicians, by Size of Practice, 1995**

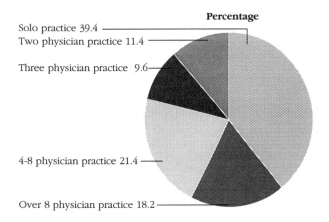

Percentage

Solo practice 39.4
Two physician practice 11.4
Three physician practice 9.6
4-8 physician practice 21.4
Over 8 physician practice 18.2

Figure 35. **Distribution of Self-Employed Nonfederal Physicians, by Size of Practice, 1995**[a]

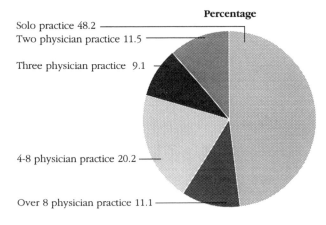

Percentage

Solo practice 48.2
Two physician practice 11.5
Three physician practice 9.1
4-8 physician practice 20.2
Over 8 physician practice 11.1

a. Figures do not add to 100 because of rounding.

Figure 36. **Distribution of Employee Nonfederal Physicians, by Size of Practice, 1995**

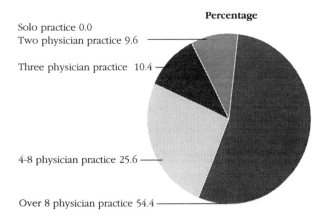

Percentage

Solo practice 0.0
Two physician practice 9.6
Three physician practice 10.4
4-8 physician practice 25.6
Over 8 physician practice 54.4

Table 99. **Distribution of Nonfederal Physicians by Employment Status, 1995**

| | Number of Responses | Percent | | |
| --- | --- | --- | --- | --- |
| | | Self-Employed | Employees | Independent Contractor |
| All Physicians | 4026 | 54.6 | 39.0 | 6.4 |
| *Specialty* | | | | |
| General/Family Practice | 517 | 50.3 | 42.9 | 6.7 |
| Internal Medicine | 769 | 53.5 | 42.1 | 4.4 |
| · General Internal Medicine | 525 | 48.0 | 47.2 | 4.8 |
| · Cardiovascular Diseases | 102 | 61.3 | 36.2 | 2.5 |
| · Other | 142 | 69.0 | 26.7 | 4.3 |
| Surgery | 894 | 70.2 | 26.1 | 3.7 |
| · General Surgery | 222 | 73.3 | 22.7 | 4.1 |
| · Otolaryngology | 77 | 75.3 | 17.6 | 7.1 |
| · Orthopedic Surgery | 188 | 67.6 | 29.3 | 3.1 |
| · Ophthalmology | 188 | 66.6 | 28.3 | 5.1 |
| · Urological Surgery | 99 | 70.7 | 29.3 | 0.0 |
| · Other | 120 | 69.8 | 27.5 | 2.7 |
| Pediatrics | 310 | 49.5 | 47.7 | 2.7 |
| Obstetrics/Gynecology | 251 | 66.0 | 31.0 | 3.0 |
| Radiology | 284 | 49.0 | 42.9 | 8.1 |
| Psychiatry | 276 | 48.6 | 44.5 | 6.8 |
| Anesthesiology | 231 | 48.6 | 35.5 | 15.9 |
| Pathology | 121 | 30.4 | 54.2 | 15.4 |
| Other Specialty | 373 | 42.1 | 44.3 | 13.6 |
| · Emergency Medicine | 133 | 25.6 | 40.2 | 34.1 |
| · Other | 240 | 50.7 | 46.4 | 2.8 |
| *Geographic Area* | | | | |
| New England | 256 | 44.1 | 51.4 | 4.4 |
| · Massachusetts | 119 | 42.9 | 52.7 | 4.4 |
| · Other | 137 | 45.4 | 50.2 | 4.5 |
| Middle Atlantic | 629 | 57.6 | 37.1 | 5.4 |
| · New Jersey | 111 | 67.4 | 28.9 | 3.8 |
| · New York | 251 | 52.1 | 40.8 | 7.1 |
| · Pennsylvania | 267 | 58.4 | 37.4 | 4.2 |
| East North Central | 607 | 52.9 | 41.2 | 5.9 |
| · Illinois | 188 | 56.3 | 35.9 | 7.8 |
| · Michigan | 114 | 45.6 | 47.3 | 7.1 |
| · Ohio | 134 | 56.1 | 40.7 | 3.3 |
| · Other | 171 | 50.8 | 44.4 | 4.8 |
| West North Central | 295 | 49.3 | 44.6 | 6.1 |
| South Atlantic | 723 | 58.9 | 35.6 | 5.5 |
| · Florida | 203 | 63.7 | 28.3 | 7.9 |
| · Other | 520 | 56.9 | 38.7 | 4.4 |
| East South Central | 236 | 64.5 | 29.1 | 6.4 |
| West South Central | 370 | 53.2 | 41.5 | 5.3 |
| · Texas | 245 | 51.7 | 41.9 | 6.4 |
| · Other | 125 | 56.6 | 40.7 | 2.7 |
| Mountain | 235 | 53.0 | 38.6 | 8.4 |
| Pacific | 675 | 53.1 | 37.0 | 9.9 |
| · California | 471 | 54.6 | 33.7 | 11.7 |
| · Other | 204 | 49.0 | 46.0 | 5.0 |

Source: 1995 Socioeconomic Monitoring System survey of nonfederal patient care physicians. See the beginning of this section, the introduction, and appendices for a discussion of the survey sample, definitions, and computation procedures. Statistics are not reported if the number of responses is less than 25.

Table 100. **Distribution of Employee Nonfederal Physicians, by Size of Practice, 1995**

| | Number of Responses | Health Maintenance Organizations | Group Practices or Free-Standing Centers | Private Hospitals | Medical Schools, Universities or Colleges | State or Local Gov't, Others |
|---|---|---|---|---|---|---|
| All Physicians | 1417 | 8.0 | 32.5 | 18.3 | 20.4 | 20.8 |
| *Specialty* | | | | | | |
| General/Family Practice | 205 | 12.0 | 26.4 | 27.3 | 7.8 | 26.5 |
| Internal Medicine | 295 | 10.1 | 31.4 | 15.6 | 22.2 | 20.8 |
| · General Internal Medicine | 221 | 12.2 | 24.8 | 18.1 | 21.5 | 23.3 |
| · Cardiovascular Diseases | 37 | 0.0 | 55.3 | 5.2 | 30.6 | 8.9 |
| · Other | 37 | 5.3 | 53.3 | 8.2 | 18.7 | 14.5 |
| Surgery | 218 | 3.7 | 44.8 | 8.8 | 27.2 | 15.5 |
| · General Surgery | 57 | 5.3 | 42.3 | 10.4 | 27.2 | 14.9 |
| · Otolaryngology | 13 | . | . | . | . | . |
| · Orthopedic Surgery | 51 | 0.0 | 51.5 | 11.0 | 22.5 | 14.9 |
| · Ophthalmology | 48 | 3.5 | 73.1 | 1.7 | 12.8 | 9.0 |
| · Urological Surgery | 23 | . | . | . | . | . |
| · Other | 26 | 3.0 | 14.8 | 21.9 | 33.0 | 27.3 |
| Pediatrics | 133 | 11.7 | 30.2 | 19.1 | 20.1 | 19.0 |
| Obstetrics/Gynecology | 73 | 8.4 | 43.3 | 19.3 | 20.3 | 8.6 |
| Radiology | 110 | 9.0 | 43.3 | 12.2 | 22.3 | 13.1 |
| Psychiatry | 102 | 4.5 | 3.0 | 29.3 | 13.5 | 49.7 |
| Anesthesiology | 74 | 3.1 | 43.4 | 10.3 | 25.8 | 17.4 |
| Pathology | 58 | 2.8 | 29.4 | 23.6 | 28.5 | 15.6 |
| Other Specialty | 149 | 6.3 | 34.7 | 21.6 | 22.4 | 15.1 |
| · Emergency Medicine | 52 | 2.8 | 44.0 | 34.9 | 10.8 | 7.5 |
| · Other | 97 | 8.0 | 30.1 | 14.9 | 28.1 | 18.8 |
| *Geographic Area* | | | | | | |
| New England | 113 | 0.9 | 31.1 | 32.0 | 16.5 | 19.5 |
| · Massachusetts | 50 | 1.7 | 26.4 | 41.2 | 14.1 | 16.6 |
| · Other | 63 | 0.0 | 36.2 | 22.0 | 19.1 | 22.6 |
| Middle Atlantic | 217 | 1.4 | 21.3 | 31.3 | 31.8 | 14.3 |
| · New Jersey | 32 | 2.3 | 25.5 | 39.6 | 24.4 | 8.2 |
| · New York | 93 | 0.0 | 14.3 | 32.3 | 31.9 | 21.5 |
| · Pennsylvania | 92 | 2.7 | 28.2 | 26.5 | 34.8 | 7.8 |
| East North Central | 223 | 6.7 | 34.3 | 23.3 | 18.3 | 17.4 |
| · Illinois | 64 | 7.3 | 34.4 | 20.5 | 18.9 | 18.9 |
| · Michigan | 43 | 6.1 | 29.7 | 38.0 | 22.7 | 3.5 |
| · Ohio | 49 | 2.1 | 29.7 | 14.1 | 24.1 | 30.0 |
| · Other | 67 | 10.4 | 41.8 | 21.6 | 9.3 | 16.8 |
| West North Central | 117 | 8.0 | 32.5 | 22.6 | 10.7 | 26.3 |
| South Atlantic | 234 | 6.4 | 33.7 | 12.0 | 21.2 | 26.6 |
| · Florida | 52 | 2.1 | 34.8 | 16.3 | 22.3 | 24.5 |
| · Other | 182 | 7.7 | 33.4 | 10.8 | 20.9 | 27.3 |
| East South Central | 60 | 4.7 | 30.0 | 19.2 | 20.9 | 25.2 |
| West South Central | 133 | 3.2 | 34.4 | 7.5 | 28.9 | 26.0 |
| · Texas | 89 | 3.5 | 32.2 | 4.6 | 30.6 | 29.0 |
| · Other | 44 | 2.5 | 39.7 | 14.3 | 24.7 | 18.7 |
| Mountain | 85 | 18.0 | 35.4 | 11.8 | 15.0 | 19.7 |
| Pacific | 235 | 22.0 | 39.6 | 5.4 | 13.9 | 19.0 |
| · California | 150 | 22.0 | 41.5 | 2.7 | 17.0 | 16.8 |
| · Other | 85 | 22.0 | 36.1 | 10.7 | 7.9 | 23.3 |

Source: 1995 Socioeconomic Monitoring System survey of nonfederal patient care physicians. See the beginning of this section, the introduction, and appendices for a discussion of the survey sample, definitions, and computation procedures. Statistics are not reported if the number of responses is less than 25.

## Table 101. **Distribution of Nonfederal Physicians, by Size of Practice, 1995**

| | Number of Responses | Solo Practice | Two Physician Practice | Three Physician Practice | 4-8 Physician Practice | Over 8 Physician Practice |
|---|---|---|---|---|---|---|
| All Physicians | 2789 | 39.4 | 11.4 | 9.6 | 21.4 | 18.2 |
| *Specialty* | | | | | | |
| General/Family Practice | 329 | 46.2 | 14.2 | 10.2 | 18.3 | 11.1 |
| Internal Medicine | 546 | 40.8 | 10.6 | 10.3 | 17.5 | 20.8 |
| · General Internal Medicine | 345 | 43.7 | 11.4 | 9.9 | 16.1 | 18.9 |
| · Cardiovascular Diseases | 83 | 25.5 | 8.0 | 8.8 | 20.7 | 37.0 |
| · Other | 118 | 42.6 | 10.3 | 12.3 | 19.2 | 15.6 |
| Surgery | 735 | 43.7 | 13.8 | 11.2 | 21.3 | 10.0 |
| · General Surgery | 182 | 53.7 | 9.6 | 9.4 | 18.8 | 8.5 |
| · Otolaryngology | 64 | 50.0 | 19.4 | 7.2 | 15.9 | 7.5 |
| · Orthopedic Surgery | 156 | 32.7 | 12.5 | 11.4 | 27.5 | 15.9 |
| · Ophthalmology | 161 | 35.0 | 16.3 | 13.2 | 22.5 | 13.0 |
| · Urological Surgery | 82 | 37.2 | 17.5 | 14.3 | 26.9 | 4.1 |
| · Other | 90 | 54.5 | 14.8 | 11.6 | 13.5 | 5.6 |
| Pediatrics | 199 | 38.0 | 16.3 | 10.8 | 21.2 | 13.7 |
| Obstetrics/Gynecology | 195 | 41.8 | 13.5 | 9.8 | 24.8 | 10.1 |
| Radiology | 197 | 3.0 | 6.5 | 8.8 | 36.9 | 44.8 |
| Psychiatry | 162 | 80.0 | 7.2 | 1.3 | 6.0 | 5.4 |
| Anesthesiology | 148 | 19.2 | 0.5 | 8.0 | 21.8 | 50.5 |
| Pathology | 61 | 4.9 | 23.3 | 8.2 | 41.3 | 22.2 |
| Other Specialty | 217 | 31.4 | 5.5 | 6.8 | 29.4 | 26.9 |
| · Emergency Medicine | 59 | 3.8 | 1.3 | 1.3 | 38.4 | 55.2 |
| · Other | 158 | 41.1 | 7.0 | 8.7 | 26.2 | 17.0 |
| *Geographic Area* | | | | | | |
| New England | 167 | 41.7 | 11.6 | 7.8 | 20.4 | 18.6 |
| · Massachusetts | 74 | 40.5 | 10.5 | 6.9 | 19.5 | 22.6 |
| · Other | 93 | 42.9 | 12.5 | 8.6 | 21.2 | 14.8 |
| Middle Atlantic | 428 | 43.1 | 14.8 | 9.2 | 22.2 | 10.6 |
| · New Jersey | 81 | 46.8 | 22.2 | 7.7 | 19.0 | 4.3 |
| · New York | 158 | 50.2 | 15.4 | 8.0 | 12.6 | 13.8 |
| · Pennsylvania | 189 | 34.1 | 9.9 | 11.4 | 33.4 | 11.1 |
| East North Central | 420 | 35.1 | 8.5 | 11.9 | 23.0 | 21.6 |
| · Illinois | 132 | 45.3 | 6.0 | 12.7 | 17.4 | 18.6 |
| · Michigan | 78 | 29.4 | 8.7 | 18.1 | 26.8 | 17.0 |
| · Ohio | 94 | 33.5 | 12.3 | 10.2 | 22.7 | 21.2 |
| · Other | 116 | 27.1 | 8.0 | 8.3 | 28.1 | 28.5 |
| West North Central | 196 | 25.3 | 6.6 | 13.2 | 30.3 | 24.5 |
| South Atlantic | 518 | 42.5 | 11.3 | 8.6 | 22.0 | 15.6 |
| · Florida | 148 | 49.6 | 9.2 | 6.2 | 20.7 | 14.3 |
| · Other | 370 | 39.4 | 12.2 | 9.7 | 22.6 | 16.1 |
| East South Central | 178 | 32.1 | 17.7 | 13.0 | 20.6 | 16.7 |
| West South Central | 267 | 41.8 | 13.5 | 7.6 | 17.4 | 19.6 |
| · Texas | 174 | 45.5 | 13.3 | 6.7 | 15.5 | 19.1 |
| · Other | 93 | 34.6 | 14.1 | 9.5 | 21.3 | 20.5 |
| Mountain | 155 | 37.3 | 10.4 | 11.8 | 18.7 | 21.8 |
| Pacific | 460 | 42.8 | 9.5 | 7.3 | 19.0 | 21.3 |
| · California | 316 | 47.4 | 10.6 | 7.3 | 15.3 | 19.3 |
| · Other | 144 | 30.1 | 6.3 | 7.4 | 29.3 | 26.9 |

Source: 1995 Socioeconomic Monitoring System survey of nonfederal patient care physicians. See the beginning of this section, the introduction, and appendices for a discussion of the survey sample, definitions, and computation procedures. Statistics are not reported if the number of responses is less than 25.

Table 102. **Distribution of Self Employed Nonfederal Physicians, by Size of Practice, 1995**

| | Number of Responses | Solo Practice | Two Physician Practice | Three Physician Practice | 4-8 Physician Practice | Over 8 Physician Practice |
|---|---|---|---|---|---|---|
| All Physicians | 2276 | 48.2 | 11.5 | 9.1 | 20.2 | 11.1 |
| *Specialty* | | | | | | |
| General/Family Practice | 265 | 56.1 | 15.3 | 7.4 | 16.6 | 4.6 |
| Internal Medicine | 437 | 51.1 | 9.2 | 10.9 | 17.4 | 11.3 |
| · General Internal Medicine | 276 | 54.9 | 10.1 | 10.9 | 14.8 | 9.3 |
| · Cardiovascular Diseases | 62 | 34.2 | 9.2 | 9.2 | 26.4 | 21.0 |
| · Other | 99 | 51.0 | 6.9 | 11.9 | 19.3 | 11.0 |
| Surgery | 635 | 50.4 | 13.9 | 10.8 | 20.1 | 4.8 |
| · General Surgery | 156 | 59.9 | 9.3 | 7.9 | 19.4 | 3.5 |
| · Otolaryngology | 61 | 52.5 | 20.3 | 7.5 | 16.7 | 3.0 |
| · Orthopedic Surgery | 130 | 40.1 | 13.7 | 12.3 | 25.0 | 8.9 |
| · Ophthalmology | 128 | 45.5 | 17.3 | 12.5 | 19.6 | 5.1 |
| · Urological Surgery | 74 | 41.4 | 15.8 | 14.8 | 25.8 | 2.2 |
| · Other | 86 | 57.2 | 13.7 | 11.3 | 13.3 | 4.5 |
| Pediatrics | 154 | 47.3 | 19.4 | 9.0 | 17.3 | 7.0 |
| Obstetrics/Gynecology | 165 | 49.9 | 13.3 | 8.3 | 21.8 | 6.7 |
| Radiology | 142 | 3.7 | 7.9 | 5.7 | 43.9 | 38.8 |
| Psychiatry | 157 | 81.5 | 7.4 | 1.4 | 5.7 | 4.0 |
| Anesthesiology | 118 | 25.1 | 0.7 | 10.5 | 22.9 | 40.8 |
| Pathology | 42 | 7.5 | 19.8 | 8.9 | 48.9 | 14.9 |
| Other Specialty | 161 | 42.1 | 5.9 | 8.7 | 24.1 | 19.1 |
| · Emergency Medicine | 36 | 6.3 | 2.2 | 2.2 | 32.3 | 56.9 |
| · Other | 125 | 51.6 | 6.9 | 10.5 | 22.0 | 9.1 |
| *Geographic Area* | | | | | | |
| New England | 124 | 57.5 | 10.9 | 8.2 | 16.1 | 7.2 |
| · Massachusetts | 58 | 55.7 | 11.1 | 7.6 | 14.7 | 10.9 |
| · Other | 66 | 59.2 | 10.7 | 8.8 | 17.5 | 3.9 |
| Middle Atlantic | 371 | 49.0 | 15.5 | 8.7 | 20.3 | 6.5 |
| · New Jersey | 71 | 51.6 | 21.9 | 5.6 | 18.9 | 2.0 |
| · New York | 143 | 56.1 | 16.0 | 8.1 | 11.1 | 8.7 |
| · Pennsylvania | 157 | 40.0 | 10.9 | 11.2 | 30.8 | 7.1 |
| East North Central | 335 | 43.7 | 8.8 | 11.0 | 21.5 | 15.0 |
| · Illinois | 108 | 53.5 | 6.3 | 11.5 | 16.5 | 12.2 |
| · Michigan | 61 | 38.6 | 6.5 | 17.4 | 24.4 | 13.1 |
| · Ohio | 78 | 40.2 | 13.8 | 7.3 | 20.2 | 18.5 |
| · Other | 88 | 36.3 | 8.8 | 10.1 | 27.9 | 16.9 |
| West North Central | 154 | 32.5 | 6.3 | 14.8 | 30.0 | 16.4 |
| South Atlantic | 432 | 50.6 | 10.9 | 7.6 | 20.7 | 10.2 |
| · Florida | 128 | 56.3 | 9.3 | 4.7 | 20.1 | 9.6 |
| · Other | 304 | 47.9 | 11.7 | 9.0 | 21.0 | 10.5 |
| East South Central | 157 | 36.8 | 15.1 | 12.4 | 23.0 | 12.8 |
| West South Central | 213 | 52.3 | 14.6 | 8.0 | 15.2 | 9.8 |
| · Texas | 139 | 55.7 | 12.7 | 6.4 | 13.9 | 11.3 |
| · Other | 74 | 45.5 | 18.5 | 11.3 | 17.8 | 6.8 |
| Mountain | 125 | 46.3 | 11.0 | 10.9 | 17.3 | 14.5 |
| Pacific | 365 | 54.1 | 9.8 | 6.4 | 18.2 | 11.5 |
| · California | 257 | 58.5 | 10.9 | 5.6 | 15.6 | 9.4 |
| · Other | 108 | 40.7 | 6.3 | 9.1 | 26.2 | 17.7 |

Source: 1995 Socioeconomic Monitoring System survey of nonfederal patient care physicians. See the beginning of this section, the introduction, and appendices for a discussion of the survey sample, definitions, and computation procedures. Statistics are not reported if the number of responses is less than 25.

Table 103. **Distribution of Employee Nonfederal Physicians, by Size of Practice, 1995**

| | Number of Responses | Solo Practice | Two Physician Practice | Three Physician Practice | 4-8 Physician Practice | Over 8 Physician Practice |
|---|---|---|---|---|---|---|
| All Physicians | 600 | 0.0 | 9.6 | 10.4 | 25.6 | 54.4 |
| *Specialty* | | | | | | |
| General/Family Practice | 85 | 0.0 | 6.8 | 18.3 | 24.0 | 50.9 |
| Internal Medicine | 128 | 0.0 | 14.7 | 7.2 | 17.3 | 60.8 |
| · General Internal Medicine | 88 | 0.0 | 14.1 | 5.5 | 19.8 | 60.6 |
| · Cardiovascular Diseases | 21 | . | . | . | . | . |
| · Other | 19 | . | . | . | . | . |
| Surgery | 107 | 0.0 | 12.8 | 13.2 | 27.7 | 46.3 |
| · General Surgery | 28 | 0.0 | 11.6 | 19.9 | 12.7 | 55.8 |
| · Otolaryngology | 4 | . | . | . | . | . |
| · Orthopedic Surgery | 26 | 0.0 | 7.0 | 7.5 | 38.7 | 46.8 |
| · Ophthalmology | 34 | 0.0 | 12.7 | 15.4 | 31.2 | 40.7 |
| · Urological Surgery | 10 | . | . | . | . | . |
| · Other | 5 | . | . | . | . | . |
| Pediatrics | 60 | 0.0 | 4.4 | 13.2 | 28.6 | 53.8 |
| Obstetrics/Gynecology | 36 | 0.0 | 11.9 | 16.7 | 40.3 | 31.1 |
| Radiology | 62 | 0.0 | 4.1 | 14.9 | 15.3 | 65.7 |
| Psychiatry | 6 | . | . | . | . | . |
| Anesthesiology | 32 | 0.0 | 0.0 | 0.0 | 17.2 | 82.8 |
| Pathology | 20 | . | . | . | . | . |
| Other Specialty | 64 | 0.0 | 3.8 | 1.1 | 43.9 | 51.2 |
| · Emergency Medicine | 24 | . | . | . | . | . |
| · Other | 40 | 0.0 | 6.2 | 1.7 | 43.5 | 48.6 |
| *Geographic Area* | | | | | | |
| New England | 43 | 0.0 | 13.3 | 6.6 | 31.5 | 48.6 |
| · Massachusetts | 16 | . | . | . | . | . |
| · Other | 27 | 0.0 | 17.2 | 8.2 | 31.0 | 43.5 |
| Middle Atlantic | 60 | 0.0 | 9.6 | 12.7 | 33.9 | 43.8 |
| · New Jersey | 11 | . | . | . | . | . |
| · New York | 15 | . | . | . | . | . |
| · Pennsylvania | 34 | 0.0 | 4.3 | 11.8 | 44.6 | 39.3 |
| East North Central | 95 | 0.0 | 6.2 | 13.1 | 28.0 | 52.7 |
| · Illinois | 26 | 0.0 | 3.7 | 16.3 | 18.2 | 61.8 |
| · Michigan | 20 | . | . | . | . | . |
| · Ohio | 17 | . | . | . | . | . |
| · Other | 32 | 0.0 | 5.0 | 2.6 | 28.0 | 64.4 |
| West North Central | 48 | 0.0 | 8.7 | 9.0 | 26.1 | 56.2 |
| South Atlantic | 95 | 0.0 | 11.9 | 12.4 | 28.3 | 47.4 |
| · Florida | 20 | . | . | . | . | . |
| · Other | 75 | 0.0 | 12.7 | 11.4 | 29.5 | 46.3 |
| East South Central | 25 | 0.0 | 31.1 | 18.6 | 8.6 | 41.8 |
| West South Central | 56 | 0.0 | 9.5 | 6.0 | 24.7 | 59.8 |
| · Texas | 36 | 0.0 | 15.1 | 7.6 | 21.2 | 56.2 |
| · Other | 20 | . | . | . | . | . |
| Mountain | 44 | 0.0 | 10.4 | 13.3 | 27.5 | 48.8 |
| Pacific | 134 | 0.0 | 5.9 | 7.4 | 19.2 | 67.6 |
| · California | 82 | 0.0 | 6.8 | 10.2 | 15.0 | 68.0 |
| · Other | 52 | 0.0 | 4.1 | 1.8 | 27.4 | 66.7 |

Source: 1995 Socioeconomic Monitoring System survey of nonfederal patient care physicians. See the beginning of this section, the introduction, and appendices for a discussion of the survey sample, definitions, and computation procedures. Statistics are not reported if the number of responses is less than 25.

## Table 104. Number of Nonfederal Physicians per Medical Practice, 1995

| | Number of Responses | Mean | Standard Error | 25th Percentile | Median | 75th Percentile |
|---|---|---|---|---|---|---|
| All Physicians | 2789 | 13.7 | 1.1 | 1.0 | 2.0 | 6.0 |
| *Specialty* | | | | | | |
| General/Family Practice | 329 | 8.7 | 2.1 | 1.0 | 2.0 | 4.0 |
| Internal Medicine | 546 | 17.4 | 3.4 | 1.0 | 2.0 | 6.0 |
| · General Internal Medicine | 345 | 15.7 | 4.2 | 1.0 | 2.0 | 5.0 |
| · Cardiovascular Diseases | 83 | 15.4 | 6.6 | 1.0 | 5.0 | 12.0 |
| · Other | 118 | 23.3 | 8.3 | 1.0 | 2.0 | 4.0 |
| Surgery | 735 | 9.6 | 1.6 | 1.0 | 2.0 | 4.0 |
| · General Surgery | 182 | 12.5 | 4.9 | 1.0 | 1.0 | 4.0 |
| · Otolaryngology | 64 | 6.4 | 1.8 | 1.0 | 1.0 | 3.0 |
| · Orthopedic Surgery | 156 | 11.5 | 3.8 | 1.0 | 3.0 | 5.0 |
| · Ophthalmology | 161 | 10.5 | 2.9 | 1.0 | 2.0 | 5.0 |
| · Urological Surgery | 82 | 3.5 | 0.6 | 1.0 | 2.0 | 4.0 |
| · Other | 90 | 5.5 | 2.6 | 1.0 | 1.0 | 3.0 |
| Pediatrics | 199 | 12.5 | 2.7 | 1.0 | 2.0 | 5.0 |
| Obstetrics/Gynecology | 195 | 10.3 | 3.1 | 1.0 | 2.0 | 5.0 |
| Radiology | 197 | 33.1 | 6.6 | 5.0 | 8.0 | 17.0 |
| Psychiatry | 162 | 5.1 | 2.1 | 1.0 | 1.0 | 1.0 |
| Anesthesiology | 148 | 16.1 | 2.8 | 3.0 | 9.0 | 16.0 |
| Pathology | 61 | 11.8 | 3.7 | 2.0 | 5.0 | 8.0 |
| Other Specialty | 217 | 18.7 | 4.3 | 1.0 | 4.0 | 9.0 |
| · Emergency Medicine | 59 | 19.3 | 5.8 | 7.0 | 9.0 | 13.0 |
| · Other | 158 | 18.4 | 5.5 | 1.0 | 3.0 | 6.0 |
| *Geographic Area* | | | | | | |
| New England | 167 | 17.8 | 7.1 | 1.0 | 2.0 | 6.0 |
| · Massachusetts | 74 | 11.4 | 4.3 | 1.0 | 2.0 | 8.0 |
| · Other | 93 | 23.8 | 12.3 | 1.0 | 2.0 | 5.0 |
| Middle Atlantic | 428 | 5.4 | 0.9 | 1.0 | 2.0 | 5.0 |
| · New Jersey | 81 | 4.1 | 1.2 | 1.0 | 2.0 | 3.0 |
| · New York | 158 | 7.3 | 2.4 | 1.0 | 1.0 | 4.0 |
| · Pennsylvania | 189 | 4.4 | 0.4 | 1.0 | 3.0 | 5.0 |
| East North Central | 420 | 21.5 | 3.9 | 1.0 | 3.0 | 8.0 |
| · Illinois | 132 | 12.8 | 4.6 | 1.0 | 2.0 | 6.0 |
| · Michigan | 78 | 22.8 | 12.2 | 1.0 | 3.0 | 5.0 |
| · Ohio | 94 | 14.0 | 6.3 | 1.0 | 3.0 | 8.0 |
| · Other | 116 | 38.5 | 8.8 | 1.0 | 4.0 | 14.0 |
| West North Central | 196 | 17.8 | 3.0 | 1.0 | 4.0 | 8.0 |
| South Atlantic | 518 | 7.9 | 1.7 | 1.0 | 2.0 | 5.0 |
| · Florida | 148 | 5.6 | 1.3 | 1.0 | 2.0 | 5.0 |
| · Other | 370 | 9.0 | 2.3 | 1.0 | 2.0 | 6.0 |
| East South Central | 178 | 17.7 | 4.9 | 1.0 | 3.0 | 5.0 |
| West South Central | 267 | 12.7 | 2.6 | 1.0 | 2.0 | 5.0 |
| · Texas | 174 | 7.9 | 1.8 | 1.0 | 2.0 | 5.0 |
| · Other | 93 | 22.2 | 6.4 | 1.0 | 3.0 | 6.0 |
| Mountain | 155 | 14.2 | 4.3 | 1.0 | 3.0 | 6.0 |
| Pacific | 460 | 17.1 | 2.9 | 1.0 | 2.0 | 6.0 |
| · California | 316 | 17.1 | 4.1 | 1.0 | 2.0 | 5.0 |
| · Other | 144 | 17.0 | 3.0 | 1.0 | 4.0 | 10.0 |

Source: 1995 Socioeconomic Monitoring System survey of nonfederal patient care physicians. See the beginning of this section, the introduction, and appendices for a discussion of the survey sample, definitions, and computation procedures. Statistics are not reported if the number of responses is less than 25.

Table 105. **Number of Nonfederal Physicians per Medical Practice, in Practices of Two or More Physicians, 1995**

| | Number of Responses | Mean | Standard Error | 25th Percentile | Median | 75th Percentile |
|---|---|---|---|---|---|---|
| All Physicians | 1767 | 22.0 | 1.7 | 3.0 | 5.0 | 10.0 |
| *Specialty* | | | | | | |
| General/Family Practice | 174 | 15.3 | 3.8 | 2.0 | 4.0 | 6.0 |
| Internal Medicine | 346 | 28.6 | 5.2 | 3.0 | 5.0 | 13.0 |
| · General Internal Medicine | 206 | 27.1 | 6.9 | 3.0 | 5.0 | 15.0 |
| · Cardiovascular Diseases | 65 | 20.3 | 8.4 | 4.0 | 8.0 | 14.0 |
| · Other | 75 | 39.8 | 12.8 | 3.0 | 4.0 | 9.0 |
| Surgery | 446 | 16.2 | 2.7 | 3.0 | 4.0 | 6.0 |
| · General Surgery | 101 | 25.9 | 8.7 | 3.0 | 4.0 | 6.0 |
| · Otolaryngology | 31 | 11.7 | 3.6 | 2.0 | 3.0 | 4.0 |
| · Orthopedic Surgery | 110 | 16.6 | 5.3 | 3.0 | 4.0 | 8.0 |
| · Ophthalmology | 101 | 15.7 | 4.6 | 2.0 | 4.0 | 7.0 |
| · Urological Surgery | 53 | 5.0 | 0.8 | 2.0 | 3.0 | 5.0 |
| · Other | 50 | 10.8 | 4.6 | 2.0 | 3.0 | 5.0 |
| Pediatrics | 128 | 19.6 | 4.1 | 2.0 | 4.0 | 7.0 |
| Obstetrics/Gynecology | 121 | 17.0 | 5.0 | 3.0 | 4.0 | 6.0 |
| Radiology | 189 | 34.0 | 6.8 | 5.0 | 8.0 | 18.0 |
| Psychiatry | 28 | 21.5 | 11.6 | 2.0 | 4.0 | 9.0 |
| Anesthesiology | 126 | 19.7 | 3.2 | 6.0 | 11.0 | 18.0 |
| Pathology | 58 | 12.4 | 3.9 | 3.0 | 5.0 | 8.0 |
| Other Specialty | 151 | 26.7 | 6.0 | 4.0 | 7.0 | 12.0 |
| · Emergency Medicine | 56 | 20.0 | 6.1 | 7.0 | 9.0 | 13.0 |
| · Other | 95 | 30.6 | 8.9 | 3.0 | 5.0 | 9.0 |
| *Geographic Area* | | | | | | |
| New England | 100 | 29.8 | 11.8 | 3.0 | 5.0 | 12.0 |
| · Massachusetts | 44 | 18.5 | 7.0 | 3.0 | 6.0 | 12.0 |
| · Other | 56 | 40.9 | 20.3 | 3.0 | 5.0 | 9.0 |
| Middle Atlantic | 253 | 8.8 | 1.5 | 2.0 | 4.0 | 7.0 |
| · New Jersey | 50 | 6.7 | 1.9 | 2.0 | 3.0 | 6.0 |
| · New York | 77 | 13.7 | 4.8 | 2.0 | 4.0 | 9.0 |
| · Pennsylvania | 126 | 6.2 | 0.5 | 3.0 | 4.0 | 7.0 |
| East North Central | 295 | 32.6 | 5.5 | 3.0 | 5.0 | 12.0 |
| · Illinois | 83 | 22.5 | 7.2 | 3.0 | 5.0 | 12.0 |
| · Michigan | 56 | 31.9 | 16.9 | 3.0 | 4.0 | 8.0 |
| · Ohio | 69 | 20.6 | 8.5 | 3.0 | 5.0 | 11.0 |
| · Other | 87 | 52.4 | 11.4 | 4.0 | 6.0 | 22.0 |
| West North Central | 150 | 23.5 | 3.8 | 3.0 | 6.0 | 14.0 |
| South Atlantic | 324 | 13.1 | 2.6 | 3.0 | 5.0 | 9.0 |
| · Florida | 83 | 10.2 | 2.3 | 3.0 | 5.0 | 9.0 |
| · Other | 241 | 14.1 | 3.4 | 3.0 | 5.0 | 10.0 |
| East South Central | 122 | 25.6 | 7.1 | 2.0 | 4.0 | 8.0 |
| West South Central | 156 | 21.1 | 4.3 | 3.0 | 5.0 | 13.0 |
| · Texas | 97 | 13.7 | 3.2 | 3.0 | 5.0 | 14.0 |
| · Other | 59 | 33.5 | 9.9 | 3.0 | 5.0 | 12.0 |
| Mountain | 96 | 22.1 | 6.8 | 3.0 | 5.0 | 10.0 |
| Pacific | 271 | 29.2 | 4.9 | 3.0 | 5.0 | 15.0 |
| · California | 171 | 31.7 | 7.3 | 3.0 | 5.0 | 15.0 |
| · Other | 100 | 23.9 | 4.2 | 4.0 | 6.0 | 17.0 |

Source: 1995 Socioeconomic Monitoring System survey of nonfederal patient care physicians. See the beginning of this section, the introduction, and appendices for a discussion of the survey sample, definitions, and computation procedures. Statistics are not reported if the number of responses is less than 25.

Table 106. **Number of Self-Employed Nonfederal Physicians per Medical Practice, in Practices of Two or More Physicians, 1995**

| | Number of Responses | Mean | Standard Error | 25th Percentile | Median | 75th Percentile |
|---|---|---|---|---|---|---|
| All Physicians | 1740 | 13.4 | 1.2 | 2.0 | 3.0 | 6.0 |
| *Specialty* | | | | | | |
| General/Family Practice | 171 | 8.3 | 2.6 | 1.0 | 2.0 | 4.0 |
| Internal Medicine | 342 | 19.9 | 4.3 | 2.0 | 3.0 | 7.0 |
| · General Internal Medicine | 203 | 14.8 | 5.1 | 2.0 | 3.0 | 6.0 |
| · Cardiovascular Diseases | 65 | 15.7 | 7.5 | 3.0 | 6.0 | 9.0 |
| · Other | 74 | 37.1 | 12.4 | 2.0 | 3.0 | 7.0 |
| Surgery | 441 | 8.8 | 1.5 | 2.0 | 3.0 | 4.0 |
| · General Surgery | 100 | 12.2 | 4.3 | 2.0 | 3.0 | 5.0 |
| · Otolaryngology | 31 | 8.1 | 2.5 | 2.0 | 3.0 | 4.0 |
| · Orthopedic Surgery | 108 | 9.2 | 3.3 | 2.0 | 4.0 | 6.0 |
| · Ophthalmology | 99 | 7.0 | 2.5 | 1.0 | 2.0 | 4.0 |
| · Urological Surgery | 53 | 4.2 | 0.7 | 2.0 | 3.0 | 4.0 |
| · Other | 50 | 9.9 | 4.6 | 1.0 | 3.0 | 4.0 |
| Pediatrics | 127 | 9.7 | 2.6 | 1.0 | 2.0 | 5.0 |
| Obstetrics/Gynecology | 120 | 13.7 | 4.7 | 2.0 | 3.0 | 5.0 |
| Radiology | 183 | 23.4 | 4.3 | 4.0 | 6.0 | 13.0 |
| Psychiatry | 27 | 13.7 | 9.7 | 2.0 | 3.0 | 7.0 |
| Anesthesiology | 124 | 14.0 | 2.0 | 4.0 | 7.0 | 15.0 |
| Pathology | 57 | 5.4 | 1.4 | 2.0 | 3.0 | 6.0 |
| Other Specialty | 148 | 9.2 | 2.4 | 1.0 | 4.0 | 8.0 |
| · Emergency Medicine | 56 | 7.0 | 0.9 | 3.0 | 7.0 | 9.0 |
| · Other | 92 | 10.5 | 3.8 | 1.0 | 3.0 | 4.0 |
| *Geographic Area* | | | | | | |
| New England | 97 | 11.2 | 5.5 | 1.0 | 3.0 | 5.0 |
| · Massachusetts | 43 | 8.2 | 6.1 | 0.0 | 2.0 | 6.0 |
| · Other | 54 | 14.1 | 8.7 | 2.0 | 4.0 | 5.0 |
| Middle Atlantic | 251 | 6.0 | 1.5 | 2.0 | 3.0 | 5.0 |
| · New Jersey | 50 | 4.2 | 1.0 | 2.0 | 2.0 | 5.0 |
| · New York | 77 | 9.0 | 4.6 | 1.0 | 2.0 | 4.0 |
| · Pennsylvania | 124 | 4.7 | 0.5 | 2.0 | 3.0 | 5.0 |
| East North Central | 293 | 16.8 | 2.8 | 2.0 | 4.0 | 8.0 |
| · Illinois | 82 | 12.6 | 3.7 | 2.0 | 4.0 | 8.0 |
| · Michigan | 56 | 8.2 | 2.6 | 2.0 | 3.0 | 6.0 |
| · Ohio | 68 | 7.8 | 1.4 | 2.0 | 4.0 | 8.0 |
| · Other | 87 | 33.1 | 8.5 | 2.0 | 4.0 | 14.0 |
| West North Central | 150 | 13.3 | 2.3 | 2.0 | 4.0 | 8.0 |
| South Atlantic | 321 | 7.6 | 1.3 | 2.0 | 3.0 | 6.0 |
| · Florida | 82 | 7.6 | 2.1 | 2.0 | 3.0 | 6.0 |
| · Other | 239 | 7.6 | 1.6 | 2.0 | 3.0 | 6.0 |
| East South Central | 122 | 22.9 | 7.0 | 2.0 | 3.0 | 6.0 |
| West South Central | 148 | 13.7 | 3.6 | 2.0 | 3.0 | 6.0 |
| · Texas | 93 | 10.1 | 3.2 | 2.0 | 3.0 | 7.0 |
| · Other | 55 | 19.7 | 8.2 | 2.0 | 2.0 | 5.0 |
| Mountain | 94 | 18.5 | 6.7 | 2.0 | 4.0 | 9.0 |
| Pacific | 264 | 18.3 | 4.3 | 2.0 | 4.0 | 8.0 |
| · California | 167 | 19.7 | 6.6 | 1.0 | 3.0 | 8.0 |
| · Other | 97 | 15.3 | 2.5 | 3.0 | 5.0 | 14.0 |

Source: 1995 Socioeconomic Monitoring System survey of nonfederal patient care physicians. See the beginning of this section, the introduction, and appendices for a discussion of the survey sample, definitions, and computation procedures. Statistics are not reported if the number of responses is less than 25.

Table 107. **Number of Employee Nonfederal Physicians per Medical Practice, in Practices of Two or More Physicians, 1995**

| | Number of Responses | Mean | Standard Error | 25th Percentile | Median | 75th Percentile |
|---|---|---|---|---|---|---|
| All Physicians | 1740 | 7.1 | 0.9 | 0.0 | 1.0 | 2.0 |
| *Specialty* | | | | | | |
| General/Family Practice | 171 | 6.9 | 2.4 | 0.0 | 1.0 | 2.0 |
| Internal Medicine | 342 | 8.5 | 2.9 | 0.0 | 1.0 | 3.0 |
| · General Internal Medicine | 203 | 11.8 | 4.8 | 0.0 | 1.0 | 4.0 |
| · Cardiovascular Diseases | 65 | 4.6 | 1.2 | 0.0 | 1.0 | 4.0 |
| · Other | 74 | 3.0 | 1.3 | 0.0 | 1.0 | 1.0 |
| Surgery | 441 | 6.4 | 1.9 | 0.0 | 1.0 | 2.0 |
| · General Surgery | 100 | 9.0 | 6.4 | 0.0 | 0.0 | 1.0 |
| · Otolaryngology | 31 | 3.6 | 1.9 | 0.0 | 0.0 | 1.0 |
| · Orthopedic Surgery | 108 | 7.5 | 4.4 | 0.0 | 1.0 | 2.0 |
| · Ophthalmology | 99 | 8.8 | 2.9 | 0.0 | 1.0 | 3.0 |
| · Urological Surgery | 53 | 0.8 | 0.3 | 0.0 | 0.0 | 1.0 |
| · Other | 50 | 1.0 | 0.2 | 0.0 | 1.0 | 1.0 |
| Pediatrics | 127 | 10.0 | 2.4 | 0.0 | 1.0 | 3.0 |
| Obstetrics/Gynecology | 120 | 3.5 | 1.9 | 0.0 | 1.0 | 2.0 |
| Radiology | 183 | 2.6 | 0.3 | 0.0 | 1.0 | 2.0 |
| Psychiatry | 27 | 3.2 | 1.1 | 0.0 | 1.0 | 7.0 |
| Anesthesiology | 124 | 5.7 | 1.5 | 0.0 | 2.0 | 4.0 |
| Pathology | 57 | 6.3 | 3.7 | 0.0 | 1.0 | 2.0 |
| Other Specialty | 148 | 12.0 | 4.0 | 0.0 | 1.0 | 5.0 |
| · Emergency Medicine | 56 | 13.0 | 6.3 | 0.0 | 1.0 | 6.0 |
| · Other | 92 | 11.4 | 5.2 | 0.0 | 1.0 | 3.0 |
| *Geographic Area* | | | | | | |
| New England | 97 | 6.5 | 1.4 | 0.0 | 1.0 | 5.0 |
| · Massachusetts | 43 | 10.3 | 3.0 | 1.0 | 2.0 | 11.0 |
| · Other | 54 | 2.6 | 0.5 | 0.0 | 1.0 | 3.0 |
| Middle Atlantic | 251 | 2.8 | 0.5 | 0.0 | 1.0 | 2.0 |
| · New Jersey | 50 | 2.5 | 1.3 | 0.0 | 1.0 | 2.0 |
| · New York | 77 | 4.7 | 1.2 | 0.0 | 1.0 | 3.0 |
| · Pennsylvania | 124 | 1.5 | 0.2 | 0.0 | 1.0 | 2.0 |
| East North Central | 293 | 13.4 | 4.1 | 0.0 | 1.0 | 2.0 |
| · Illinois | 82 | 9.8 | 5.7 | 0.0 | 1.0 | 2.0 |
| · Michigan | 56 | 23.7 | 16.8 | 0.0 | 1.0 | 2.0 |
| · Ohio | 68 | 2.2 | 0.6 | 0.0 | 1.0 | 2.0 |
| · Other | 87 | 19.3 | 6.7 | 0.0 | 1.0 | 3.0 |
| West North Central | 150 | 10.2 | 3.1 | 0.0 | 1.0 | 3.0 |
| South Atlantic | 321 | 5.4 | 2.1 | 0.0 | 1.0 | 2.0 |
| · Florida | 82 | 2.5 | 0.4 | 0.0 | 1.0 | 2.0 |
| · Other | 239 | 6.5 | 2.8 | 0.0 | 1.0 | 2.0 |
| East South Central | 122 | 2.6 | 1.1 | 0.0 | 1.0 | 1.0 |
| West South Central | 148 | 6.6 | 1.5 | 0.0 | 1.0 | 3.0 |
| · Texas | 93 | 3.3 | 0.7 | 0.0 | 1.0 | 3.0 |
| · Other | 55 | 12.1 | 3.7 | 0.0 | 1.0 | 4.0 |
| Mountain | 94 | 1.9 | 0.3 | 0.0 | 1.0 | 2.0 |
| Pacific | 264 | 9.1 | 1.7 | 0.0 | 1.0 | 3.0 |
| · California | 167 | 9.8 | 2.0 | 0.0 | 1.0 | 4.0 |
| · Other | 97 | 7.4 | 3.2 | 0.0 | 1.0 | 2.0 |

Source: 1995 Socioeconomic Monitoring System survey of nonfederal patient care physicians. See the beginning of this section, the introduction, and appendices for a discussion of the survey sample, definitions, and computation procedures. Statistics are not reported if the number of responses is less than 25.

Table 108. **Total Nonphysician Employees per Nonfederal Physician in Medical Practices (excluding non-self-employed physicians), 1994**

| | Number of Responses | Mean | Standard Error | 25th Percentile | Median | 75th Percentile |
|---|---|---|---|---|---|---|
| All Physicians | 2247 | 3.4 | 0.1 | 1.7 | 3.0 | 4.7 |
| *Specialty* | | | | | | |
| General/Family Practice | 264 | 4.5 | 0.2 | 3.0 | 4.0 | 5.2 |
| Internal Medicine | 433 | 3.5 | 0.1 | 2.0 | 3.0 | 4.3 |
| · General Internal Medicine | 273 | 3.5 | 0.2 | 2.0 | 3.0 | 4.2 |
| · Cardiovascular Diseases | 61 | 3.6 | 0.3 | 2.0 | 3.0 | 5.0 |
| · Other | 99 | 3.3 | 0.2 | 2.0 | 3.0 | 4.0 |
| Surgery | 631 | 3.8 | 0.1 | 2.0 | 3.0 | 5.0 |
| · General Surgery | 153 | 2.5 | 0.1 | 1.5 | 2.0 | 3.2 |
| · Otolaryngology | 61 | 5.1 | 0.5 | 3.0 | 4.0 | 6.0 |
| · Orthopedic Surgery | 130 | 4.7 | 0.2 | 3.0 | 4.5 | 6.0 |
| · Ophthalmology | 128 | 5.2 | 0.3 | 3.0 | 5.0 | 6.8 |
| · Urological Surgery | 73 | 3.6 | 0.2 | 2.7 | 3.0 | 4.3 |
| · Other | 86 | 2.9 | 0.2 | 2.0 | 2.5 | 3.5 |
| Pediatrics | 153 | 3.6 | 0.2 | 2.0 | 3.0 | 4.5 |
| Obstetrics/Gynecology | 162 | 4.1 | 0.2 | 2.7 | 3.5 | 5.0 |
| Radiology | 134 | 2.1 | 0.2 | 0.3 | 1.1 | 3.5 |
| Psychiatry | 156 | 1.6 | 0.2 | 0.0 | 1.0 | 2.0 |
| Anesthesiology | 113 | 0.8 | 0.1 | 0.0 | 0.5 | 1.0 |
| Pathology | 42 | 1.9 | 0.4 | 0.0 | 0.5 | 4.0 |
| Other Specialty | 159 | 3.0 | 0.2 | 1.0 | 2.5 | 5.0 |
| · Emergency Medicine | 36 | 0.7 | 0.2 | 0.0 | 0.1 | 0.6 |
| · Other | 123 | 3.7 | 0.3 | 1.8 | 3.3 | 5.0 |
| *Geographic Area* | | | | | | |
| New England | 123 | 2.9 | 0.2 | 1.5 | 3.0 | 4.0 |
| · Massachusetts | 57 | 2.8 | 0.3 | 1.5 | 3.0 | 4.0 |
| · Other | 66 | 3.0 | 0.2 | 1.8 | 3.0 | 4.0 |
| Middle Atlantic | 364 | 3.1 | 0.1 | 1.0 | 2.7 | 4.0 |
| · New Jersey | 70 | 3.1 | 0.3 | 2.0 | 2.7 | 4.0 |
| · New York | 139 | 2.8 | 0.2 | 1.0 | 2.0 | 4.0 |
| · Pennsylvania | 155 | 3.3 | 0.2 | 1.0 | 3.0 | 4.6 |
| East North Central | 331 | 3.5 | 0.2 | 1.5 | 3.0 | 5.0 |
| · Illinois | 107 | 3.4 | 0.3 | 1.3 | 3.0 | 5.0 |
| · Michigan | 59 | 3.7 | 0.3 | 2.0 | 4.0 | 4.5 |
| · Ohio | 78 | 3.1 | 0.3 | 1.9 | 2.5 | 4.0 |
| · Other | 87 | 3.9 | 0.5 | 1.4 | 3.0 | 5.0 |
| West North Central | 150 | 3.8 | 0.2 | 2.0 | 3.0 | 5.0 |
| South Atlantic | 427 | 3.6 | 0.1 | 2.0 | 3.0 | 5.0 |
| · Florida | 128 | 3.9 | 0.3 | 2.0 | 4.0 | 5.0 |
| · Other | 299 | 3.4 | 0.1 | 1.7 | 3.0 | 5.0 |
| East South Central | 156 | 3.7 | 0.2 | 2.0 | 3.0 | 4.7 |
| West South Central | 211 | 3.4 | 0.2 | 1.7 | 3.0 | 4.3 |
| · Texas | 139 | 3.4 | 0.3 | 1.5 | 3.0 | 4.0 |
| · Other | 72 | 3.5 | 0.3 | 1.7 | 3.0 | 5.0 |
| Mountain | 123 | 3.6 | 0.3 | 2.0 | 3.0 | 4.5 |
| Pacific | 362 | 3.2 | 0.1 | 1.8 | 3.0 | 4.4 |
| · California | 255 | 3.3 | 0.2 | 1.8 | 3.0 | 4.1 |
| · Other | 107 | 3.0 | 0.2 | 1.3 | 3.0 | 4.5 |
| *Practice Arrangement* | | | | | | |
| Solo Practice | 1015 | 3.5 | 0.1 | 2.0 | 3.0 | 5.0 |
| Two Physician Practice | 270 | 3.7 | 0.1 | 2.0 | 3.0 | 5.0 |
| Three Physician Practice | 213 | 3.3 | 0.1 | 1.7 | 2.7 | 4.7 |
| 4-8 Physician Practice | 497 | 3.4 | 0.1 | 1.7 | 3.0 | 4.5 |
| Over 8 Physician Practice | 252 | 2.7 | 0.1 | 0.5 | 2.3 | 4.3 |

Source: 1995 Socioeconomic Monitoring System survey of nonfederal patient care physicians. See the beginning of this section, the introduction, and appendices for a discussion of the survey sample, definitions, and computation procedures. Statistics are not reported if the number of responses is less than 25.

## Table 109. **Full-Time Nonphysician Employees per Nonfederal Physician in Medical Practices (excluding non-self-employed physicians), 1994**

| | Number of Responses | Mean | Standard Error | 25th Percentile | Median | 75th Percentile |
|---|---|---|---|---|---|---|
| All Physicians | 2039 | 2.5 | 0.0 | 1.0 | 2.0 | 3.0 |
| *Specialty* | | | | | | |
| General/Family Practice | 259 | 2.8 | 0.1 | 2.0 | 3.0 | 4.0 |
| Internal Medicine | 426 | 2.5 | 0.1 | 1.0 | 2.0 | 3.0 |
| · General Internal Medicine | 267 | 2.5 | 0.2 | 1.0 | 2.0 | 3.0 |
| · Cardiovascular Diseases | 61 | 2.7 | 0.2 | 1.5 | 2.5 | 3.2 |
| · Other | 98 | 2.4 | 0.2 | 1.0 | 2.0 | 3.0 |
| Surgery | 619 | 2.8 | 0.1 | 1.3 | 2.0 | 3.5 |
| · General Surgery | 149 | 1.7 | 0.1 | 1.0 | 1.7 | 2.0 |
| · Otolaryngology | 61 | 3.7 | 0.3 | 2.0 | 3.0 | 4.0 |
| · Orthopedic Surgery | 127 | 3.6 | 0.2 | 2.0 | 3.0 | 4.5 |
| · Ophthalmology | 124 | 4.0 | 0.3 | 2.0 | 3.3 | 5.0 |
| · Urological Surgery | 73 | 2.6 | 0.1 | 2.0 | 2.0 | 3.2 |
| · Other | 85 | 1.9 | 0.2 | 1.0 | 2.0 | 2.8 |
| Pediatrics | 147 | 2.2 | 0.1 | 1.0 | 2.0 | 3.0 |
| Obstetrics/Gynecology | 158 | 2.9 | 0.2 | 1.5 | 2.2 | 3.3 |
| Radiology | 100 | 2.2 | 0.2 | 0.6 | 1.3 | 3.0 |
| Psychiatry | 86 | 1.5 | 0.3 | 0.0 | 1.0 | 2.0 |
| Anesthesiology | 81 | 0.8 | 0.1 | 0.1 | 0.5 | 1.0 |
| Pathology | 25 | 2.7 | 0.4 | 0.8 | 2.0 | 4.0 |
| Other Specialty | 138 | 2.2 | 0.2 | 1.0 | 2.0 | 3.0 |
| · Emergency Medicine | 21 | . | . | . | . | . |
| · Other | 117 | 2.5 | 0.2 | 1.0 | 2.0 | 3.5 |
| *Geographic Area* | | | | | | |
| New England | 107 | 1.9 | 0.1 | 1.0 | 2.0 | 2.5 |
| · Massachusetts | 49 | 1.9 | 0.2 | 1.0 | 2.0 | 2.3 |
| · Other | 58 | 1.8 | 0.2 | 1.0 | 2.0 | 2.7 |
| Middle Atlantic | 319 | 1.9 | 0.1 | 1.0 | 1.5 | 2.7 |
| · New Jersey | 63 | 1.3 | 0.2 | 0.5 | 1.0 | 2.0 |
| · New York | 119 | 1.9 | 0.2 | 1.0 | 1.5 | 2.5 |
| · Pennsylvania | 137 | 2.2 | 0.1 | 1.0 | 2.0 | 3.0 |
| East North Central | 300 | 2.4 | 0.1 | 1.0 | 2.0 | 3.0 |
| · Illinois | 97 | 2.3 | 0.2 | 1.0 | 2.0 | 2.8 |
| · Michigan | 56 | 2.1 | 0.2 | 1.1 | 2.0 | 2.8 |
| · Ohio | 69 | 2.4 | 0.2 | 1.0 | 2.0 | 3.1 |
| · Other | 78 | 2.9 | 0.3 | 1.0 | 2.0 | 3.7 |
| West North Central | 140 | 2.9 | 0.2 | 1.7 | 2.3 | 3.6 |
| South Atlantic | 402 | 2.8 | 0.1 | 1.0 | 2.5 | 4.0 |
| · Florida | 124 | 3.1 | 0.2 | 1.5 | 3.0 | 4.0 |
| · Other | 278 | 2.6 | 0.1 | 1.0 | 2.3 | 3.8 |
| East South Central | 148 | 3.0 | 0.2 | 1.7 | 2.5 | 4.0 |
| West South Central | 192 | 3.0 | 0.2 | 1.5 | 2.5 | 4.0 |
| · Texas | 124 | 3.0 | 0.3 | 1.5 | 2.5 | 3.6 |
| · Other | 68 | 3.0 | 0.2 | 1.5 | 2.5 | 4.0 |
| Mountain | 113 | 2.8 | 0.3 | 1.3 | 2.0 | 3.0 |
| Pacific | 318 | 2.3 | 0.1 | 1.0 | 2.0 | 3.0 |
| · California | 222 | 2.4 | 0.1 | 1.0 | 2.0 | 3.0 |
| · Other | 96 | 2.2 | 0.2 | 1.0 | 2.0 | 3.0 |
| *Practice Arrangement* | | | | | | |
| Solo Practice | 900 | 2.4 | 0.1 | 1.0 | 2.0 | 3.0 |
| Two Physician Practice | 259 | 2.6 | 0.1 | 1.5 | 2.0 | 3.5 |
| Three Physician Practice | 203 | 2.4 | 0.1 | 1.3 | 2.0 | 3.3 |
| 4-8 Physician Practice | 455 | 2.8 | 0.1 | 1.4 | 2.5 | 3.6 |
| Over 8 Physician Practice | 222 | 2.4 | 0.1 | 0.5 | 2.2 | 3.8 |

Source: 1995 Socioeconomic Monitoring System survey of nonfederal patient care physicians. See the beginning of this section, the introduction, and appendices for a discussion of the survey sample, definitions, and computation procedures. Statistics are not reported if the number of responses is less than 25.

Table 110. **Total Nonphysician Administrative, Secretarial, and Clerical Employees per Nonfederal Physician in Medical Practices (excluding non-self-employed physicians), 1994**

| | Number of Responses | Mean | Standard Error | 25th Percentile | Median | 75th Percentile |
|---|---|---|---|---|---|---|
| All Physicians | 2231 | 1.9 | 0.0 | 1.0 | 2.0 | 2.5 |
| *Specialty* | | | | | | |
| General/Family Practice | 263 | 2.3 | 0.1 | 1.3 | 2.0 | 3.0 |
| Internal Medicine | 429 | 1.9 | 0.1 | 1.0 | 2.0 | 2.3 |
| · General Internal Medicine | 272 | 1.9 | 0.1 | 1.0 | 1.7 | 2.4 |
| · Cardiovascular Diseases | 60 | 2.1 | 0.2 | 1.3 | 2.0 | 2.3 |
| · Other | 97 | 1.8 | 0.1 | 1.0 | 1.8 | 2.0 |
| Surgery | 628 | 2.3 | 0.1 | 1.3 | 2.0 | 3.0 |
| · General Surgery | 153 | 1.6 | 0.1 | 1.0 | 1.5 | 2.0 |
| · Otolaryngology | 61 | 2.9 | 0.3 | 1.5 | 2.5 | 3.5 |
| · Orthopedic Surgery | 129 | 3.1 | 0.1 | 2.0 | 2.8 | 4.0 |
| · Ophthalmology | 126 | 2.7 | 0.1 | 1.7 | 2.4 | 3.8 |
| · Urological Surgery | 73 | 2.2 | 0.1 | 1.7 | 2.0 | 2.9 |
| · Other | 86 | 2.2 | 0.2 | 1.0 | 2.0 | 2.9 |
| Pediatrics | 152 | 1.9 | 0.1 | 1.0 | 2.0 | 2.3 |
| Obstetrics/Gynecology | 162 | 2.3 | 0.1 | 1.1 | 2.0 | 3.0 |
| Radiology | 132 | 1.1 | 0.1 | 0.1 | 0.9 | 1.6 |
| Psychiatry | 154 | 0.9 | 0.1 | 0.0 | 0.8 | 1.0 |
| Anesthesiology | 112 | 0.3 | 0.0 | 0.0 | 0.1 | 0.4 |
| Pathology | 40 | 1.1 | 0.2 | 0.0 | 0.3 | 1.7 |
| Other Specialty | 159 | 1.9 | 0.1 | 0.5 | 1.8 | 3.0 |
| · Emergency Medicine | 36 | 0.3 | 0.1 | 0.0 | 0.0 | 0.2 |
| · Other | 123 | 2.3 | 0.2 | 1.0 | 2.0 | 3.0 |
| *Geographic Area* | | | | | | |
| New England | 121 | 1.9 | 0.1 | 1.0 | 2.0 | 2.7 |
| · Massachusetts | 56 | 1.9 | 0.2 | 1.0 | 2.0 | 2.3 |
| · Other | 65 | 1.9 | 0.1 | 1.0 | 2.0 | 3.0 |
| Middle Atlantic | 364 | 1.9 | 0.1 | 1.0 | 1.7 | 2.5 |
| · New Jersey | 70 | 1.9 | 0.2 | 1.0 | 2.0 | 2.5 |
| · New York | 139 | 1.8 | 0.1 | 1.0 | 1.5 | 2.6 |
| · Pennsylvania | 155 | 1.9 | 0.1 | 1.0 | 1.7 | 2.5 |
| East North Central | 325 | 1.9 | 0.1 | 1.0 | 1.6 | 2.5 |
| · Illinois | 106 | 1.7 | 0.1 | 1.0 | 1.0 | 2.3 |
| · Michigan | 57 | 2.4 | 0.3 | 1.0 | 2.0 | 3.0 |
| · Ohio | 76 | 1.8 | 0.2 | 1.0 | 1.7 | 2.0 |
| · Other | 86 | 2.0 | 0.2 | 1.0 | 1.4 | 2.0 |
| West North Central | 148 | 2.0 | 0.1 | 1.0 | 1.7 | 2.5 |
| South Atlantic | 426 | 2.0 | 0.1 | 1.0 | 2.0 | 3.0 |
| · Florida | 128 | 2.1 | 0.1 | 1.0 | 2.0 | 3.0 |
| · Other | 298 | 2.0 | 0.1 | 1.0 | 2.0 | 2.8 |
| East South Central | 156 | 1.9 | 0.1 | 1.0 | 2.0 | 2.6 |
| West South Central | 209 | 1.8 | 0.1 | 1.0 | 2.0 | 2.5 |
| · Texas | 138 | 1.8 | 0.1 | 1.0 | 1.8 | 2.5 |
| · Other | 71 | 1.9 | 0.1 | 1.0 | 2.0 | 2.5 |
| Mountain | 122 | 2.1 | 0.2 | 1.0 | 1.6 | 2.7 |
| Pacific | 360 | 1.9 | 0.1 | 1.0 | 1.8 | 2.5 |
| · California | 253 | 2.0 | 0.1 | 1.0 | 1.8 | 2.9 |
| · Other | 107 | 1.7 | 0.1 | 1.0 | 1.6 | 2.3 |
| *Practice Arrangement* | | | | | | |
| Solo Practice | 1014 | 2.1 | 0.1 | 1.0 | 2.0 | 3.0 |
| Two Physician Practice | 270 | 2.1 | 0.1 | 1.0 | 1.5 | 3.0 |
| Three Physician Practice | 213 | 1.8 | 0.1 | 1.0 | 1.7 | 2.3 |
| 4-8 Physician Practice | 494 | 1.8 | 0.1 | 1.0 | 1.6 | 2.5 |
| Over 8 Physician Practice | 240 | 1.3 | 0.1 | 0.2 | 0.8 | 2.0 |

Source: 1995 Socioeconomic Monitoring System survey of nonfederal patient care physicians. See the beginning of this section, the introduction, and appendices for a discussion of the survey sample, definitions, and computation procedures. Statistics are not reported if the number of responses is less than 25.

# Selected Statistics for Federal Physicians

Annual Weeks of Practice

Total Professional and Patient Care hours

Patient Visit Hours by Setting

Hours in Surgery

Total Patient Visits

Patient Visits by Setting

Surgical Procedures Including and Excluding Assists

Hospital Discharges and Lengths of Stay

Net Income after Expenses before Taxes

Percentage of Time Spent in Primary Care Activities

Appointment Delays and Waiting Time

## Selected Statistics for Federal Physicians

In 1995, a special survey was conducted with the purpose of learning more about the practice patterns of physicians employed by the federal government. Physicians employed by either the Department of Defense or the Department of Veterans Affairs were surveyed regarding their practice activities. Figures 37-39 and Tables 111-113 contain information on selected practice characteristics derived from this survey of federal physicians. Information presented in Figures 37-39 and Tables 111-113 can be categorized under the following headings:

- Weeks and hours of practice (Table 111);

- Physician service and hospital utilization (Table 112);

- Net income, time spent in primary care activities, appointment delays and waiting times (Table 113).

Because of sample size considerations only national level data for all federal physicians are presented in Tables 111-113. For this reason it was also not possible to show separate statistics for physicians employed by the Defense Department and physicians employed by the Department of Veterans Affairs.

When comparing results of the nonfederal and federal surveys it is important to note that federal physicians are probably most like employee nonfederal physicians. In addition, all of the federal physicians surveyed were hospital based. A discussion of the survey methodology, weighting techniques and definitions is presented in the appendices.

### Questionnaire Summary and Computations

Screener Questions

1. The American Medical Association Physician Masterfile indicates that (name physician's specialty) is the specialty from which you derive most of your medical income. Is that correct?

[IF YES GO TO QUESTION 2]

    a. What is your primary specialty?

2. During a typical week, do you provide direct patient care for 20 hours a week or more? Direct patient care includes seeing patients and performing surgery, as well as related patient services performed by anesthesiologists, radiologists, and pathologists.

3. Are you currently a full-time, salaried employee of a federal agency such as the U.S. Public Health Service, Veterans Administration, or military services? Full-time in this case is defined as 20 hours a week or more.

[IF YES GO TO QUESTION 4, IF NO END SURVEY]

4. Who are you currently employed by:

    a. U.S. Public Health Service;

    b. Veterans Administration; or

    c. A branch of the military?

[IF B OR C GO TO QUESTION 5, IF A END SURVEY]

*Physicians employed by the military or Veterans Administration*

5. Do you practice medicine other than for the federal government?

[If NO GO TO QUESTION 7]

6. What percentage of your time is spent working for the federal government?

7. Do you provide primary care services such as preventive care, routine physical exams or treatment of common ailments as part of your practice? Primary care services include routine comprehensive physical exams not related to a specific complaint or symptom, coordinating your patients general medical care and treating common ailments.

[IF NO GO TO QUESTION 9]

8. About what percentage of your time in your last complete week of practice was spent providing primary care services? Primary care services include routine comprehensive physical exams not related to a specific complaint or symptom, coordinating your patients general medical care and treating common ailments.

Responses to Questions 7 and 8 were used to calculate the information on the percentage of time spent in primary care activities (Table 113). Two figures are presented for this characteristic. The first figure shows the percentage of time spent in primary care activities for all physicians. The second figure shows the percentage of time spent in primary care activities only for physicians who engage in primary care activities.

9. In what year did you begin medical practice after completing your undergraduate and graduate medical training? A residency would be considered graduate medical training.

10. In what year did you start working at your current main medical practice? By current practice we mean the main medical practice you are in now.

**Weeks of Practice**

Weeks of practice in 1994 was ascertained from responses to the following survey questions:

11. During 1994, how many weeks of medical practice did you miss because of:

    a. illness or vacation, military service, professional conferences, or any other reason?

    b. Altogether then, you missed (Number) weeks of practice and practiced (Number) weeks?

*If physician began practice in 1994*

    c. Excluding the (Number) of weeks of practice you missed in 1994 due to illness or vacation, military service, professional conferences, or any other reason, for how many weeks did you practice in 1994.

Weeks worked in Table 111 was derived from responses to parts a and b of Question 11. If the physician began practicing in 1994, weeks worked was derived from part c of Question 11.

**Hours in Practice**

The time spent in practice by physicians was measured in weeks per year and hours per week. Two measures of total hours in practice can be distinguished. Total professional hours combines hours in patient care with those in other professional activities, such as teaching, research, and administration. Hours in patient care activities excludes other professional hours. Hours spent in various patient care activities were ascertained from the following question:

*All specialties except radiology, psychiatry, anesthesiology, and pathology*

12. During your most recent complete week of practice, how many hours did you spend (If necessary, at any point in the course of eliciting responses to these questions, the interviewer may give the following clarification: "By complete week of practice, we mean the most recent week in which you worked your normal work schedule. We want to exclude weeks when you were sick or on vacation."):

    a. in the office or in freestanding primary care or urgent care centers seeing patients? Include time spent in all offices if the practice includes multiple offices. Freestanding or urgent care centers may be owned by a hospital or chain.

    b. seeing patients in outpatient clinics or hospital emergency rooms?

    c. on house calls and with patients in nursing homes, convalescent homes or other extended care facilities?

    d. in the operating, labor or delivery room, including waiting time before surgery?

    e. making hospital rounds, including visits to newborn infants, but excluding hours spent on call when you are not actually working?

    f. having telephone conversations with patients or their families, consulting with other physicians and providing other services to patients such as interpreting lab tests and x-rays?

*Radiology*

    g. reading films, including time spent preparing reports on films read?

    h. personally performing radiodiagnostic procedures?

    i. personally providing radiotherapy to patients?

    j. supervising technicians and paraprofessionals?

    k. in consultation with other physicians?

*Psychiatry*

    l. seeing individual patients in the office and in all other settings?

    m. seeing nonfamily groups in the office and in all other settings? Nonfamily groups are sessions with unrelated individuals.

    n. seeing family groups in the office and in all other settings?

o. supervising psychiatric teams, consulting with other physicians, having telephone conversations with patients and their families, and providing other services to patients such as interpreting lab tests and EEG results?

*Anesthesiology*

p. personally anesthetizing patients, including waiting time before surgery?

q. supervising nurse anesthetists?

r. managing patients in intensive care units?

s. making pre-anesthesia visits, including histories and examinations as well as seeing patients on hospital rounds. Do not include time spent managing patients in intensive care units.

t. consulting with other physicians about their patients and providing any other services to patients,such as interpreting lab tests and x-rays?

*Pathology*

u. in consultations during surgery, including time spent interpreting frozen sections?

v. examining surgical specimens other than consultations during surgery?

w. doing autopsies, including time spent to complete the study and write the report?

x. personally performing nonsurgical laboratory procedures including time to write any reports?

y. supervising technicians and paraprofessionals?

*All physicians*

13. During your most recent complete week of practice, how many hours did you spend in administrative activities connected with your practice and other medical facilities, as well as any other professional activities that did not involve patient care? (These activities include managing your practice, medical staff functions, supervising residents and interns, teaching, lecturing, professional reading and writing, and research).

If the physician responded to all applicable parts of Question 12 and to Question 13, total professional hours was calculated from the sum of responses to these questions. For physicians not responding to all parts of Question 12 or to Question 13, an attempt was still made to obtain information on total professional hours by asking the following question:

14. During your most recent complete week of practice, how many hours altogether did you spend working at medical and administrative activities?

Hours in patient care activities was based on the sum of responses to Question 12. Hours of activity among radiologists, psychiatrists, anesthesiologists, and pathologists reflects responses to various parts of Question 12 applicable to these specialists. Total patient visit hours reflects the sum of responses to parts a, b, c, and e of Question 12. Responses to parts a (office), b (outpatient clinics and emergency rooms), c (surgery) and e (hospital) are presented individually in Table 111.

**Utilization of Physician Services and Hospital Utilization**

Physician service utilization refers to the quantity of services provided by physicians to their patients. The number of patient visits is a measure that captures a large proportion of overall physician utilization in most specialties. Surgical services account for another important share of physician services. While patient visit and surgical service measures cover a broad range of the practice activities of physicians, they do not reflect the full heterogeneity of physician services. For this reason, additional procedures are reported. Hospital utilization refers to the utilization of hospital resources by physicians. Two measures indicating the extent of hospital utilization are the number of patients discharged from the hospital and the average length of their hospital stays.

The questions from which physician service utilization information were derived are as follows:

15. During your last complete week of practice, how many:

a. patient visits did you personally have during the hours you spent in the office or in free-standing primary or urgent care centers? Please count as one visit every time you saw a patient. Do not include patient visits in outpatient clinics located in hospitals or in hospital emergency rooms.

b. of these visits were with new patients?

c. patient visits did you personally have during the hours you spent in hospital emergency rooms and outpatient clinics located in hospitals? Please count as one visit every time you saw a patient.

d. patient visits did you personally have during the hours you spent seeing patients in nursing homes, convalescent homes, and other extended care facilities? Please count as one visit every time you saw a patient.

e. operations and deliveries did you perform during the hours you spent in the operating, labor or delivery room? Do not include assists in this question.

f. assists did you perform?

g. inpatient visits did you make during the hours you spent on hospital rounds? Please count as one visit every time you saw a patient.

Total patient visits is based on the sum of responses to parts a, c, d, and g of Question 15. Responses to parts a (office), b (new patient office visit), c (outpatient clinics and emergency rooms), and g (hospital) are presented individually in Table 122. Surgical procedures including assists reflects the sum of responses to parts e and f of the same question.

Hospital utilization statistics are based on responses to the following questions:

16. During your most recent complete week of practice, how many patients did you personally discharge from the hospital?

17. For the patients you discharged from the hospital that week, what was the average length of stay in days in the hospital?

Physicians in anesthesiology, radiology, psychiatry, and pathology are not included in the information shown in Table 112.

## Physician Compensation

*Physicians employed by the Defense Department*

18a. During 1994, what was your own net income from medical practice to the nearest $1,000 after expenses but before taxes including any deferred compensation? Please include basic pay and incentive special pay. Do not include BAQ (basic allowance for quarters, BAS (basic allowance for subsistence), and moving allowances.

18b. To the nearest $1,000, how much did you receive in 1994 in BAQ, BAS, and moving allowances?

18c. Did you receive incentive special pay in 1994?

[IF NO GO TO QUESTION 20A]

18d. To the nearest $1,000 how much did you receive in 1994 in incentive special pay?

*Physicians employed by the Department of Veterans Affairs*

19a. During 1994, what was your own net income from medical practice to the nearest $1,000 after expenses but before taxes including any deferred compensation? Please include special pay and income from a performance award.

19b. Did you receive a performance award in 1994?

[IF NO GO TO QUESTION 20A]

19c. To the nearest $1,000, how much did you receive in 1994 for a performance award?

*Physicians employed by the Defense Department or the Veterans Administration*

20a. Were any contributions made for you into pension, profit sharing or other deferred compensation plans during 1994?

[IF NO GO TO QUESTION 21]

20b. How much was contributed for or by you during 1994, to the nearest $1,000?

20c. Did you include this amount (response to Question 20b) in your net income figure for 1994 (response to Question 18a or 19a)?

*Physicians who practice medicine outside of their federal practices*

Federal physicians who indicated that they had a practice outside of their employment with the federal government were also asked the following questions:

21a. To the nearest $1,000, how much did you make in 1994 for medical work performed outside of your federal practice?

21b. Did you include this amount in your net income response (response to Question 18a or 19a)?

Net income for physicians employed by the Department of Defense was obtained from Question 18a. Net income for these physicians includes incentive special pay and deferred compensation. However, it does not include BAQ (basic allowance for quarters), BAS (basic allowance for subsistence) and moving allowances. Net income for physicians employed by the Department of Veterans Affairs was obtained from Question 19a. Net income for these physicians includes special pay, deferred compensation and income from a performance award.

If physicians had deferred income (Question 20a) but did not include it in the response to Question 18a (or 19a) then the response to Question 20b was added to the response to Question 18a (or 19a).

Similarly, if physicians earned income from nonfederal practices and did not include that income in the response to Question 18a (or 19a) then the response to Question 21a was added to the response to Question 18a (or 19a).

## Appointment Delays and Waiting Times

Appointment delay and waiting time statistics were computed from responses to the following questions:

22. How many days does a new patient wishing to see you typically have to wait for an appointment?

23. How many minutes does a patient typically have to wait to see you after arriving for a scheduled appointment?

Information on net income after expenses but before taxes, appointment delays and waiting times is reported in Table 113.

**Figure 37. Mean and Median Total Professional Hours, Total Patient Care Hours, and Total Visit Hours per Week, for Federal Physicians, 1995**

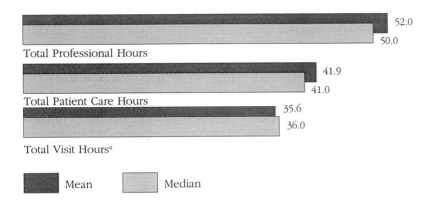

Total Professional Hours    52.0 / 50.0

Total Patient Care Hours    41.9 / 41.0

Total Visit Hours[a]    35.6 / 36.0

■ Mean     ▨ Median

a. Excludes radiologists, psychiatrists, anesthesiologists, and pathologists.

**Figure 38. Distribution of Mean Total Visit Hours per Week, for Federal Physicians, by Setting, 1995[a]**

**Hours[b]**

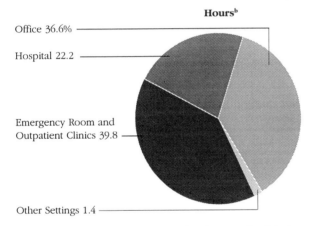

Office 36.6%

Hospital 22.2

Emergency Room and Outpatient Clinics 39.8

Other Settings 1.4

a. Excludes radiologists, psychiatrists, anesthesiologists, and pathologists.
b. Based on responses from physicians who provided hours worked information for every component of total visit hours.

**Figure 39. Distribution of Mean Total Visits per Week, for Federal Physicians, by Setting, 1995[a]**

**Visits[b]**

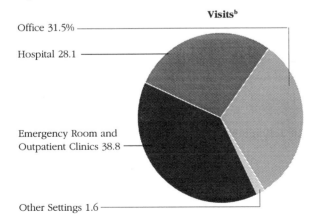

Office 31.5%

Hospital 28.1

Emergency Room and Outpatient Clinics 38.8

Other Settings 1.6

a. Excludes radiologists, psychiatrists, anesthesiologists, and pathologists.
b. Based on responses from physicians who provided visit information for every component of total visits.

## Table 111. **Weeks and Hours of Practice, for Federal Physicians, 1995**

| | Number of Responses | Mean | Standard Error | 25th Percentile | Median | 75th Percentile |
|---|---|---|---|---|---|---|
| Weeks of Practice 1994 | 114 | 47.9 | 0.2 | 46.0 | 48.0 | 49.0 |
| Hours in All Professional Activities per Week | 117 | 52.0 | 1.8 | 42.0 | 50.0 | 61.0 |
| Hours in Patient Care Activities per Week | 118 | 41.9 | 1.6 | 36.0 | 41.0 | 46.0 |
| Total Patient Visit Hours per Week | 71 | 35.6 | 1.8 | 30.0 | 36.0 | 40.0 |
| Office Hours per Week | 73 | 13.8 | 1.9 | 0.0 | 9.0 | 25.0 |
| Hours on Hospital Rounds per Week | 71 | 7.1 | 1.1 | 0.0 | 5.0 | 10.0 |
| Hours in Outpatient Clinics and Emergency Rooms per Week | 72 | 13.8 | 1.7 | 2.0 | 10.0 | 20.0 |
| Hours in Surgery per Week | 74 | 4.4 | 1.0 | 0.0 | 0.0 | 5.0 |

Source: 1995 Socioeconomic Monitoring System survey of federal patient care physicians employed by the Department of Defense or the Department of Veterans Affairs. See the beginning of this section, the introduction, and appendices for a discussion of the survey sample, definitions, and computation procedures. Statistics are not reported if the number of responses is less than 25.

## Table 112. **Physician Service and Hospital Utilization, for Federal Physicians, 1995**

| | Number of Responses | Mean | Standard Error | 25th Percentile | Median | 75th Percentile |
|---|---|---|---|---|---|---|
| Total Patient Visits per Week | 66 | 89.9 | 5.9 | 50.0 | 94.0 | 120.0 |
| Office Visits per Week | 70 | 26.4 | 4.5 | 0.0 | 12.0 | 50.0 |
| Office Visits with New Patients per Week | 29 | 15.2 | 3.4 | 5.0 | 7.0 | 20.0 |
| Visits on Hospital Rounds per Week | 69 | 27.5 | 4.7 | 0.0 | 15.0 | 45.0 |
| Visits in Outpatient Clinics and Emergency Rooms per Week | 69 | 32.9 | 4.9 | 1.0 | 24.0 | 50.0 |
| Surgical Procedures, Including Assists, per Week | 74 | 2.4 | 0.5 | 0.0 | 0.0 | 4.0 |
| Surgical Procedures, Excluding Assists, per Week | 74 | 2.0 | 0.5 | 0.0 | 0.0 | 3.0 |
| Patients Discharged from the Hospital per Week | 58 | 5.6 | 0.7 | 0.0 | 5.0 | 10.0 |
| Average Length of Stay of Patients Discharged from the Hospital | 42 | 10.5 | 3.3 | 2.0 | 4.0 | 7.0 |

Source: 1995 Socioeconomic Monitoring System survey of federal patient care physicians employed by the Department of Defense or the Department of Veterans Affairs. See the beginning of this section, the introduction, and appendices for a discussion of the survey sample, definitions, and computation procedures. Statistics are not reported if the number of responses is less than 25.

## Table 113. **Net Income, Time Spent in Primary Care Activities, Appointment Delays and Waiting Times, for Federal Physicians, 1995**

| | Number of Responses | Mean | Standard Error | 25th Percentile | Median | 75th Percentile |
|---|---|---|---|---|---|---|
| Net Income after Expenses before Taxes, 1994 | 89 | 105.7 | 3.6 | 85.0 | 110.0 | 130.0 |
| Percentage of Time Spent in Primary Care Activities, by Federal Physicians | 116 | 37.8 | 3.9 | 0.0 | 20.0 | 90.0 |
| Percentage of Time Spent in Primary Care Activities, by Federal Physicians Who Perform Primary Care Activities | 64 | 61.8 | 4.9 | 25.0 | 75.0 | 100.0 |
| Average Days Wait for an Appointment by New Patients | 70 | 11.9 | 2.1 | 1.0 | 7.0 | 14.0 |
| Average Minutes Waiting by Patients upon Arriving for a Scheduled Appointment | 77 | 21.1 | 2.4 | 10.0 | 15.0 | 30.0 |

Source: 1995 Socioeconomic Monitoring System survey of federal patient care physicians employed by the Department of Defense or the Department of Veterans Affairs. See the beginning of this section, the introduction, and appendices for a discussion of the survey sample, definitions, and computation procedures. Statistics are not reported if the number of responses is less than 25.

# Selected Statistics for Federal and Nonfederal Physicians

Annual Weeks of Practice

Total Professional and Patient Care hours

Patient Visit Hours by Setting

Hours in Surgery

Total Patient Visits

Patient Visits by Setting

Surgical Procedures Including and Excluding Assists

Hospital Discharges and Lengths of Stay

Net Income after Expenses before Taxes

Percentage of Time Spent in Primary Care Activities

Appointment Delays and Waiting Time

## Selected Statistics for Federal and Nonfederal Physicians

Responses to the SMS survey of nonfederal physicians and the survey of federal physicians were combined in an effort to better represent the practice activities of all patient care physicians. Only information asked of both federal and nonfederal physicians is included in Figures 40-43 and Tables 114-136. In each table, federal respondents are included with nonfederal respondents in the all physician category and the breakouts by specialty and region. However, because they are employee physicians, federal respondents are not included in the self-employed category. Because they include only self-employed (and therefore only nonfederal) physicians, the practice size breakouts are not shown in Tables 114-136. Similarly, because only self-employed physicians are asked practice expense questions, these questions were not asked of any federal physicians. Questions about Medicare patients, third-party payers, fees, nonphysician employees and size of practice were also deemed not applicable to federal physician practices.

Information highlighted in the tables of this section of *Physician Marketplace Statistics* is listed below. The SMS survey included 4,026 responses from physicians and the federal survey included 119 responses. The number of federal physicians that responded to the questions that were used to derive the information in each table is shown in parentheses.

- Weeks worked per year (114).

- Hours in professional activities per week (117).

- Hours in patient care activities per week (118).

- Total patient visit hours per week (71).

- Office hours per week (73).

- Hours on hospital rounds per week (71).

- Hours in outpatient clinics and emergency rooms per week (72).

- Hours in surgery per week (74).

- Total patient visits per week (66).

- Office visits per week (70).

- Office visits with new patients per week (29).

- Visits on hospital rounds per week (69).

- Visits in outpatient clinics and emergency rooms per week (69).

- Surgical procedures, including assists, per week (74).

- Surgical procedures, excluding assists, per week (74).

- Patients discharged from the hospital per week (58).

- Average length of stay of patients discharged from the hospital (42).

- Net income after expenses before taxes (89).

- Percentage of time spent in primary care activities (116).

- Percentage of time spent in primary care activities by physicians who perform primary care activities (64).

- Average days wait for an appointment by new patients (70).

- Average minutes waiting by patients upon arriving for a scheduled appointment (77).

Questions asked of federal respondents were the same or similar to those asked of nonfederal survey respondents. The SMS survey of nonfederal physicians is summarized throughout the section of this volume that pertains only to nonfederal physicians. A summary of the survey of federal physicians is found in the section: Selected Statistics for Federal Physicians.

Figures 40-43 and Tables 131-132 present information on physician net income, after expenses but before taxes. Every effort was made to ensure that only income from physicians' medical practices (including deferred income) was included in the income figures. Employee nonfederal physicians were asked not to include noncash fringe benefits in their net income. Federal physicians employed by the Department of Defense were asked not to include basic allowance for room, board and moving expenses.

When making comparisons between tables that only include nonfederal physicians and those that include federal and nonfederal physicians several points need to be considered:

- Both the federal and nonfederal surveys were designed to obtain a 1% sample of the population. However, federal physicians comprise only about 3% of patient care physicians, and the sample does not include physicians employed by the U.S. Public Health Service. Therefore, the impact of including federal physicians with nonfederal physicians should be small.

- The impact that federal respondents will have on the combined survey results, while most likely small, will depend upon the extent that federal and nonfederal physicians differ with respect to their practice characteristics.

- Federal physicians are most like nonfederal physician employees in terms of their employment status. Therefore, it would be most appropriate to compare the employee physician category of the nonfederal tables with the employee category of the federal and nonfederal tables. The tables showing net income for employee physicians will allow such comparisons by specialty and region.

Corrections for survey nonresponse were required for both the federal and nonfederal survey samples. A second weight was also applied when combining the data from the federal and nonfederal physicians. This weight ensured that the ratio of federal to nonfederal physicians in the sample was approximately the same as the ratio of federal to nonfederal physicians in the population. The weighting techniques used to correct for nonresponse bias are discussed in Appendix B.

Figure 40. **Median Net Income after Expenses before Taxes per Physician, for Federal and Nonfederal Physicians, for Selected Specialties, 1994**

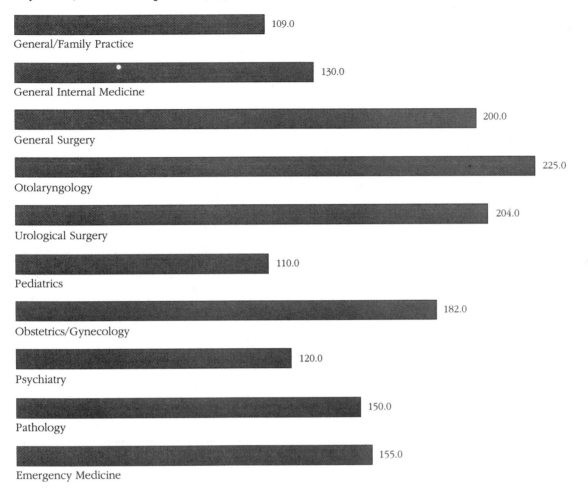

General/Family Practice — 109.0

General Internal Medicine — 130.0

General Surgery — 200.0

Otolaryngology — 225.0

Urological Surgery — 204.0

Pediatrics — 110.0

Obstetrics/Gynecology — 182.0

Psychiatry — 120.0

Pathology — 150.0

Emergency Medicine — 155.0

Figure 41. **Median Net Income after Expenses before Taxes per Physician, for Federal and Nonfederal Physicians, by Census Division, 1994**

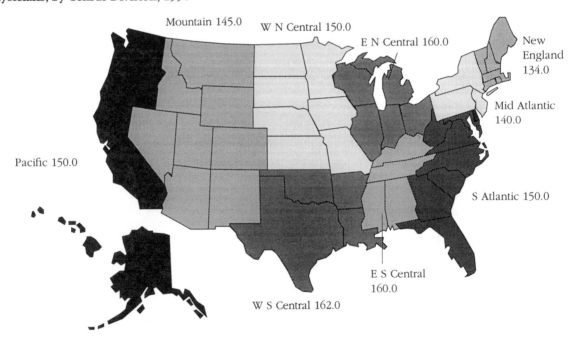

Mountain 145.0  W N Central 150.0  E N Central 160.0  New England 134.0

Mid Atlantic 140.0

Pacific 150.0

S Atlantic 150.0

E S Central 160.0

W S Central 162.0

Figure 42. **Median Net Income after Expenses before Taxes per Employee Physician, for Federal and Nonfederal Physicians, for Selected Specialties, 1994**

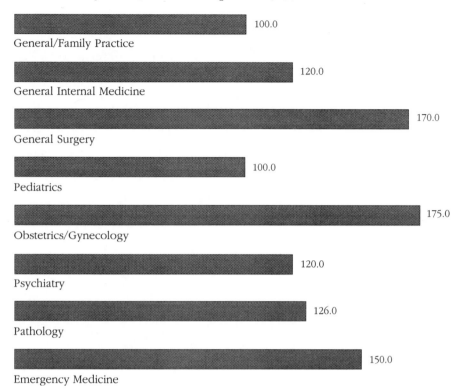

General/Family Practice   100.0

General Internal Medicine   120.0

General Surgery   170.0

Pediatrics   100.0

Obstetrics/Gynecology   175.0

Psychiatry   120.0

Pathology   126.0

Emergency Medicine   150.0

Figure 43. **Median Net Income after Expenses before Taxes per Employee Physician, for Federal and Nonfederal Physicians, by Census Division, 1994**

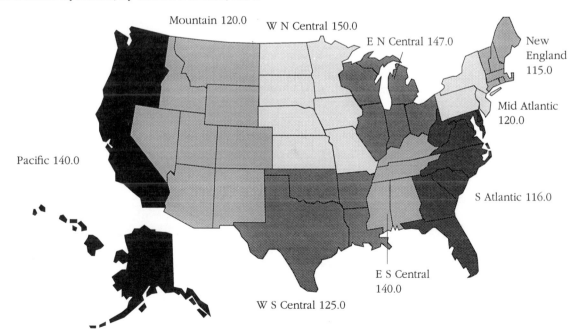

Mountain 120.0

W N Central 150.0

E N Central 147.0

New England 115.0

Mid Atlantic 120.0

Pacific 140.0

S Atlantic 116.0

E S Central 140.0

W S Central 125.0

## Table 114. **Weeks of Practice for Federal and Nonfederal Physicians, 1994**

| | Number of Responses | Mean | Standard Error | 25th Percentile | Median | 75th Percentile |
|---|---|---|---|---|---|---|
| All Physicians | 4011 | 47.3 | 0.1 | 46.0 | 48.0 | 49.0 |
| *Specialty* | | | | | | |
| General/Family Practice | 507 | 47.3 | 0.2 | 47.0 | 48.0 | 50.0 |
| Internal Medicine | 779 | 47.7 | 0.2 | 47.0 | 48.0 | 49.0 |
| · General Internal Medicine | 534 | 47.7 | 0.2 | 47.0 | 48.0 | 49.0 |
| · Cardiovascular Diseases | 101 | 47.1 | 0.4 | 46.0 | 48.0 | 49.0 |
| · Other | 144 | 48.1 | 0.2 | 47.0 | 48.0 | 50.0 |
| Surgery | 875 | 47.4 | 0.1 | 46.0 | 48.0 | 49.0 |
| · General Surgery | 222 | 47.5 | 0.2 | 46.0 | 48.0 | 50.0 |
| · Otolaryngology | 75 | 47.4 | 0.5 | 46.0 | 48.0 | 49.0 |
| · Orthopedic Surgery | 185 | 46.8 | 0.3 | 46.0 | 48.0 | 49.0 |
| · Ophthalmology | 182 | 47.6 | 0.2 | 46.0 | 48.0 | 49.0 |
| · Urological Surgery | 96 | 47.8 | 0.2 | 46.0 | 48.0 | 49.0 |
| · Other | 115 | 47.7 | 0.4 | 47.0 | 48.0 | 50.0 |
| Pediatrics | 307 | 47.7 | 0.2 | 47.0 | 48.0 | 50.0 |
| Obstetrics/Gynecology | 238 | 47.1 | 0.3 | 46.0 | 48.0 | 49.0 |
| Radiology | 288 | 44.4 | 0.3 | 43.0 | 46.0 | 48.0 |
| Psychiatry | 286 | 47.8 | 0.1 | 47.0 | 48.0 | 49.0 |
| Anesthesiology | 229 | 45.5 | 0.3 | 44.0 | 46.0 | 48.0 |
| Pathology | 127 | 47.3 | 0.3 | 46.0 | 48.0 | 49.0 |
| Other Specialty | 375 | 47.7 | 0.2 | 47.0 | 48.0 | 50.0 |
| · Emergency Medicine | 134 | 48.1 | 0.5 | 48.0 | 49.0 | 51.0 |
| · Other | 241 | 47.6 | 0.3 | 47.0 | 48.0 | 49.0 |
| *Geographic Area* | | | | | | |
| New England | 254 | 47.2 | 0.3 | 47.0 | 48.0 | 49.0 |
| · Massachusetts | 118 | 47.5 | 0.4 | 47.0 | 48.0 | 49.0 |
| · Other | 136 | 47.0 | 0.4 | 46.0 | 48.0 | 49.0 |
| Middle Atlantic | 643 | 46.8 | 0.2 | 46.0 | 48.0 | 49.0 |
| · New Jersey | 110 | 47.3 | 0.5 | 46.0 | 48.0 | 50.0 |
| · New York | 265 | 47.0 | 0.3 | 46.0 | 48.0 | 49.0 |
| · Pennsylvania | 268 | 46.3 | 0.4 | 46.0 | 48.0 | 49.0 |
| East North Central | 593 | 46.7 | 0.2 | 46.0 | 48.0 | 49.0 |
| · Illinois | 187 | 47.4 | 0.3 | 46.0 | 48.0 | 49.0 |
| · Michigan | 111 | 46.4 | 0.6 | 46.0 | 48.0 | 49.0 |
| · Ohio | 130 | 46.5 | 0.5 | 46.0 | 48.0 | 49.0 |
| · Other | 165 | 46.2 | 0.3 | 45.0 | 47.0 | 49.0 |
| West North Central | 291 | 46.8 | 0.3 | 46.0 | 48.0 | 49.0 |
| South Atlantic | 715 | 47.5 | 0.2 | 47.0 | 48.0 | 50.0 |
| · Florida | 205 | 47.7 | 0.2 | 46.0 | 48.0 | 50.0 |
| · Other | 510 | 47.5 | 0.2 | 47.0 | 48.0 | 49.0 |
| East South Central | 240 | 47.9 | 0.2 | 47.0 | 48.0 | 50.0 |
| West South Central | 371 | 48.1 | 0.2 | 48.0 | 49.0 | 50.0 |
| · Texas | 246 | 48.4 | 0.2 | 48.0 | 49.0 | 50.0 |
| · Other | 125 | 47.5 | 0.4 | 47.0 | 48.0 | 50.0 |
| Mountain | 232 | 46.9 | 0.4 | 46.0 | 48.0 | 49.0 |
| Pacific | 672 | 47.5 | 0.1 | 46.0 | 48.0 | 49.0 |
| · California | 469 | 47.8 | 0.1 | 46.0 | 48.0 | 50.0 |
| · Other | 203 | 46.7 | 0.3 | 46.0 | 47.0 | 49.0 |
| *Practice Arrangement* | | | | | | |
| Self-Employed | 2223 | 47.7 | 0.1 | 46.0 | 48.0 | 50.0 |
| Employee | 1554 | 46.6 | 0.1 | 46.0 | 48.0 | 49.0 |
| Independent Contractor | 234 | 48.0 | 0.2 | 47.0 | 49.0 | 50.0 |

Source: 1995 Socioeconomic Monitoring System surveys of nonfederal patient care physicians and federal patient care physicians employed by the Department of Defense or the Department of Veterans Affairs. See the beginning of this section, the introduction, and appendices for a discussion of the survey sample, definitions, and computation procedures. Statistics are not reported if the number of responses is less than 25.

Table 115. **Hours in Professional Activities per Week, for Federal and Nonfederal Physicians, 1995**

| | Number of Responses | Mean | Standard Error | 25th Percentile | Median | 75th Percentile |
|---|---|---|---|---|---|---|
| All Physicians | 4081 | 56.6 | 0.3 | 46.0 | 55.0 | 66.0 |
| *Specialty* | | | | | | |
| General/Family Practice | 518 | 57.1 | 0.7 | 47.0 | 55.0 | 66.0 |
| Internal Medicine | 796 | 59.5 | 0.6 | 50.0 | 60.0 | 69.0 |
| · General Internal Medicine | 546 | 58.6 | 0.8 | 49.0 | 58.0 | 68.0 |
| · Cardiovascular Diseases | 105 | 60.3 | 1.8 | 51.0 | 60.0 | 70.0 |
| · Other | 145 | 62.5 | 1.3 | 54.0 | 60.0 | 72.0 |
| Surgery | 899 | 58.9 | 0.6 | 48.0 | 59.0 | 68.0 |
| · General Surgery | 229 | 63.0 | 1.3 | 53.0 | 62.0 | 71.0 |
| · Otolaryngology | 77 | 57.9 | 1.5 | 49.0 | 56.0 | 66.0 |
| · Orthopedic Surgery | 189 | 57.9 | 1.1 | 49.0 | 55.0 | 66.0 |
| · Ophthalmology | 187 | 52.1 | 0.9 | 43.0 | 51.0 | 61.0 |
| · Urological Surgery | 98 | 62.7 | 1.6 | 51.0 | 60.0 | 72.0 |
| · Other | 119 | 59.0 | 1.9 | 48.0 | 60.0 | 72.0 |
| Pediatrics | 312 | 56.5 | 0.9 | 45.0 | 55.0 | 65.0 |
| Obstetrics/Gynecology | 246 | 59.3 | 1.2 | 49.0 | 57.0 | 70.0 |
| Radiology | 286 | 51.3 | 0.9 | 45.0 | 50.0 | 60.0 |
| Psychiatry | 288 | 49.7 | 0.9 | 40.0 | 49.0 | 59.0 |
| Anesthesiology | 227 | 55.4 | 1.2 | 46.0 | 56.0 | 65.0 |
| Pathology | 129 | 46.7 | 1.2 | 40.0 | 48.0 | 56.0 |
| Other Specialty | 380 | 53.0 | 0.8 | 43.0 | 50.0 | 61.0 |
| · Emergency Medicine | 136 | 51.8 | 1.2 | 42.0 | 49.0 | 59.0 |
| · Other | 244 | 53.6 | 1.0 | 44.0 | 52.0 | 61.0 |
| *Geographic Area* | | | | | | |
| New England | 261 | 53.8 | 1.1 | 45.0 | 52.0 | 65.0 |
| · Massachusetts | 121 | 54.2 | 1.4 | 45.0 | 53.0 | 65.0 |
| · Other | 140 | 53.4 | 1.5 | 45.0 | 52.0 | 63.0 |
| Middle Atlantic | 654 | 55.2 | 0.7 | 45.0 | 55.0 | 66.0 |
| · New Jersey | 114 | 51.4 | 1.8 | 40.0 | 50.0 | 60.0 |
| · New York | 267 | 55.2 | 1.1 | 44.0 | 56.0 | 67.0 |
| · Pennsylvania | 273 | 57.4 | 0.9 | 47.0 | 57.0 | 67.0 |
| East North Central | 605 | 56.3 | 0.7 | 47.0 | 55.0 | 65.0 |
| · Illinois | 187 | 56.0 | 1.3 | 45.0 | 54.0 | 65.0 |
| · Michigan | 115 | 56.7 | 1.2 | 50.0 | 55.0 | 63.0 |
| · Ohio | 132 | 57.9 | 1.4 | 50.0 | 55.0 | 65.0 |
| · Other | 171 | 55.2 | 1.4 | 44.0 | 55.0 | 66.0 |
| West North Central | 294 | 58.1 | 1.0 | 47.0 | 56.0 | 66.0 |
| South Atlantic | 744 | 58.3 | 0.6 | 47.0 | 58.0 | 66.0 |
| · Florida | 211 | 59.4 | 1.3 | 48.0 | 60.0 | 67.0 |
| · Other | 533 | 57.8 | 0.7 | 47.0 | 56.0 | 66.0 |
| East South Central | 240 | 57.3 | 1.1 | 47.0 | 56.0 | 70.0 |
| West South Central | 372 | 59.0 | 0.8 | 49.0 | 57.0 | 67.0 |
| · Texas | 247 | 59.1 | 1.0 | 50.0 | 58.0 | 66.0 |
| · Other | 125 | 58.9 | 1.5 | 47.0 | 55.0 | 67.0 |
| Mountain | 234 | 56.0 | 1.0 | 46.0 | 55.0 | 64.0 |
| Pacific | 677 | 55.6 | 0.7 | 45.0 | 54.0 | 65.0 |
| · California | 471 | 56.5 | 0.8 | 45.0 | 54.0 | 67.0 |
| · Other | 206 | 53.1 | 1.0 | 44.0 | 52.0 | 60.0 |
| *Practice Arrangement* | | | | | | |
| Self-Employed | 2263 | 59.0 | 0.4 | 49.0 | 59.0 | 68.0 |
| Employee | 1581 | 54.1 | 0.4 | 44.0 | 53.0 | 63.0 |
| Independent Contractor | 237 | 52.6 | 1.1 | 44.0 | 53.0 | 61.0 |

Source: 1995 Socioeconomic Monitoring System surveys of nonfederal patient care physicians and federal patient care physicians employed by the Department of Defense or the Department of Veterans Affairs. See the beginning of this section, the introduction, and appendices for a discussion of the survey sample, definitions, and computation procedures. Statistics are not reported if the number of responses is less than 25.

Table 116. **Hours in Patient Care Activities per Week, for Federal and Nonfederal Physicians, 1995**

| | Number of Responses | Mean | Standard Error | 25th Percentile | Median | 75th Percentile |
|---|---|---|---|---|---|---|
| All Physicians | 4084 | 51.0 | 0.3 | 40.0 | 50.0 | 60.0 |
| *Specialty* | | | | | | |
| General/Family Practice | 518 | 52.6 | 0.7 | 43.0 | 51.0 | 60.0 |
| Internal Medicine | 796 | 53.5 | 0.6 | 42.0 | 54.0 | 63.0 |
| · General Internal Medicine | 546 | 52.5 | 0.8 | 41.0 | 52.0 | 62.0 |
| · Cardiovascular Diseases | 105 | 54.4 | 1.8 | 45.0 | 57.0 | 65.0 |
| · Other | 145 | 56.6 | 1.3 | 48.0 | 56.0 | 65.0 |
| Surgery | 899 | 53.2 | 0.5 | 43.0 | 52.0 | 62.0 |
| · General Surgery | 229 | 57.0 | 1.2 | 47.0 | 57.0 | 66.0 |
| · Otolaryngology | 77 | 51.9 | 1.3 | 44.0 | 50.0 | 60.0 |
| · Orthopedic Surgery | 189 | 52.6 | 1.0 | 42.0 | 51.0 | 61.0 |
| · Ophthalmology | 187 | 46.5 | 0.8 | 39.0 | 46.0 | 53.0 |
| · Urological Surgery | 98 | 57.4 | 1.5 | 47.0 | 55.0 | 67.0 |
| · Other | 119 | 53.0 | 1.7 | 42.0 | 55.0 | 65.0 |
| Pediatrics | 312 | 50.4 | 0.9 | 40.0 | 48.0 | 60.0 |
| Obstetrics/Gynecology | 246 | 54.6 | 1.1 | 44.0 | 54.0 | 65.0 |
| Radiology | 288 | 49.0 | 0.9 | 41.0 | 49.0 | 55.0 |
| Psychiatry | 289 | 43.6 | 0.9 | 34.0 | 42.0 | 52.0 |
| Anesthesiology | 227 | 50.4 | 1.2 | 40.0 | 52.0 | 60.0 |
| Pathology | 129 | 40.4 | 1.0 | 33.0 | 41.0 | 50.0 |
| Other Specialty | 380 | 45.7 | 0.8 | 37.0 | 45.0 | 53.0 |
| · Emergency Medicine | 136 | 44.7 | 1.4 | 36.0 | 41.0 | 52.0 |
| · Other | 244 | 46.3 | 0.9 | 37.0 | 46.0 | 54.0 |
| *Geographic Area* | | | | | | |
| New England | 261 | 47.0 | 1.0 | 36.0 | 47.0 | 57.0 |
| · Massachusetts | 121 | 46.7 | 1.4 | 36.0 | 46.0 | 55.0 |
| · Other | 140 | 47.3 | 1.5 | 37.0 | 47.0 | 59.0 |
| Middle Atlantic | 653 | 49.9 | 0.6 | 40.0 | 50.0 | 60.0 |
| · New Jersey | 114 | 47.1 | 1.6 | 38.0 | 47.0 | 58.0 |
| · New York | 266 | 49.1 | 1.0 | 38.0 | 48.0 | 60.0 |
| · Pennsylvania | 273 | 52.4 | 0.8 | 43.0 | 50.0 | 60.0 |
| East North Central | 608 | 50.6 | 0.7 | 40.0 | 50.0 | 60.0 |
| · Illinois | 188 | 50.3 | 1.3 | 40.0 | 51.0 | 61.0 |
| · Michigan | 116 | 50.2 | 1.2 | 41.0 | 50.0 | 58.0 |
| · Ohio | 132 | 51.0 | 1.4 | 41.0 | 50.0 | 60.0 |
| · Other | 172 | 51.1 | 1.3 | 40.0 | 52.0 | 61.0 |
| West North Central | 294 | 52.3 | 1.0 | 41.0 | 50.0 | 60.0 |
| South Atlantic | 744 | 52.9 | 0.6 | 42.0 | 52.0 | 62.0 |
| · Florida | 212 | 54.2 | 1.2 | 44.0 | 54.0 | 62.0 |
| · Other | 532 | 52.3 | 0.7 | 42.0 | 51.0 | 62.0 |
| East South Central | 239 | 52.8 | 1.0 | 42.0 | 52.0 | 64.0 |
| West South Central | 372 | 53.8 | 0.8 | 44.0 | 53.0 | 62.0 |
| · Texas | 247 | 53.5 | 1.0 | 44.0 | 53.0 | 61.0 |
| · Other | 125 | 54.5 | 1.4 | 44.0 | 52.0 | 63.0 |
| Mountain | 236 | 50.4 | 1.0 | 40.0 | 50.0 | 60.0 |
| Pacific | 677 | 49.8 | 0.6 | 40.0 | 49.0 | 60.0 |
| · California | 471 | 50.5 | 0.8 | 41.0 | 50.0 | 60.0 |
| · Other | 206 | 47.8 | 1.0 | 38.0 | 48.0 | 56.0 |
| *Practice Arrangement* | | | | | | |
| Self-Employed | 2264 | 54.0 | 0.3 | 44.0 | 53.0 | 63.0 |
| Employee | 1583 | 47.4 | 0.4 | 37.0 | 46.0 | 56.0 |
| Independent Contractor | 237 | 48.7 | 1.1 | 40.0 | 50.0 | 60.0 |

Source: 1995 Socioeconomic Monitoring System surveys of nonfederal patient care physicians and federal patient care physicians employed by the Department of Defense or the Department of Veterans Affairs. See the beginning of this section, the introduction, and appendices for a discussion of the survey sample, definitions, and computation procedures. Statistics are not reported if the number of responses is less than 25.

Table 117. **Total Patient Visit Hours per Week, for Federal and Nonfederal Physicians (excluding Physicians in Radiology, Psychiatry, Anesthesiology, and Pathology), 1995**

| | Number of Responses | Mean | Standard Error | 25th Percentile | Median | 75th Percentile |
|---|---|---|---|---|---|---|
| All Physicians | 3116 | 41.2 | 0.3 | 31.0 | 40.0 | 50.0 |
| *Specialty* | | | | | | |
| General/Family Practice | 514 | 46.6 | 0.6 | 39.0 | 45.0 | 55.0 |
| Internal Medicine | 787 | 44.8 | 0.6 | 35.0 | 45.0 | 55.0 |
| · General Internal Medicine | 540 | 45.8 | 0.7 | 36.0 | 45.0 | 55.0 |
| · Cardiovascular Diseases | 103 | 41.0 | 1.5 | 27.0 | 40.0 | 52.0 |
| · Other | 144 | 43.8 | 1.3 | 35.0 | 42.0 | 52.0 |
| Surgery | 886 | 33.9 | 0.4 | 25.0 | 33.0 | 40.0 |
| · General Surgery | 222 | 31.3 | 0.9 | 23.0 | 30.0 | 39.0 |
| · Otolaryngology | 77 | 34.6 | 1.2 | 26.0 | 34.0 | 41.0 |
| · Orthopedic Surgery | 185 | 33.8 | 0.8 | 26.0 | 33.0 | 40.0 |
| · Ophthalmology | 187 | 37.5 | 0.7 | 30.0 | 37.0 | 43.0 |
| · Urological Surgery | 98 | 38.4 | 1.4 | 29.0 | 35.0 | 48.0 |
| · Other | 117 | 30.3 | 1.2 | 20.0 | 27.0 | 37.0 |
| Pediatrics | 309 | 43.5 | 0.8 | 35.0 | 42.0 | 52.0 |
| Obstetrics/Gynecology | 243 | 36.6 | 0.8 | 30.0 | 36.0 | 44.0 |
| Other Specialty | 377 | 42.2 | 1.1 | 33.0 | 40.0 | 48.0 |
| · Emergency Medicine | 136 | 41.9 | 1.3 | 34.0 | 40.0 | 49.0 |
| · Other | 241 | 42.4 | 1.5 | 33.0 | 40.0 | 48.0 |
| *Geographic Area* | | | | | | |
| New England | 195 | 38.5 | 1.0 | 30.0 | 40.0 | 47.0 |
| · Massachusetts | 90 | 37.9 | 1.4 | 28.0 | 40.0 | 46.0 |
| · Other | 105 | 39.1 | 1.3 | 30.0 | 40.0 | 48.0 |
| Middle Atlantic | 488 | 40.0 | 0.6 | 30.0 | 40.0 | 49.0 |
| · New Jersey | 89 | 38.2 | 1.6 | 27.0 | 40.0 | 46.0 |
| · New York | 195 | 39.0 | 1.0 | 29.0 | 38.0 | 49.0 |
| · Pennsylvania | 204 | 42.1 | 1.0 | 34.0 | 40.0 | 51.0 |
| East North Central | 463 | 40.4 | 0.7 | 28.0 | 39.0 | 50.0 |
| · Illinois | 154 | 40.0 | 1.4 | 27.0 | 38.0 | 50.0 |
| · Michigan | 87 | 37.5 | 1.6 | 25.0 | 36.0 | 48.0 |
| · Ohio | 103 | 42.2 | 1.6 | 31.0 | 40.0 | 53.0 |
| · Other | 119 | 41.4 | 1.3 | 30.0 | 40.0 | 51.0 |
| West North Central | 231 | 41.3 | 1.0 | 31.0 | 40.0 | 50.0 |
| South Atlantic | 577 | 42.0 | 0.6 | 32.0 | 40.0 | 51.0 |
| · Florida | 163 | 41.8 | 1.3 | 30.0 | 40.0 | 52.0 |
| · Other | 414 | 42.2 | 0.7 | 33.0 | 40.0 | 50.0 |
| East South Central | 186 | 43.7 | 1.1 | 32.0 | 43.0 | 55.0 |
| West South Central | 286 | 43.6 | 0.8 | 34.0 | 42.0 | 52.0 |
| · Texas | 192 | 43.7 | 1.0 | 34.0 | 41.0 | 52.0 |
| · Other | 94 | 43.2 | 1.3 | 35.0 | 42.0 | 52.0 |
| Mountain | 183 | 40.9 | 1.0 | 32.0 | 40.0 | 50.0 |
| Pacific | 507 | 41.2 | 0.8 | 32.0 | 40.0 | 48.0 |
| · California | 352 | 40.6 | 0.7 | 33.0 | 40.0 | 50.0 |
| · Other | 155 | 42.8 | 2.2 | 30.0 | 40.0 | 45.0 |
| *Practice Arrangement* | | | | | | |
| Self-Employed | 1793 | 42.8 | 0.4 | 33.0 | 41.0 | 51.0 |
| Employee | 1177 | 38.6 | 0.4 | 30.0 | 38.0 | 47.0 |
| Independent Contractor | 146 | 43.5 | 1.4 | 34.0 | 41.0 | 53.0 |

Source: 1995 Socioeconomic Monitoring System surveys of nonfederal patient care physicians and federal patient care physicians employed by the Department of Defense or the Department of Veterans Affairs. See the beginning of this section, the introduction, and appendices for a discussion of the survey sample, definitions, and computation procedures. Statistics are not reported if the number of responses is less than 25.

Table 118. **Office Hours per Week, for Federal and Nonfederal Physicians (excluding Physicians in Radiology, Psychiatry, Anesthesiology, and Pathology), 1995**

| | Number of Responses | Mean | Standard Error | 25th Percentile | Median | 75th Percentile |
|---|---|---|---|---|---|---|
| All Physicians | 3145 | 26.2 | 0.3 | 16.0 | 28.0 | 36.0 |
| *Specialty* | | | | | | |
| General/Family Practice | 518 | 34.4 | 0.6 | 30.0 | 36.0 | 40.0 |
| Internal Medicine | 793 | 25.7 | 0.5 | 16.0 | 28.0 | 36.0 |
| · General Internal Medicine | 544 | 27.6 | 0.7 | 20.0 | 30.0 | 40.0 |
| · Cardiovascular Diseases | 104 | 19.0 | 1.2 | 10.0 | 20.0 | 25.0 |
| · Other | 145 | 22.8 | 1.1 | 15.0 | 20.0 | 30.0 |
| Surgery | 898 | 22.7 | 0.4 | 15.0 | 20.0 | 30.0 |
| · General Surgery | 228 | 14.7 | 0.6 | 8.0 | 14.0 | 20.0 |
| · Otolaryngology | 77 | 27.6 | 1.2 | 20.0 | 27.0 | 35.0 |
| · Orthopedic Surgery | 189 | 22.7 | 0.7 | 18.0 | 22.0 | 27.0 |
| · Ophthalmology | 187 | 34.4 | 0.7 | 30.0 | 35.0 | 40.0 |
| · Urological Surgery | 98 | 25.1 | 1.1 | 20.0 | 25.0 | 30.0 |
| · Other | 119 | 18.4 | 1.0 | 10.0 | 18.0 | 25.0 |
| Pediatrics | 311 | 31.1 | 0.9 | 21.0 | 35.0 | 40.0 |
| Obstetrics/Gynecology | 246 | 28.2 | 0.8 | 20.0 | 30.0 | 35.0 |
| Other Specialty | 379 | 18.5 | 1.0 | 0.0 | 15.0 | 35.0 |
| · Emergency Medicine | 136 | 4.3 | 1.1 | 0.0 | 0.0 | 0.0 |
| · Other | 243 | 26.2 | 1.2 | 12.0 | 30.0 | 40.0 |
| *Geographic Area* | | | | | | |
| New England | 196 | 24.7 | 1.1 | 12.0 | 25.0 | 35.0 |
| · Massachusetts | 90 | 23.5 | 1.6 | 12.0 | 25.0 | 35.0 |
| · Other | 106 | 25.8 | 1.5 | 14.0 | 27.0 | 36.0 |
| Middle Atlantic | 489 | 24.8 | 0.7 | 15.0 | 25.0 | 35.0 |
| · New Jersey | 90 | 25.4 | 1.6 | 20.0 | 25.0 | 32.0 |
| · New York | 195 | 23.3 | 1.1 | 12.0 | 25.0 | 35.0 |
| · Pennsylvania | 204 | 26.2 | 1.0 | 15.0 | 26.0 | 38.0 |
| East North Central | 470 | 25.1 | 0.7 | 15.0 | 26.0 | 36.0 |
| · Illinois | 156 | 23.4 | 1.3 | 12.0 | 24.0 | 35.0 |
| · Michigan | 88 | 24.9 | 1.7 | 16.0 | 25.0 | 35.0 |
| · Ohio | 104 | 26.3 | 1.5 | 15.0 | 30.0 | 38.0 |
| · Other | 122 | 26.6 | 1.2 | 18.0 | 30.0 | 38.0 |
| West North Central | 234 | 27.7 | 1.0 | 20.0 | 29.0 | 36.0 |
| South Atlantic | 583 | 25.9 | 0.7 | 15.0 | 28.0 | 37.0 |
| · Florida | 164 | 24.2 | 1.3 | 12.0 | 25.0 | 38.0 |
| · Other | 419 | 26.6 | 0.7 | 18.0 | 28.0 | 37.0 |
| East South Central | 189 | 26.1 | 1.1 | 16.0 | 30.0 | 36.0 |
| West South Central | 291 | 28.7 | 0.9 | 20.0 | 31.0 | 40.0 |
| · Texas | 194 | 29.0 | 1.1 | 18.0 | 32.0 | 40.0 |
| · Other | 97 | 28.1 | 1.4 | 20.0 | 30.0 | 40.0 |
| Mountain | 183 | 26.7 | 1.1 | 16.0 | 30.0 | 40.0 |
| Pacific | 510 | 27.2 | 0.7 | 18.0 | 30.0 | 36.0 |
| · California | 354 | 26.7 | 0.8 | 16.0 | 30.0 | 36.0 |
| · Other | 156 | 28.8 | 1.3 | 20.0 | 30.0 | 36.0 |
| *Practice Arrangement* | | | | | | |
| Self-Employed | 1810 | 29.4 | 0.3 | 20.0 | 30.0 | 40.0 |
| Employee | 1188 | 22.5 | 0.5 | 8.0 | 24.0 | 35.0 |
| Independent Contractor | 147 | 19.4 | 1.6 | 0.0 | 17.0 | 36.0 |

Source: 1995 Socioeconomic Monitoring System surveys of nonfederal patient care physicians and federal patient care physicians employed by the Department of Defense or the Department of Veterans Affairs. See the beginning of this section, the introduction, and appendices for a discussion of the survey sample, definitions, and computation procedures. Statistics are not reported if the number of responses is less than 25.

Table 119. **Hours on Hospital Rounds per Week, for Federal and Nonfederal Physicians (excluding Physicians in Radiology, Psychiatry, Anesthesiology, and Pathology), 1995**

| | Number of Responses | Mean | Standard Error | 25th Percentile | Median | 75th Percentile |
|---|---|---|---|---|---|---|
| All Physicians | 3123 | 7.7 | 0.2 | 0.0 | 5.0 | 10.0 |
| *Specialty* | | | | | | |
| General/Family Practice | 515 | 5.1 | 0.3 | 0.0 | 4.0 | 8.0 |
| Internal Medicine | 788 | 12.0 | 0.5 | 2.0 | 10.0 | 20.0 |
| · General Internal Medicine | 541 | 10.8 | 0.5 | 1.0 | 8.0 | 15.0 |
| · Cardiovascular Diseases | 103 | 17.0 | 1.3 | 9.0 | 15.0 | 25.0 |
| · Other | 144 | 13.7 | 1.2 | 5.0 | 10.0 | 20.0 |
| Surgery | 889 | 6.3 | 0.2 | 1.0 | 5.0 | 10.0 |
| · General Surgery | 224 | 10.7 | 0.5 | 5.0 | 10.0 | 15.0 |
| · Otolaryngology | 77 | 3.7 | 0.4 | 1.0 | 3.0 | 5.0 |
| · Orthopedic Surgery | 186 | 5.2 | 0.2 | 3.0 | 5.0 | 7.0 |
| · Ophthalmology | 187 | 0.7 | 0.1 | 0.0 | 0.0 | 1.0 |
| · Urological Surgery | 98 | 7.5 | 0.5 | 4.0 | 5.0 | 10.0 |
| · Other | 117 | 7.3 | 0.7 | 2.0 | 6.0 | 10.0 |
| Pediatrics | 309 | 8.8 | 0.6 | 2.0 | 6.0 | 10.0 |
| Obstetrics/Gynecology | 243 | 4.7 | 0.2 | 2.0 | 5.0 | 6.0 |
| Other Specialty | 379 | 4.8 | 0.5 | 0.0 | 0.0 | 5.0 |
| · Emergency Medicine | 136 | 0.2 | 0.1 | 0.0 | 0.0 | 0.0 |
| · Other | 243 | 7.2 | 0.7 | 0.0 | 2.0 | 10.0 |
| *Geographic Area* | | | | | | |
| New England | 195 | 5.9 | 0.5 | 0.0 | 5.0 | 9.0 |
| · Massachusetts | 90 | 5.7 | 0.7 | 0.0 | 5.0 | 10.0 |
| · Other | 105 | 6.1 | 0.8 | 0.0 | 4.0 | 8.0 |
| Middle Atlantic | 488 | 8.6 | 0.5 | 0.0 | 5.0 | 12.0 |
| · New Jersey | 89 | 6.6 | 1.0 | 0.0 | 5.0 | 10.0 |
| · New York | 195 | 7.7 | 0.8 | 0.0 | 5.0 | 10.0 |
| · Pennsylvania | 204 | 10.7 | 0.7 | 2.0 | 8.0 | 15.0 |
| East North Central | 463 | 8.4 | 0.4 | 1.0 | 5.0 | 12.0 |
| · Illinois | 154 | 8.7 | 0.7 | 2.0 | 6.0 | 15.0 |
| · Michigan | 87 | 6.6 | 0.9 | 0.0 | 4.0 | 10.0 |
| · Ohio | 103 | 9.8 | 1.1 | 1.0 | 6.0 | 15.0 |
| · Other | 119 | 8.0 | 0.9 | 1.0 | 5.0 | 10.0 |
| West North Central | 232 | 7.0 | 0.5 | 1.0 | 5.0 | 10.0 |
| South Atlantic | 580 | 8.3 | 0.4 | 0.0 | 5.0 | 10.0 |
| · Florida | 164 | 9.4 | 1.0 | 0.0 | 5.0 | 15.0 |
| · Other | 416 | 7.8 | 0.5 | 1.0 | 5.0 | 10.0 |
| East South Central | 187 | 9.5 | 0.8 | 1.0 | 6.0 | 15.0 |
| West South Central | 287 | 7.2 | 0.5 | 0.0 | 5.0 | 10.0 |
| · Texas | 192 | 6.6 | 0.6 | 0.0 | 5.0 | 10.0 |
| · Other | 95 | 8.6 | 1.0 | 1.0 | 6.0 | 10.0 |
| Mountain | 183 | 6.6 | 0.6 | 0.0 | 4.0 | 10.0 |
| Pacific | 508 | 6.6 | 0.4 | 0.0 | 4.0 | 10.0 |
| · California | 353 | 6.7 | 0.5 | 0.0 | 4.0 | 10.0 |
| · Other | 155 | 6.2 | 0.6 | 0.0 | 4.0 | 7.0 |
| *Practice Arrangement* | | | | | | |
| Self-Employed | 1797 | 8.2 | 0.2 | 2.0 | 5.0 | 10.0 |
| Employee | 1180 | 7.5 | 0.3 | 0.0 | 5.0 | 10.0 |
| Independent Contractor | 146 | 4.1 | 0.8 | 0.0 | 0.0 | 5.0 |

Source: 1995 Socioeconomic Monitoring System surveys of nonfederal patient care physicians and federal patient care physicians employed by the Department of Defense or the Department of Veterans Affairs. See the beginning of this section, the introduction, and appendices for a discussion of the survey sample, definitions, and computation procedures. Statistics are not reported if the number of responses is less than 25.

Table 120. **Hours in Outpatient Clinics and Emergency Rooms per Week, for Federal and Nonfederal Physicians (excluding Physicians in Radiology, Psychiatry, Anesthesiology, and Pathology), 1995**

| | Number of Responses | Mean | Standard Error | 25th Percentile | Median | 75th Percentile |
|---|---|---|---|---|---|---|
| All Physicians | 3131 | 6.3 | 0.2 | 0.0 | 1.0 | 6.0 |
| *Specialty* | | | | | | |
| General/Family Practice | 516 | 5.0 | 0.5 | 0.0 | 0.0 | 4.0 |
| Internal Medicine | 791 | 5.6 | 0.4 | 0.0 | 2.0 | 6.0 |
| · General Internal Medicine | 542 | 5.4 | 0.5 | 0.0 | 1.0 | 6.0 |
| · Cardiovascular Diseases | 104 | 4.7 | 0.6 | 1.0 | 3.0 | 5.0 |
| · Other | 145 | 7.1 | 1.0 | 0.0 | 2.0 | 10.0 |
| Surgery | 891 | 4.3 | 0.2 | 0.0 | 2.0 | 5.0 |
| · General Surgery | 224 | 5.4 | 0.4 | 1.0 | 3.0 | 6.0 |
| · Otolaryngology | 77 | 3.1 | 0.4 | 0.0 | 2.0 | 4.0 |
| · Orthopedic Surgery | 186 | 5.1 | 0.4 | 1.0 | 4.0 | 8.0 |
| · Ophthalmology | 187 | 1.9 | 0.3 | 0.0 | 0.0 | 1.0 |
| · Urological Surgery | 98 | 5.5 | 0.9 | 0.0 | 1.0 | 5.0 |
| · Other | 119 | 3.9 | 0.6 | 0.0 | 2.0 | 5.0 |
| Pediatrics | 310 | 3.4 | 0.4 | 0.0 | 0.0 | 4.0 |
| Obstetrics/Gynecology | 245 | 3.6 | 0.4 | 0.0 | 1.0 | 4.0 |
| Other Specialty | 378 | 18.3 | 1.1 | 0.0 | 6.0 | 36.0 |
| · Emergency Medicine | 136 | 37.4 | 1.5 | 30.0 | 38.0 | 45.0 |
| · Other | 242 | 7.9 | 0.9 | 0.0 | 0.0 | 8.0 |
| *Geographic Area* | | | | | | |
| New England | 196 | 6.1 | 0.9 | 0.0 | 2.0 | 5.0 |
| · Massachusetts | 90 | 6.4 | 1.3 | 0.0 | 2.0 | 5.0 |
| · Other | 106 | 5.9 | 1.1 | 0.0 | 1.0 | 5.0 |
| Middle Atlantic | 490 | 5.3 | 0.4 | 0.0 | 1.0 | 5.0 |
| · New Jersey | 90 | 5.3 | 1.0 | 0.0 | 1.0 | 5.0 |
| · New York | 195 | 6.3 | 0.9 | 0.0 | 2.0 | 8.0 |
| · Pennsylvania | 205 | 4.0 | 0.5 | 0.0 | 1.0 | 5.0 |
| East North Central | 466 | 5.8 | 0.6 | 0.0 | 1.0 | 5.0 |
| · Illinois | 155 | 6.7 | 1.3 | 0.0 | 1.0 | 5.0 |
| · Michigan | 87 | 5.6 | 1.1 | 0.0 | 2.0 | 5.0 |
| · Ohio | 103 | 4.3 | 1.0 | 0.0 | 0.0 | 3.0 |
| · Other | 121 | 6.3 | 1.0 | 0.0 | 2.0 | 5.0 |
| West North Central | 233 | 5.7 | 0.7 | 0.0 | 2.0 | 5.0 |
| South Atlantic | 578 | 7.1 | 0.5 | 0.0 | 2.0 | 8.0 |
| · Florida | 163 | 7.2 | 1.1 | 0.0 | 2.0 | 8.0 |
| · Other | 415 | 7.1 | 0.6 | 0.0 | 2.0 | 8.0 |
| East South Central | 188 | 7.6 | 1.1 | 0.0 | 1.0 | 6.0 |
| West South Central | 288 | 7.1 | 0.7 | 0.0 | 2.0 | 8.0 |
| · Texas | 193 | 7.5 | 0.9 | 0.0 | 2.0 | 10.0 |
| · Other | 95 | 6.1 | 0.9 | 0.0 | 2.0 | 5.0 |
| Mountain | 183 | 6.8 | 0.9 | 0.0 | 2.0 | 6.0 |
| Pacific | 509 | 6.2 | 0.5 | 0.0 | 1.0 | 5.0 |
| · California | 354 | 6.0 | 0.6 | 0.0 | 1.0 | 5.0 |
| · Other | 155 | 6.7 | 1.0 | 0.0 | 1.0 | 5.0 |
| *Practice Arrangement* | | | | | | |
| Self-Employed | 1801 | 4.1 | 0.2 | 0.0 | 1.0 | 5.0 |
| Employee | 1183 | 7.7 | 0.4 | 0.0 | 2.0 | 10.0 |
| Independent Contractor | 147 | 19.2 | 2.2 | 0.0 | 3.0 | 40.0 |

Source: 1995 Socioeconomic Monitoring System surveys of nonfederal patient care physicians and federal patient care physicians employed by the Department of Defense or the Department of Veterans Affairs. See the beginning of this section, the introduction, and appendices for a discussion of the survey sample, definitions, and computation procedures. Statistics are not reported if the number of responses is less than 25.

Table 121. **Hours in Surgery per Week, for Federal and Nonfederal Physicians (excluding Physicians in Radiology, Psychiatry, Anesthesiology, and Pathology), 1995**

| | Number of Responses | Mean | Standard Error | 25th Percentile | Median | 75th Percentile |
|---|---|---|---|---|---|---|
| All Physicians | 3137 | 6.4 | 0.2 | 0.0 | 0.0 | 10.0 |
| *Specialty* | | | | | | |
| General/Family Practice | 516 | 1.1 | 0.1 | 0.0 | 0.0 | 0.0 |
| Internal Medicine | 793 | 2.8 | 0.3 | 0.0 | 0.0 | 0.0 |
| · General Internal Medicine | 544 | 0.7 | 0.2 | 0.0 | 0.0 | 0.0 |
| · Cardiovascular Diseases | 104 | 8.4 | 1.2 | 0.0 | 2.0 | 14.0 |
| · Other | 145 | 7.4 | 0.9 | 0.0 | 0.0 | 15.0 |
| Surgery | 893 | 15.8 | 0.3 | 8.0 | 15.0 | 20.0 |
| · General Surgery | 226 | 21.6 | 0.7 | 15.0 | 20.0 | 28.0 |
| · Otolaryngology | 77 | 13.7 | 0.8 | 8.0 | 12.0 | 20.0 |
| · Orthopedic Surgery | 187 | 15.6 | 0.6 | 10.0 | 15.0 | 20.0 |
| · Ophthalmology | 187 | 6.3 | 0.3 | 4.0 | 6.0 | 8.0 |
| · Urological Surgery | 98 | 15.2 | 0.7 | 9.0 | 15.0 | 20.0 |
| · Other | 118 | 18.9 | 1.1 | 10.0 | 20.0 | 28.0 |
| Pediatrics | 311 | 1.5 | 0.2 | 0.0 | 0.0 | 1.0 |
| Obstetrics/Gynecology | 244 | 13.3 | 0.7 | 6.0 | 10.0 | 20.0 |
| Other Specialty | 380 | 1.1 | 0.3 | 0.0 | 0.0 | 0.0 |
| · Emergency Medicine | 136 | 0.1 | 0.0 | 0.0 | 0.0 | 0.0 |
| · Other | 244 | 1.7 | 0.4 | 0.0 | 0.0 | 0.0 |
| *Geographic Area* | | | | | | |
| New England | 195 | 5.0 | 0.6 | 0.0 | 0.0 | 8.0 |
| · Massachusetts | 90 | 4.7 | 0.9 | 0.0 | 0.0 | 6.0 |
| · Other | 105 | 5.3 | 0.8 | 0.0 | 0.0 | 8.0 |
| Middle Atlantic | 490 | 5.6 | 0.5 | 0.0 | 0.0 | 8.0 |
| · New Jersey | 90 | 4.1 | 1.0 | 0.0 | 0.0 | 3.0 |
| · New York | 195 | 5.8 | 0.7 | 0.0 | 0.0 | 9.0 |
| · Pennsylvania | 205 | 6.4 | 0.8 | 0.0 | 0.0 | 8.0 |
| East North Central | 467 | 6.7 | 0.5 | 0.0 | 0.0 | 12.0 |
| · Illinois | 156 | 6.6 | 0.9 | 0.0 | 0.0 | 10.0 |
| · Michigan | 88 | 8.4 | 1.2 | 0.0 | 0.0 | 20.0 |
| · Ohio | 103 | 5.3 | 0.9 | 0.0 | 0.0 | 7.0 |
| · Other | 120 | 7.1 | 0.8 | 0.0 | 1.0 | 15.0 |
| West North Central | 232 | 7.3 | 0.7 | 0.0 | 2.0 | 12.0 |
| South Atlantic | 583 | 7.1 | 0.4 | 0.0 | 0.0 | 12.0 |
| · Florida | 164 | 8.5 | 1.0 | 0.0 | 0.0 | 16.0 |
| · Other | 419 | 6.6 | 0.5 | 0.0 | 0.0 | 10.0 |
| East South Central | 188 | 6.3 | 0.7 | 0.0 | 0.0 | 10.0 |
| West South Central | 291 | 6.9 | 0.6 | 0.0 | 0.0 | 12.0 |
| · Texas | 194 | 6.4 | 0.8 | 0.0 | 0.0 | 10.0 |
| · Other | 97 | 7.8 | 1.0 | 0.0 | 4.0 | 13.0 |
| Mountain | 182 | 5.7 | 0.6 | 0.0 | 0.0 | 10.0 |
| Pacific | 509 | 6.2 | 0.4 | 0.0 | 0.0 | 10.0 |
| · California | 354 | 6.5 | 0.6 | 0.0 | 0.0 | 10.0 |
| · Other | 155 | 5.3 | 0.6 | 0.0 | 0.0 | 10.0 |
| *Practice Arrangement* | | | | | | |
| Self-Employed | 1806 | 7.5 | 0.2 | 0.0 | 2.0 | 13.0 |
| Employee | 1184 | 5.2 | 0.3 | 0.0 | 0.0 | 6.0 |
| Independent Contractor | 147 | 3.4 | 0.7 | 0.0 | 0.0 | 1.0 |

Source: 1995 Socioeconomic Monitoring System surveys of nonfederal patient care physicians and federal patient care physicians employed by the Department of Defense or the Department of Veterans Affairs. See the beginning of this section, the introduction, and appendices for a discussion of the survey sample, definitions, and computation procedures. Statistics are not reported if the number of responses is less than 25.

Table 122. **Total Patients Visits per Week, for Federal and Nonfederal Physicians (excluding Physicians in Radiology, Psychiatry, Anesthesiology, and Pathology), 1995**

| | Number of Responses | Mean | Standard Error | 25th Percentile | Median | 75th Percentile |
|---|---|---|---|---|---|---|
| All Physicians | 2929 | 107.2 | 1.0 | 69.0 | 100.0 | 136.0 |
| *Specialty* | | | | | | |
| General/Family Practice | 483 | 132.5 | 2.8 | 95.0 | 125.0 | 160.0 |
| Internal Medicine | 737 | 99.2 | 2.0 | 64.0 | 94.0 | 127.0 |
| · General Internal Medicine | 511 | 102.8 | 2.4 | 69.0 | 100.0 | 130.0 |
| · Cardiovascular Diseases | 92 | 88.5 | 5.9 | 57.0 | 71.0 | 113.0 |
| · Other | 134 | 92.4 | 4.2 | 60.0 | 88.0 | 122.0 |
| Surgery | 826 | 97.4 | 1.6 | 64.0 | 93.0 | 126.0 |
| · General Surgery | 206 | 84.8 | 2.9 | 57.0 | 78.0 | 104.0 |
| · Otolaryngology | 73 | 105.2 | 4.0 | 75.0 | 105.0 | 130.0 |
| · Orthopedic Surgery | 168 | 109.7 | 3.4 | 75.0 | 105.0 | 136.0 |
| · Ophthalmology | 182 | 117.8 | 3.7 | 80.0 | 110.0 | 150.0 |
| · Urological Surgery | 93 | 96.5 | 3.3 | 72.0 | 90.0 | 120.0 |
| · Other | 104 | 70.8 | 4.0 | 40.0 | 70.0 | 92.0 |
| Pediatrics | 294 | 125.6 | 3.8 | 81.0 | 120.0 | 160.0 |
| Obstetrics/Gynecology | 227 | 94.0 | 3.2 | 61.0 | 87.0 | 119.0 |
| Other Specialty | 362 | 107.9 | 3.2 | 68.0 | 100.0 | 140.0 |
| · Emergency Medicine | 134 | 125.0 | 5.8 | 85.0 | 110.0 | 150.0 |
| · Other | 228 | 98.3 | 3.6 | 60.0 | 90.0 | 131.0 |
| *Geographic Area* | | | | | | |
| New England | 184 | 99.0 | 3.7 | 74.0 | 90.0 | 122.0 |
| · Massachusetts | 85 | 99.0 | 5.5 | 75.0 | 95.0 | 124.0 |
| · Other | 99 | 99.0 | 4.9 | 71.0 | 89.0 | 120.0 |
| Middle Atlantic | 460 | 101.6 | 2.6 | 60.0 | 99.0 | 132.0 |
| · New Jersey | 84 | 99.4 | 7.2 | 60.0 | 101.0 | 134.0 |
| · New York | 180 | 94.9 | 3.8 | 56.0 | 90.0 | 130.0 |
| · Pennsylvania | 196 | 110.2 | 4.0 | 71.0 | 104.0 | 136.0 |
| East North Central | 438 | 108.2 | 2.7 | 70.0 | 100.0 | 140.0 |
| · Illinois | 146 | 100.8 | 4.6 | 61.0 | 90.0 | 130.0 |
| · Michigan | 79 | 111.2 | 7.4 | 71.0 | 100.0 | 134.0 |
| · Ohio | 98 | 110.4 | 5.1 | 73.0 | 107.0 | 146.0 |
| · Other | 115 | 114.9 | 5.0 | 75.0 | 101.0 | 151.0 |
| West North Central | 210 | 121.3 | 4.1 | 80.0 | 116.0 | 146.0 |
| South Atlantic | 540 | 107.4 | 2.5 | 68.0 | 100.0 | 140.0 |
| · Florida | 149 | 111.0 | 4.7 | 68.0 | 100.0 | 142.0 |
| · Other | 391 | 106.0 | 2.9 | 68.0 | 100.0 | 139.0 |
| East South Central | 180 | 128.9 | 5.1 | 80.0 | 116.0 | 154.0 |
| West South Central | 258 | 108.4 | 3.2 | 71.0 | 100.0 | 140.0 |
| · Texas | 173 | 106.2 | 4.0 | 70.0 | 96.0 | 137.0 |
| · Other | 85 | 113.8 | 5.6 | 80.0 | 109.0 | 143.0 |
| Mountain | 173 | 105.1 | 3.8 | 70.0 | 95.0 | 131.0 |
| Pacific | 486 | 101.4 | 2.3 | 64.0 | 95.0 | 129.0 |
| · California | 336 | 103.2 | 2.9 | 64.0 | 95.0 | 130.0 |
| · Other | 150 | 96.5 | 3.7 | 61.0 | 92.0 | 125.0 |
| *Practice Arrangement* | | | | | | |
| Self-Employed | 1675 | 113.1 | 1.4 | 74.0 | 107.0 | 143.0 |
| Employee | 1113 | 97.6 | 1.6 | 60.0 | 90.0 | 125.0 |
| Independent Contractor | 141 | 114.4 | 5.7 | 70.0 | 100.0 | 145.0 |

Source: 1995 Socioeconomic Monitoring System surveys of nonfederal patient care physicians and federal patient care physicians employed by the Department of Defense or the Department of Veterans Affairs. See the beginning of this section, the introduction, and appendices for a discussion of the survey sample, definitions, and computation procedures. Statistics are not reported if the number of responses is less than 25.

Table 123. **Total Office Visits per Week, for Federal and Nonfederal Physicians (excluding Physicians in Radiology, Psychiatry, Anesthesiology, and Pathology), 1995**

| | Number of Responses | Mean | Standard Error | 25th Percentile | Median | 75th Percentile |
|---|---|---|---|---|---|---|
| All Physicians | 3109 | 72.7 | 1.0 | 30.0 | 65.0 | 100.0 |
| *Specialty* | | | | | | |
| General/Family Practice | 509 | 106.6 | 2.7 | 75.0 | 100.0 | 135.0 |
| Internal Medicine | 784 | 58.3 | 1.5 | 30.0 | 55.0 | 80.0 |
| · General Internal Medicine | 540 | 64.0 | 2.0 | 33.0 | 65.0 | 90.0 |
| · Cardiovascular Diseases | 101 | 42.8 | 3.5 | 15.0 | 35.0 | 60.0 |
| · Other | 143 | 46.3 | 2.7 | 30.0 | 40.0 | 60.0 |
| Surgery | 891 | 69.3 | 1.6 | 35.0 | 60.0 | 100.0 |
| · General Surgery | 226 | 40.8 | 1.8 | 20.0 | 40.0 | 55.0 |
| · Otolaryngology | 77 | 89.3 | 4.2 | 60.0 | 100.0 | 120.0 |
| · Orthopedic Surgery | 186 | 79.9 | 2.9 | 54.0 | 76.0 | 100.0 |
| · Ophthalmology | 186 | 113.1 | 4.0 | 70.0 | 108.0 | 150.0 |
| · Urological Surgery | 98 | 68.1 | 2.7 | 50.0 | 65.0 | 80.0 |
| · Other | 118 | 42.0 | 3.1 | 20.0 | 35.0 | 58.0 |
| Pediatrics | 307 | 99.1 | 4.0 | 50.0 | 100.0 | 140.0 |
| Obstetrics/Gynecology | 242 | 78.0 | 3.0 | 45.0 | 75.0 | 100.0 |
| Other Specialty | 376 | 46.2 | 3.2 | 0.0 | 20.0 | 75.0 |
| · Emergency Medicine | 136 | 14.3 | 4.4 | 0.0 | 0.0 | 0.0 |
| · Other | 240 | 63.6 | 3.9 | 12.0 | 50.0 | 100.0 |
| *Geographic Area* | | | | | | |
| New England | 193 | 64.8 | 3.5 | 30.0 | 60.0 | 90.0 |
| · Massachusetts | 88 | 59.6 | 4.9 | 20.0 | 60.0 | 90.0 |
| · Other | 105 | 70.0 | 5.0 | 32.0 | 64.0 | 96.0 |
| Middle Atlantic | 484 | 66.1 | 2.5 | 25.0 | 60.0 | 100.0 |
| · New Jersey | 89 | 65.1 | 5.6 | 20.0 | 60.0 | 90.0 |
| · New York | 194 | 61.2 | 4.1 | 20.0 | 50.0 | 90.0 |
| · Pennsylvania | 201 | 72.3 | 3.8 | 35.0 | 65.0 | 100.0 |
| East North Central | 468 | 71.9 | 2.6 | 30.0 | 65.0 | 105.0 |
| · Illinois | 156 | 66.5 | 4.6 | 23.0 | 60.0 | 100.0 |
| · Michigan | 86 | 71.2 | 5.9 | 40.0 | 60.0 | 100.0 |
| · Ohio | 104 | 72.3 | 5.4 | 30.0 | 65.0 | 110.0 |
| · Other | 122 | 80.0 | 4.8 | 40.0 | 75.0 | 120.0 |
| West North Central | 226 | 92.1 | 4.8 | 45.0 | 85.0 | 120.0 |
| South Atlantic | 571 | 71.5 | 2.5 | 30.0 | 60.0 | 100.0 |
| · Florida | 160 | 69.7 | 4.9 | 35.0 | 58.0 | 100.0 |
| · Other | 411 | 72.2 | 2.9 | 30.0 | 65.0 | 100.0 |
| East South Central | 188 | 82.5 | 4.7 | 38.0 | 75.0 | 120.0 |
| West South Central | 290 | 76.5 | 3.1 | 35.0 | 70.0 | 110.0 |
| · Texas | 194 | 75.5 | 3.8 | 36.0 | 70.0 | 110.0 |
| · Other | 96 | 78.7 | 5.2 | 35.0 | 80.0 | 120.0 |
| Mountain | 183 | 71.3 | 3.7 | 35.0 | 70.0 | 100.0 |
| Pacific | 506 | 71.5 | 2.3 | 35.0 | 64.0 | 100.0 |
| · California | 352 | 70.8 | 2.9 | 34.0 | 60.0 | 100.0 |
| · Other | 154 | 73.5 | 3.8 | 40.0 | 70.0 | 100.0 |
| *Practice Arrangement* | | | | | | |
| Self-Employed | 1791 | 84.1 | 1.3 | 45.0 | 75.0 | 115.0 |
| Employee | 1175 | 58.3 | 1.6 | 15.0 | 50.0 | 90.0 |
| Independent Contractor | 143 | 56.9 | 6.8 | 0.0 | 40.0 | 90.0 |

Source: 1995 Socioeconomic Monitoring System surveys of nonfederal patient care physicians and federal patient care physicians employed by the Department of Defense or the Department of Veterans Affairs. See the beginning of this section, the introduction, and appendices for a discussion of the survey sample, definitions, and computation procedures. Statistics are not reported if the number of responses is less than 25.

Table 124. **Office Visits with New Patients per Week, for Federal and Nonfederal Physicians (excluding Physicians in Radiology, Psychiatry, Anesthesiology, and Pathology), 1995**

| | Number of Responses | Mean | Standard Error | 25th Percentile | Median | 75th Percentile |
|---|---|---|---|---|---|---|
| All Physicians | 2284 | 14.7 | 0.3 | 5.0 | 11.0 | 20.0 |
| *Specialty* | | | | | | |
| General/Family Practice | 390 | 13.6 | 0.8 | 5.0 | 8.0 | 20.0 |
| Internal Medicine | 575 | 10.1 | 0.5 | 4.0 | 6.0 | 15.0 |
| · General Internal Medicine | 382 | 9.4 | 0.6 | 4.0 | 6.0 | 15.0 |
| · Cardiovascular Diseases | 80 | 7.1 | 0.7 | 4.0 | 6.0 | 8.0 |
| · Other | 113 | 14.7 | 1.5 | 6.0 | 12.0 | 20.0 |
| Surgery | 721 | 17.5 | 0.5 | 8.0 | 15.0 | 20.0 |
| · General Surgery | 178 | 12.1 | 0.7 | 5.0 | 9.0 | 15.0 |
| · Otolaryngology | 66 | 27.1 | 1.5 | 18.0 | 25.0 | 35.0 |
| · Orthopedic Surgery | 155 | 22.0 | 1.4 | 15.0 | 20.0 | 25.0 |
| · Ophthalmology | 157 | 22.1 | 1.0 | 15.0 | 20.0 | 26.0 |
| · Urological Surgery | 68 | 15.2 | 0.7 | 12.0 | 15.0 | 20.0 |
| · Other | 97 | 11.3 | 1.0 | 4.0 | 8.0 | 15.0 |
| Pediatrics | 198 | 13.1 | 1.0 | 5.0 | 8.0 | 20.0 |
| Obstetrics/Gynecology | 198 | 12.8 | 1.1 | 5.0 | 8.0 | 15.0 |
| Other Specialty | 202 | 26.7 | 2.0 | 8.0 | 20.0 | 35.0 |
| · Emergency Medicine | 21 | . | . | . | . | . |
| · Other | 181 | 23.8 | 1.7 | 8.0 | 20.0 | 30.0 |
| *Geographic Area* | | | | | | |
| New England | 138 | 11.3 | 1.0 | 5.0 | 7.0 | 15.0 |
| · Massachusetts | 65 | 9.9 | 1.1 | 4.0 | 8.0 | 15.0 |
| · Other | 73 | 12.7 | 1.7 | 5.0 | 6.0 | 20.0 |
| Middle Atlantic | 366 | 11.7 | 0.7 | 4.0 | 6.0 | 17.0 |
| · New Jersey | 62 | 10.5 | 1.5 | 5.0 | 6.0 | 15.0 |
| · New York | 146 | 13.0 | 1.2 | 4.0 | 8.0 | 18.0 |
| · Pennsylvania | 158 | 11.0 | 1.0 | 4.0 | 6.0 | 18.0 |
| East North Central | 339 | 13.8 | 0.8 | 5.0 | 9.0 | 20.0 |
| · Illinois | 103 | 13.3 | 1.2 | 5.0 | 12.0 | 16.0 |
| · Michigan | 68 | 17.3 | 1.8 | 6.0 | 15.0 | 25.0 |
| · Ohio | 76 | 11.2 | 1.2 | 5.0 | 8.0 | 15.0 |
| · Other | 92 | 14.2 | 2.1 | 5.0 | 8.0 | 15.0 |
| West North Central | 163 | 15.5 | 1.2 | 5.0 | 11.0 | 20.0 |
| South Atlantic | 429 | 15.5 | 0.9 | 6.0 | 12.0 | 20.0 |
| · Florida | 113 | 15.9 | 1.8 | 6.0 | 12.0 | 20.0 |
| · Other | 316 | 15.4 | 1.1 | 5.0 | 12.0 | 20.0 |
| East South Central | 134 | 17.0 | 1.7 | 5.0 | 14.0 | 20.0 |
| West South Central | 212 | 15.7 | 1.1 | 5.0 | 15.0 | 20.0 |
| · Texas | 138 | 16.1 | 1.5 | 5.0 | 15.0 | 20.0 |
| · Other | 74 | 15.0 | 1.5 | 5.0 | 12.0 | 20.0 |
| Mountain | 141 | 17.9 | 1.7 | 6.0 | 15.0 | 20.0 |
| Pacific | 362 | 15.8 | 0.8 | 5.0 | 12.0 | 20.0 |
| · California | 250 | 15.3 | 1.0 | 5.0 | 12.0 | 20.0 |
| · Other | 112 | 17.3 | 1.5 | 5.0 | 15.0 | 20.0 |
| *Practice Arrangement* | | | | | | |
| Self-Employed | 1433 | 14.1 | 0.4 | 5.0 | 11.0 | 20.0 |
| Employee | 774 | 14.8 | 0.6 | 5.0 | 8.0 | 20.0 |
| Independent Contractor | 77 | 22.1 | 3.6 | 6.0 | 15.0 | 20.0 |

Source: 1995 Socioeconomic Monitoring System surveys of nonfederal patient care physicians and federal patient care physicians employed by the Department of Defense or the Department of Veterans Affairs. See the beginning of this section, the introduction, and appendices for a discussion of the survey sample, definitions, and computation procedures. Statistics are not reported if the number of responses is less than 25.

Table 125. **Visits on Hospital Rounds per Week, for Federal and Nonfederal Physicians (excluding Physicians in Radiology, Psychiatry, Anesthesiology, and Pathology), 1995**

| | Number of Responses | Mean | Standard Error | 25th Percentile | Median | 75th Percentile |
|---|---|---|---|---|---|---|
| All Physicians | 3009 | 19.1 | 0.5 | 0.0 | 10.0 | 25.0 |
| *Specialty* | | | | | | |
| General/Family Practice | 504 | 11.9 | 0.7 | 0.0 | 7.0 | 18.0 |
| Internal Medicine | 755 | 28.1 | 1.4 | 3.0 | 20.0 | 40.0 |
| · General Internal Medicine | 522 | 24.2 | 1.5 | 0.0 | 15.0 | 30.0 |
| · Cardiovascular Diseases | 97 | 42.7 | 4.7 | 16.0 | 34.0 | 50.0 |
| · Other | 136 | 33.8 | 3.3 | 10.0 | 25.0 | 50.0 |
| Surgery | 849 | 18.8 | 0.8 | 2.0 | 10.0 | 25.0 |
| · General Surgery | 211 | 33.5 | 2.2 | 12.0 | 28.0 | 40.0 |
| · Otolaryngology | 74 | 9.0 | 1.3 | 2.0 | 5.0 | 12.0 |
| · Orthopedic Surgery | 178 | 18.2 | 1.3 | 5.0 | 15.0 | 24.0 |
| · Ophthalmology | 186 | 1.3 | 0.2 | 0.0 | 0.0 | 1.0 |
| · Urological Surgery | 93 | 20.7 | 1.9 | 8.0 | 15.0 | 25.0 |
| · Other | 107 | 20.8 | 2.6 | 3.0 | 14.0 | 25.0 |
| Pediatrics | 299 | 20.2 | 2.0 | 4.0 | 10.0 | 20.0 |
| Obstetrics/Gynecology | 230 | 12.1 | 0.7 | 4.0 | 10.0 | 16.0 |
| Other Specialty | 372 | 11.1 | 1.5 | 0.0 | 0.0 | 7.0 |
| · Emergency Medicine | 136 | 1.8 | 1.3 | 0.0 | 0.0 | 0.0 |
| · Other | 236 | 16.3 | 2.1 | 0.0 | 2.0 | 20.0 |
| *Geographic Area* | | | | | | |
| New England | 187 | 14.6 | 1.5 | 0.0 | 7.0 | 20.0 |
| · Massachusetts | 87 | 16.5 | 2.6 | 0.0 | 7.0 | 25.0 |
| · Other | 100 | 12.7 | 1.9 | 0.0 | 6.0 | 15.0 |
| Middle Atlantic | 476 | 22.8 | 1.7 | 0.0 | 11.0 | 30.0 |
| · New Jersey | 86 | 18.8 | 4.7 | 0.0 | 10.0 | 21.0 |
| · New York | 188 | 20.9 | 2.4 | 0.0 | 8.0 | 25.0 |
| · Pennsylvania | 202 | 27.2 | 2.5 | 3.0 | 15.0 | 35.0 |
| East North Central | 447 | 20.6 | 1.3 | 1.0 | 12.0 | 30.0 |
| · Illinois | 149 | 21.0 | 2.6 | 2.0 | 15.0 | 30.0 |
| · Michigan | 82 | 20.5 | 3.1 | 0.0 | 10.0 | 30.0 |
| · Ohio | 100 | 20.3 | 2.4 | 0.0 | 14.0 | 30.0 |
| · Other | 116 | 20.2 | 2.3 | 1.0 | 12.0 | 30.0 |
| West North Central | 220 | 18.7 | 1.6 | 2.0 | 12.0 | 25.0 |
| South Atlantic | 554 | 19.4 | 1.3 | 0.0 | 10.0 | 25.0 |
| · Florida | 154 | 23.7 | 3.0 | 0.0 | 10.0 | 30.0 |
| · Other | 400 | 17.6 | 1.4 | 0.0 | 10.0 | 23.0 |
| East South Central | 183 | 24.4 | 2.0 | 1.0 | 15.0 | 36.0 |
| West South Central | 272 | 18.2 | 1.7 | 0.0 | 10.0 | 21.0 |
| · Texas | 181 | 15.7 | 1.9 | 0.0 | 7.0 | 20.0 |
| · Other | 91 | 24.0 | 3.4 | 1.0 | 15.0 | 30.0 |
| Mountain | 176 | 16.2 | 2.1 | 0.0 | 9.0 | 20.0 |
| Pacific | 494 | 15.2 | 1.1 | 0.0 | 6.0 | 20.0 |
| · California | 343 | 16.1 | 1.5 | 0.0 | 6.0 | 20.0 |
| · Other | 151 | 12.8 | 1.4 | 0.0 | 8.0 | 15.0 |
| *Practice Arrangement* | | | | | | |
| Self-Employed | 1723 | 19.2 | 0.6 | 2.0 | 12.0 | 25.0 |
| Employee | 1142 | 20.0 | 1.0 | 0.0 | 10.0 | 25.0 |
| Independent Contractor | 144 | 11.5 | 2.5 | 0.0 | 0.0 | 10.0 |

Source: 1995 Socioeconomic Monitoring System surveys of nonfederal patient care physicians and federal patient care physicians employed by the Department of Defense or the Department of Veterans Affairs. See the beginning of this section, the introduction, and appendices for a discussion of the survey sample, definitions, and computation procedures. Statistics are not reported if the number of responses is less than 25.

Table 126. **Visits in Outpatient Clinics and Emergency Rooms per Week, for Federal and Nonfederal Physicians (excluding Physicians in Radiology, Psychiatry, Anesthesiology, and Pathology), 1995**

| | Number of Responses | Mean | Standard Error | 25th Percentile | Median | 75th Percentile |
|---|---|---|---|---|---|---|
| All Physicians | 3040 | 12.9 | 0.6 | 0.0 | 2.0 | 9.0 |
| *Specialty* | | | | | | |
| General/Family Practice | 501 | 8.7 | 1.1 | 0.0 | 0.0 | 5.0 |
| Internal Medicine | 764 | 9.9 | 0.8 | 0.0 | 2.0 | 10.0 |
| · General Internal Medicine | 530 | 9.9 | 1.0 | 0.0 | 2.0 | 10.0 |
| · Cardiovascular Diseases | 94 | 7.4 | 1.5 | 0.0 | 4.0 | 7.0 |
| · Other | 140 | 11.5 | 2.4 | 0.0 | 2.0 | 15.0 |
| Surgery | 860 | 6.7 | 0.4 | 0.0 | 3.0 | 8.0 |
| · General Surgery | 215 | 8.0 | 0.8 | 2.0 | 5.0 | 10.0 |
| · Otolaryngology | 77 | 5.4 | 1.0 | 0.0 | 3.0 | 5.0 |
| · Orthopedic Surgery | 173 | 9.3 | 1.0 | 1.0 | 5.0 | 10.0 |
| · Ophthalmology | 185 | 4.2 | 0.9 | 0.0 | 0.0 | 2.0 |
| · Urological Surgery | 95 | 5.1 | 1.0 | 0.0 | 2.0 | 6.0 |
| · Other | 115 | 5.9 | 1.0 | 0.0 | 2.0 | 5.0 |
| Pediatrics | 305 | 6.4 | 1.2 | 0.0 | 0.0 | 5.0 |
| Obstetrics/Gynecology | 240 | 5.6 | 0.8 | 0.0 | 2.0 | 5.0 |
| Other Specialty | 370 | 49.0 | 3.4 | 0.0 | 8.0 | 100.0 |
| · Emergency Medicine | 134 | 108.4 | 5.3 | 75.0 | 100.0 | 150.0 |
| · Other | 236 | 16.6 | 2.4 | 0.0 | 0.0 | 10.0 |
| *Geographic Area* | | | | | | |
| New England | 188 | 15.6 | 2.9 | 0.0 | 2.0 | 10.0 |
| · Massachusetts | 89 | 18.9 | 5.3 | 0.0 | 3.0 | 10.0 |
| · Other | 99 | 12.0 | 2.7 | 0.0 | 0.0 | 7.0 |
| Middle Atlantic | 474 | 9.8 | 1.0 | 0.0 | 2.0 | 8.0 |
| · New Jersey | 87 | 10.3 | 2.2 | 0.0 | 2.0 | 10.0 |
| · New York | 186 | 10.8 | 1.9 | 0.0 | 2.0 | 10.0 |
| · Pennsylvania | 201 | 8.4 | 1.4 | 0.0 | 2.0 | 5.0 |
| East North Central | 453 | 12.5 | 1.5 | 0.0 | 1.0 | 8.0 |
| · Illinois | 150 | 10.4 | 2.1 | 0.0 | 0.0 | 10.0 |
| · Michigan | 84 | 14.2 | 3.3 | 0.0 | 2.0 | 10.0 |
| · Ohio | 100 | 12.1 | 3.2 | 0.0 | 0.0 | 5.0 |
| · Other | 119 | 14.5 | 3.3 | 0.0 | 2.0 | 8.0 |
| West North Central | 221 | 11.1 | 1.9 | 0.0 | 2.0 | 8.0 |
| South Atlantic | 567 | 14.6 | 1.5 | 0.0 | 3.0 | 9.0 |
| · Florida | 161 | 15.4 | 2.8 | 0.0 | 2.0 | 15.0 |
| · Other | 406 | 14.2 | 1.8 | 0.0 | 3.0 | 9.0 |
| East South Central | 186 | 17.7 | 2.9 | 0.0 | 2.0 | 10.0 |
| West South Central | 271 | 13.2 | 1.9 | 0.0 | 4.0 | 10.0 |
| · Texas | 180 | 13.9 | 2.5 | 0.0 | 4.0 | 10.0 |
| · Other | 91 | 11.6 | 2.6 | 0.0 | 4.0 | 10.0 |
| Mountain | 177 | 15.4 | 2.9 | 0.0 | 1.0 | 10.0 |
| Pacific | 503 | 11.6 | 1.3 | 0.0 | 1.0 | 7.0 |
| · California | 350 | 12.7 | 1.8 | 0.0 | 0.0 | 7.0 |
| · Other | 153 | 8.5 | 1.4 | 0.0 | 1.0 | 8.0 |
| *Practice Arrangement* | | | | | | |
| Self-Employed | 1745 | 6.8 | 0.4 | 0.0 | 2.0 | 6.0 |
| Employee | 1149 | 17.0 | 1.1 | 0.0 | 2.0 | 15.0 |
| Independent Contractor | 146 | 47.0 | 6.2 | 0.0 | 4.0 | 71.0 |

Source: 1995 Socioeconomic Monitoring System surveys of nonfederal patient care physicians and federal patient care physicians employed by the Department of Defense or the Department of Veterans Affairs. See the beginning of this section, the introduction, and appendices for a discussion of the survey sample, definitions, and computation procedures. Statistics are not reported if the number of responses is less than 25.

Table 127. **Surgical Procedures, Including Assists, per Week, for Federal and Nonfederal Physicians (excluding Physicians in Radiology, Psychiatry, Anesthesiology, and Pathology), 1995**

| | Number of Responses | Mean | Standard Error | 25th Percentile | Median | 75th Percentile |
|---|---|---|---|---|---|---|
| All Physicians | 3131 | 3.6 | 0.1 | 0.0 | 0.0 | 6.0 |
| *Specialty* | | | | | | |
| General/Family Practice | 515 | 0.6 | 0.1 | 0.0 | 0.0 | 0.0 |
| Internal Medicine | 793 | 2.3 | 0.2 | 0.0 | 0.0 | 0.0 |
| · General Internal Medicine | 544 | 0.6 | 0.2 | 0.0 | 0.0 | 0.0 |
| · Cardiovascular Diseases | 104 | 5.1 | 0.7 | 0.0 | 0.0 | 9.0 |
| · Other | 145 | 7.2 | 0.9 | 0.0 | 0.0 | 15.0 |
| Surgery | 889 | 8.3 | 0.2 | 5.0 | 8.0 | 11.0 |
| · General Surgery | 224 | 10.8 | 0.4 | 7.0 | 10.0 | 14.0 |
| · Otolaryngology | 76 | 9.3 | 0.7 | 5.0 | 8.0 | 11.0 |
| · Orthopedic Surgery | 187 | 7.6 | 0.3 | 5.0 | 7.0 | 10.0 |
| · Ophthalmology | 187 | 5.6 | 0.4 | 2.0 | 4.0 | 7.0 |
| · Urological Surgery | 97 | 8.7 | 0.4 | 6.0 | 8.0 | 10.0 |
| · Other | 118 | 7.2 | 0.5 | 4.0 | 7.0 | 10.0 |
| Pediatrics | 311 | 0.9 | 0.2 | 0.0 | 0.0 | 0.0 |
| Obstetrics/Gynecology | 243 | 7.1 | 0.4 | 3.0 | 6.0 | 9.0 |
| Other Specialty | 380 | 0.8 | 0.3 | 0.0 | 0.0 | 0.0 |
| · Emergency Medicine | 136 | 0.0 | 0.0 | 0.0 | 0.0 | 0.0 |
| · Other | 244 | 1.1 | 0.4 | 0.0 | 0.0 | 0.0 |
| *Geographic Area* | | | | | | |
| New England | 196 | 2.8 | 0.3 | 0.0 | 0.0 | 5.0 |
| · Massachusetts | 90 | 2.7 | 0.6 | 0.0 | 0.0 | 4.0 |
| · Other | 106 | 2.8 | 0.4 | 0.0 | 0.0 | 5.0 |
| Middle Atlantic | 490 | 2.9 | 0.3 | 0.0 | 0.0 | 4.0 |
| · New Jersey | 90 | 2.3 | 0.6 | 0.0 | 0.0 | 2.0 |
| · New York | 195 | 2.9 | 0.4 | 0.0 | 0.0 | 4.0 |
| · Pennsylvania | 205 | 3.2 | 0.4 | 0.0 | 0.0 | 6.0 |
| East North Central | 466 | 3.7 | 0.3 | 0.0 | 0.0 | 6.0 |
| · Illinois | 155 | 3.3 | 0.5 | 0.0 | 0.0 | 6.0 |
| · Michigan | 88 | 4.8 | 0.7 | 0.0 | 0.0 | 9.0 |
| · Ohio | 103 | 2.8 | 0.6 | 0.0 | 0.0 | 4.0 |
| · Other | 120 | 4.4 | 0.5 | 0.0 | 1.0 | 7.0 |
| West North Central | 230 | 4.3 | 0.4 | 0.0 | 2.0 | 7.0 |
| South Atlantic | 579 | 4.0 | 0.3 | 0.0 | 0.0 | 8.0 |
| · Florida | 164 | 5.3 | 0.6 | 0.0 | 0.0 | 10.0 |
| · Other | 415 | 3.5 | 0.3 | 0.0 | 0.0 | 6.0 |
| East South Central | 188 | 4.3 | 0.5 | 0.0 | 0.0 | 7.0 |
| West South Central | 289 | 3.8 | 0.3 | 0.0 | 0.0 | 6.0 |
| · Texas | 193 | 3.4 | 0.4 | 0.0 | 0.0 | 5.0 |
| · Other | 96 | 4.7 | 0.6 | 0.0 | 3.0 | 8.0 |
| Mountain | 183 | 3.8 | 0.5 | 0.0 | 0.0 | 7.0 |
| Pacific | 510 | 3.6 | 0.3 | 0.0 | 0.0 | 5.0 |
| · California | 356 | 3.8 | 0.4 | 0.0 | 0.0 | 5.0 |
| · Other | 154 | 3.1 | 0.4 | 0.0 | 0.0 | 5.0 |
| *Practice Arrangement* | | | | | | |
| Self-Employed | 1798 | 4.4 | 0.2 | 0.0 | 1.0 | 7.0 |
| Employee | 1186 | 2.8 | 0.2 | 0.0 | 0.0 | 4.0 |
| Independent Contractor | 147 | 1.9 | 0.4 | 0.0 | 0.0 | 0.0 |

Source: 1995 Socioeconomic Monitoring System surveys of nonfederal patient care physicians and federal patient care physicians employed by the Department of Defense or the Department of Veterans Affairs. See the beginning of this section, the introduction, and appendices for a discussion of the survey sample, definitions, and computation procedures. Statistics are not reported if the number of responses is less than 25.

Table 128. **Surgical Procedures, Excluding Assists, per Week, for Federal and Nonfederal Physicians (excluding Physicians in Radiology, Psychiatry, Anesthesiology, and Pathology), 1995**

| | Number of Responses | Mean | Standard Error | 25th Percentile | Median | 75th Percentile |
|---|---|---|---|---|---|---|
| All Physicians | 3118 | 3.2 | 0.1 | 0.0 | 0.0 | 5.0 |
| *Specialty* | | | | | | |
| General/Family Practice | 513 | 0.4 | 0.1 | 0.0 | 0.0 | 0.0 |
| Internal Medicine | 791 | 2.2 | 0.2 | 0.0 | 0.0 | 0.0 |
| · General Internal Medicine | 544 | 0.5 | 0.1 | 0.0 | 0.0 | 0.0 |
| · Cardiovascular Diseases | 102 | 4.7 | 0.7 | 0.0 | 0.0 | 8.0 |
| · Other | 145 | 7.0 | 0.9 | 0.0 | 0.0 | 12.0 |
| Surgery | 881 | 7.5 | 0.2 | 4.0 | 7.0 | 10.0 |
| · General Surgery | 223 | 9.0 | 0.4 | 5.0 | 8.0 | 11.0 |
| · Otolaryngology | 76 | 8.8 | 0.6 | 4.0 | 8.0 | 11.0 |
| · Orthopedic Surgery | 184 | 7.1 | 0.3 | 4.0 | 7.0 | 10.0 |
| · Ophthalmology | 187 | 5.5 | 0.4 | 2.0 | 4.0 | 7.0 |
| · Urological Surgery | 96 | 8.0 | 0.4 | 5.0 | 8.0 | 10.0 |
| · Other | 115 | 6.6 | 0.4 | 4.0 | 6.0 | 10.0 |
| Pediatrics | 311 | 0.7 | 0.2 | 0.0 | 0.0 | 0.0 |
| Obstetrics/Gynecology | 242 | 6.1 | 0.4 | 3.0 | 5.0 | 8.0 |
| Other Specialty | 380 | 0.7 | 0.3 | 0.0 | 0.0 | 0.0 |
| · Emergency Medicine | 136 | 0.0 | 0.0 | 0.0 | 0.0 | 0.0 |
| · Other | 244 | 1.0 | 0.4 | 0.0 | 0.0 | 0.0 |
| *Geographic Area* | | | | | | |
| New England | 195 | 2.5 | 0.3 | 0.0 | 0.0 | 4.0 |
| · Massachusetts | 90 | 2.5 | 0.5 | 0.0 | 0.0 | 4.0 |
| · Other | 105 | 2.5 | 0.4 | 0.0 | 0.0 | 4.0 |
| Middle Atlantic | 488 | 2.5 | 0.2 | 0.0 | 0.0 | 3.0 |
| · New Jersey | 90 | 1.9 | 0.5 | 0.0 | 0.0 | 2.0 |
| · New York | 193 | 2.6 | 0.4 | 0.0 | 0.0 | 4.0 |
| · Pennsylvania | 205 | 2.8 | 0.4 | 0.0 | 0.0 | 5.0 |
| East North Central | 464 | 3.5 | 0.3 | 0.0 | 0.0 | 6.0 |
| · Illinois | 154 | 3.1 | 0.4 | 0.0 | 0.0 | 6.0 |
| · Michigan | 87 | 4.5 | 0.7 | 0.0 | 0.0 | 9.0 |
| · Ohio | 103 | 2.6 | 0.5 | 0.0 | 0.0 | 4.0 |
| · Other | 120 | 4.2 | 0.5 | 0.0 | 0.0 | 6.0 |
| West North Central | 229 | 3.8 | 0.4 | 0.0 | 1.0 | 7.0 |
| South Atlantic | 576 | 3.7 | 0.2 | 0.0 | 0.0 | 6.0 |
| · Florida | 164 | 4.9 | 0.6 | 0.0 | 0.0 | 9.0 |
| · Other | 412 | 3.1 | 0.3 | 0.0 | 0.0 | 5.0 |
| East South Central | 187 | 3.9 | 0.5 | 0.0 | 0.0 | 6.0 |
| West South Central | 288 | 3.5 | 0.3 | 0.0 | 0.0 | 5.0 |
| · Texas | 192 | 3.1 | 0.4 | 0.0 | 0.0 | 5.0 |
| · Other | 96 | 4.2 | 0.6 | 0.0 | 2.0 | 7.0 |
| Mountain | 183 | 3.0 | 0.3 | 0.0 | 0.0 | 5.0 |
| Pacific | 508 | 3.0 | 0.3 | 0.0 | 0.0 | 4.0 |
| · California | 354 | 3.2 | 0.4 | 0.0 | 0.0 | 4.0 |
| · Other | 154 | 2.5 | 0.3 | 0.0 | 0.0 | 4.0 |
| *Practice Arrangement* | | | | | | |
| Self-Employed | 1794 | 3.9 | 0.1 | 0.0 | 0.0 | 6.0 |
| Employee | 1177 | 2.5 | 0.2 | 0.0 | 0.0 | 3.0 |
| Independent Contractor | 147 | 1.7 | 0.4 | 0.0 | 0.0 | 0.0 |

Source: 1995 Socioeconomic Monitoring System surveys of nonfederal patient care physicians and federal patient care physicians employed by the Department of Defense or the Department of Veterans Affairs. See the beginning of this section, the introduction, and appendices for a discussion of the survey sample, definitions, and computation procedures. Statistics are not reported if the number of responses is less than 25.

Table 129. **Patients Discharged from the Hospital per Week, for Federal and Nonfederal Physicians (excluding Physicians in Radiology, Psychiatry, Anesthesiology, and Pathology), 1995**

|  | Number of Responses | Mean | Standard Error | 25th Percentile | Median | 75th Percentile |
|---|---|---|---|---|---|---|
| All Physicians | 1924 | 5.4 | 0.1 | 2.0 | 4.0 | 6.0 |
| *Specialty* | | | | | | |
| General/Family Practice | 335 | 5.1 | 0.5 | 2.0 | 3.0 | 5.0 |
| Internal Medicine | 589 | 5.2 | 0.3 | 2.0 | 4.0 | 6.0 |
| · General Internal Medicine | 398 | 4.7 | 0.2 | 2.0 | 4.0 | 6.0 |
| · Cardiovascular Diseases | 84 | 8.2 | 1.0 | 3.0 | 5.0 | 10.0 |
| · Other | 107 | 4.8 | 0.6 | 1.0 | 4.0 | 6.0 |
| Surgery | 642 | 5.7 | 0.2 | 3.0 | 5.0 | 7.0 |
| · General Surgery | 190 | 7.5 | 0.4 | 4.0 | 6.0 | 10.0 |
| · Otolaryngology | 64 | 4.3 | 0.5 | 1.0 | 3.0 | 6.0 |
| · Orthopedic Surgery | 153 | 4.9 | 0.3 | 2.0 | 4.0 | 6.0 |
| · Ophthalmology | 61 | 1.7 | 0.3 | 0.0 | 1.0 | 2.0 |
| · Urological Surgery | 85 | 5.4 | 0.4 | 3.0 | 4.0 | 6.0 |
| · Other | 89 | 6.3 | 0.6 | 3.0 | 5.0 | 8.0 |
| Pediatrics | 51 | 7.6 | 1.5 | 3.0 | 5.0 | 10.0 |
| Obstetrics/Gynecology | 191 | 6.0 | 0.4 | 3.0 | 5.0 | 7.0 |
| Other Specialty | 116 | 3.3 | 0.7 | 0.0 | 2.0 | 4.0 |
| · Emergency Medicine | 5 | . | . | . | . | . |
| · Other | 111 | 2.6 | 0.3 | 0.0 | 2.0 | 4.0 |
| *Geographic Area* | | | | | | |
| New England | 117 | 4.1 | 0.3 | 2.0 | 3.0 | 6.0 |
| · Massachusetts | 57 | 4.8 | 0.5 | 2.0 | 4.0 | 7.0 |
| · Other | 60 | 3.2 | 0.4 | 1.0 | 2.0 | 5.0 |
| Middle Atlantic | 311 | 5.2 | 0.3 | 2.0 | 4.0 | 6.0 |
| · New Jersey | 53 | 4.5 | 0.6 | 2.0 | 3.0 | 5.0 |
| · New York | 118 | 5.1 | 0.5 | 2.0 | 3.0 | 5.0 |
| · Pennsylvania | 140 | 5.4 | 0.4 | 2.0 | 4.0 | 7.0 |
| East North Central | 306 | 5.8 | 0.4 | 2.0 | 4.0 | 8.0 |
| · Illinois | 106 | 6.3 | 0.7 | 2.0 | 5.0 | 8.0 |
| · Michigan | 58 | 5.5 | 1.2 | 1.0 | 4.0 | 6.0 |
| · Ohio | 64 | 4.4 | 0.5 | 1.0 | 4.0 | 5.0 |
| · Other | 78 | 6.5 | 0.6 | 3.0 | 5.0 | 8.0 |
| West North Central | 151 | 5.9 | 0.6 | 2.0 | 5.0 | 8.0 |
| South Atlantic | 334 | 5.2 | 0.3 | 2.0 | 4.0 | 7.0 |
| · Florida | 83 | 5.5 | 0.7 | 2.0 | 3.0 | 6.0 |
| · Other | 251 | 5.1 | 0.3 | 2.0 | 4.0 | 8.0 |
| East South Central | 126 | 7.0 | 0.8 | 3.0 | 5.0 | 8.0 |
| West South Central | 166 | 6.2 | 0.6 | 2.0 | 5.0 | 8.0 |
| · Texas | 108 | 5.5 | 0.5 | 3.0 | 5.0 | 6.0 |
| · Other | 58 | 7.9 | 1.5 | 2.0 | 4.0 | 10.0 |
| Mountain | 112 | 5.1 | 0.5 | 2.0 | 4.0 | 6.0 |
| Pacific | 301 | 4.6 | 0.4 | 2.0 | 3.0 | 6.0 |
| · California | 210 | 4.6 | 0.5 | 2.0 | 3.0 | 5.0 |
| · Other | 91 | 4.7 | 0.3 | 3.0 | 4.0 | 6.0 |
| *Practice Arrangement* | | | | | | |
| Self-Employed | 1214 | 5.6 | 0.2 | 2.0 | 4.0 | 7.0 |
| Employee | 662 | 4.9 | 0.2 | 2.0 | 4.0 | 6.0 |
| Independent Contractor | 48 | 5.8 | 1.6 | 2.0 | 3.0 | 6.0 |

Source: 1995 Socioeconomic Monitoring System surveys of nonfederal patient care physicians and federal patient care physicians employed by the Department of Defense or the Department of Veterans Affairs. See the beginning of this section, the introduction, and appendices for a discussion of the survey sample, definitions, and computation procedures. Statistics are not reported if the number of responses is less than 25.

Table 130. **Average Length of Hospital Stay of Patients Discharged from the Hospital, for Federal and Nonfederal Physicians (excluding Physicians in Radiology, Psychiatry, Anesthesiology, and Pathology), 1995**

| | Number of Responses | Mean | Standard Error | 25th Percentile | Median | 75th Percentile |
|---|---|---|---|---|---|---|
| All Physicians | 1660 | 4.2 | 0.1 | 2.0 | 3.0 | 5.0 |
| *Specialty* | | | | | | |
| General/Family Practice | 303 | 4.2 | 0.2 | 3.0 | 4.0 | 5.0 |
| Internal Medicine | 493 | 5.5 | 0.3 | 3.0 | 4.0 | 5.0 |
| · General Internal Medicine | 334 | 5.4 | 0.3 | 3.0 | 5.0 | 5.0 |
| · Cardiovascular Diseases | 73 | 4.3 | 0.3 | 3.0 | 4.0 | 5.0 |
| · Other | 86 | 6.6 | 1.2 | 3.0 | 4.0 | 6.0 |
| Surgery | 572 | 3.2 | 0.1 | 2.0 | 3.0 | 4.0 |
| · General Surgery | 179 | 3.4 | 0.1 | 2.0 | 3.0 | 4.0 |
| · Otolaryngology | 56 | 2.3 | 0.2 | 1.0 | 2.0 | 3.0 |
| · Orthopedic Surgery | 144 | 3.5 | 0.1 | 2.0 | 3.0 | 5.0 |
| · Ophthalmology | 29 | 1.6 | 0.3 | 1.0 | 1.0 | 1.0 |
| · Urological Surgery | 81 | 2.9 | 0.2 | 2.0 | 3.0 | 3.0 |
| · Other | 83 | 3.5 | 0.2 | 2.0 | 3.0 | 4.0 |
| Pediatrics | 44 | 4.2 | 0.8 | 2.0 | 2.0 | 5.0 |
| Obstetrics/Gynecology | 181 | 2.0 | 0.1 | 1.0 | 2.0 | 2.0 |
| Other Specialty | 67 | 8.7 | 0.9 | 4.0 | 5.0 | 14.0 |
| · Emergency Medicine | 3 | . | . | . | . | . |
| · Other | 64 | 9.0 | 0.9 | 4.0 | 5.0 | 15.0 |
| *Geographic Area* | | | | | | |
| New England | 98 | 4.4 | 0.4 | 2.0 | 4.0 | 5.0 |
| · Massachusetts | 49 | 3.9 | 0.3 | 2.0 | 4.0 | 5.0 |
| · Other | 49 | 4.9 | 0.7 | 2.0 | 4.0 | 6.0 |
| Middle Atlantic | 262 | 5.0 | 0.3 | 3.0 | 4.0 | 5.0 |
| · New Jersey | 41 | 4.5 | 0.6 | 3.0 | 4.0 | 5.0 |
| · New York | 98 | 4.7 | 0.4 | 3.0 | 4.0 | 5.0 |
| · Pennsylvania | 123 | 5.4 | 0.6 | 3.0 | 4.0 | 6.0 |
| East North Central | 259 | 4.4 | 0.4 | 2.0 | 3.0 | 5.0 |
| · Illinois | 89 | 3.5 | 0.3 | 2.0 | 3.0 | 5.0 |
| · Michigan | 45 | 4.8 | 0.6 | 2.0 | 4.0 | 5.0 |
| · Ohio | 53 | 5.4 | 1.4 | 3.0 | 4.0 | 5.0 |
| · Other | 72 | 4.6 | 0.8 | 2.0 | 3.0 | 5.0 |
| West North Central | 129 | 3.6 | 0.2 | 2.0 | 3.0 | 5.0 |
| South Atlantic | 288 | 3.9 | 0.2 | 2.0 | 3.0 | 5.0 |
| · Florida | 73 | 4.5 | 0.6 | 3.0 | 4.0 | 5.0 |
| · Other | 215 | 3.7 | 0.2 | 2.0 | 3.0 | 5.0 |
| East South Central | 116 | 6.1 | 0.9 | 3.0 | 4.0 | 5.0 |
| West South Central | 145 | 3.8 | 0.2 | 2.0 | 3.0 | 5.0 |
| · Texas | 96 | 4.0 | 0.3 | 2.0 | 3.0 | 5.0 |
| · Other | 49 | 3.4 | 0.2 | 2.0 | 3.0 | 5.0 |
| Mountain | 101 | 3.4 | 0.3 | 2.0 | 3.0 | 4.0 |
| Pacific | 262 | 3.8 | 0.2 | 2.0 | 3.0 | 5.0 |
| · California | 181 | 3.9 | 0.3 | 2.0 | 3.0 | 5.0 |
| · Other | 81 | 3.5 | 0.2 | 2.0 | 3.0 | 4.0 |
| *Practice Arrangement* | | | | | | |
| Self-Employed | 1079 | 3.9 | 0.1 | 2.0 | 3.0 | 5.0 |
| Employee | 541 | 4.7 | 0.2 | 2.0 | 4.0 | 5.0 |
| Independent Contractor | 40 | 5.7 | 1.7 | 3.0 | 3.0 | 5.0 |

Source: 1995 Socioeconomic Monitoring System surveys of nonfederal patient care physicians and federal patient care physicians employed by the Department of Defense or the Department of Veterans Affairs. See the beginning of this section, the introduction, and appendices for a discussion of the survey sample, definitions, and computation procedures. Statistics are not reported if the number of responses is less than 25.

Table 131. **Net Income after Expenses before Taxes per Federal and Nonfederal Physician (in thousands of dollars), 1994**

| | Number of Responses | Mean | Standard Error | 25th Percentile | Median | 75th Percentile |
|---|---|---|---|---|---|---|
| All Physicians | 3195 | 180.4 | 2.1 | 104.0 | 150.0 | 220.0 |
| *Specialty* | | | | | | |
| General/Family Practice | 420 | 120.2 | 2.9 | 85.0 | 109.0 | 144.0 |
| Internal Medicine | 600 | 173.4 | 5.3 | 100.0 | 145.0 | 197.0 |
| · General Internal Medicine | 427 | 147.1 | 4.4 | 99.0 | 130.0 | 172.0 |
| · Cardiovascular Diseases | 66 | 276.6 | 24.8 | 150.0 | 220.0 | 400.0 |
| · Other | 107 | 217.9 | 14.5 | 127.0 | 180.0 | 280.0 |
| Surgery | 680 | 251.9 | 6.2 | 146.0 | 215.0 | 300.0 |
| · General Surgery | 181 | 232.6 | 10.8 | 132.0 | 200.0 | 275.0 |
| · Otolaryngology | 55 | 245.5 | 14.0 | 175.0 | 225.0 | 300.0 |
| · Orthopedic Surgery | 140 | 306.7 | 16.5 | 185.0 | 265.0 | 375.0 |
| · Ophthalmology | 138 | 225.0 | 13.9 | 125.0 | 175.0 | 250.0 |
| · Urological Surgery | 77 | 223.1 | 11.3 | 150.0 | 204.0 | 277.0 |
| · Other | 89 | 277.3 | 19.9 | 142.0 | 225.0 | 350.0 |
| Pediatrics | 242 | 124.8 | 4.6 | 80.0 | 110.0 | 150.0 |
| Obstetrics/Gynecology | 183 | 200.4 | 8.9 | 130.0 | 182.0 | 248.0 |
| Radiology | 205 | 232.6 | 6.8 | 156.0 | 210.0 | 300.0 |
| Psychiatry | 250 | 127.7 | 3.8 | 90.0 | 120.0 | 150.0 |
| Anesthesiology | 197 | 217.9 | 5.8 | 168.0 | 200.0 | 262.0 |
| Pathology | 109 | 179.8 | 8.5 | 115.0 | 150.0 | 210.0 |
| Other Specialty | 309 | 155.8 | 4.4 | 100.0 | 150.0 | 185.0 |
| · Emergency Medicine | 125 | 164.8 | 5.8 | 120.0 | 155.0 | 197.0 |
| · Other | 184 | 150.0 | 6.2 | 96.0 | 140.0 | 175.0 |
| *Geographic Area* | | | | | | |
| New England | 203 | 155.1 | 7.0 | 100.0 | 134.0 | 180.0 |
| Middle Atlantic | 487 | 174.8 | 6.3 | 100.0 | 140.0 | 213.0 |
| East North Central | 462 | 190.8 | 5.9 | 116.0 | 160.0 | 230.0 |
| West North Central | 243 | 183.1 | 7.8 | 110.0 | 150.0 | 225.0 |
| South Atlantic | 559 | 184.9 | 5.2 | 100.0 | 150.0 | 240.0 |
| East South Central | 194 | 197.7 | 8.9 | 120.0 | 160.0 | 230.0 |
| West South Central | 290 | 194.3 | 7.4 | 110.0 | 162.0 | 234.0 |
| Mountain | 190 | 174.5 | 8.1 | 100.0 | 145.0 | 205.0 |
| Pacific | 567 | 170.3 | 4.3 | 101.0 | 150.0 | 208.0 |
| *Practice Arrangement* | | | | | | |
| Self-Employed | 1698 | 210.2 | 3.4 | 121.0 | 176.0 | 260.0 |
| Employee | 1293 | 145.5 | 2.3 | 97.0 | 129.0 | 175.0 |
| Independent Contractor | 204 | 168.5 | 7.3 | 100.0 | 140.0 | 230.0 |

Source: 1995 Socioeconomic Monitoring System surveys of nonfederal patient care physicians and federal patient care physicians employed by the Department of Defense or the Department of Veterans Affairs. See the beginning of this section, the introduction, and appendices for a discussion of the survey sample, definitions, and computation procedures. Statistics are not reported if the number of responses is less than 25.

Table 132. **Net Income after Expenses before Taxes per Federal and Employee Nonfederal Physician (in thousands of dollars), 1994**

| | Number of Responses | Mean | Standard Error | 25th Percentile | Median | 75th Percentile |
|---|---|---|---|---|---|---|
| All Physicians | 1293 | 145.5 | 2.3 | 97.0 | 129.0 | 175.0 |
| *Specialty* | | | | | | |
| General/Family Practice | 188 | 107.1 | 3.3 | 81.0 | 100.0 | 125.0 |
| Internal Medicine | 258 | 131.7 | 3.9 | 97.0 | 120.0 | 157.0 |
| · General Internal Medicine | 202 | 125.6 | 3.8 | 97.0 | 120.0 | 150.0 |
| · Cardiovascular Diseases | 24 | . | . | . | . | . |
| · Other | 32 | 153.5 | 11.1 | 115.0 | 127.0 | 202.0 |
| Surgery | 192 | 204.4 | 9.7 | 127.0 | 170.0 | 240.0 |
| · General Surgery | 59 | 201.7 | 16.9 | 120.0 | 170.0 | 250.0 |
| · Otolaryngology | 11 | . | . | . | . | . |
| · Orthopedic Surgery | 40 | 203.6 | 16.3 | 143.0 | 190.0 | 235.0 |
| · Ophthalmology | 41 | 157.9 | 10.8 | 115.0 | 150.0 | 190.0 |
| · Urological Surgery | 19 | . | . | . | . | . |
| · Other | 22 | . | . | . | . | . |
| Pediatrics | 119 | 113.9 | 5.6 | 72.0 | 100.0 | 131.0 |
| Obstetrics/Gynecology | 57 | 188.6 | 13.5 | 122.0 | 175.0 | 235.0 |
| Radiology | 98 | 192.3 | 7.9 | 140.0 | 180.0 | 225.0 |
| Psychiatry | 111 | 117.0 | 3.5 | 90.0 | 120.0 | 140.0 |
| Anesthesiology | 67 | 184.5 | 8.4 | 136.0 | 180.0 | 218.0 |
| Pathology | 60 | 140.6 | 6.4 | 104.0 | 126.0 | 175.0 |
| Other Specialty | 143 | 139.1 | 4.9 | 100.0 | 140.0 | 170.0 |
| · Emergency Medicine | 51 | 149.3 | 7.1 | 110.0 | 150.0 | 172.0 |
| · Other | 92 | 133.8 | 6.4 | 96.0 | 130.0 | 165.0 |
| *Geographic Area* | | | | | | |
| New England | 105 | 126.9 | 5.4 | 90.0 | 115.0 | 150.0 |
| Middle Atlantic | 200 | 131.5 | 4.8 | 90.0 | 120.0 | 150.0 |
| East North Central | 192 | 163.4 | 6.9 | 110.0 | 147.0 | 195.0 |
| West North Central | 108 | 170.9 | 12.7 | 112.0 | 150.0 | 190.0 |
| South Atlantic | 224 | 134.2 | 4.9 | 88.0 | 116.0 | 168.0 |
| East South Central | 55 | 144.8 | 7.5 | 112.0 | 140.0 | 181.0 |
| West South Central | 110 | 153.6 | 9.4 | 97.0 | 125.0 | 180.0 |
| Mountain | 83 | 134.5 | 8.8 | 90.0 | 120.0 | 150.0 |
| Pacific | 216 | 153.1 | 4.7 | 100.0 | 140.0 | 190.0 |

Source: 1995 Socioeconomic Monitoring System surveys of nonfederal patient care physicians and federal patient care physicians employed by the Department of Defense or the Department of Veterans Affairs. See the beginning of this section, the introduction, and appendices for a discussion of the survey sample, definitions, and computation procedures. Statistics are not reported if the number of responses is less than 25.

## Table 133. **Percentage of Time Spent in Primary Care Activities by Federal and Nonfederal Physicians, 1995**

| | Number of Responses | Mean | Standard Error | 25th Percentile | Median | 75th Percentile |
|---|---|---|---|---|---|---|
| All Physicians | 3822 | 31.1 | 0.6 | 0.0 | 1.0 | 70.0 |
| *Specialty* | | | | | | |
| General/Family Practice | 515 | 80.7 | 1.3 | 75.0 | 100.0 | 100.0 |
| Internal Medicine | 786 | 39.7 | 1.6 | 0.0 | 25.0 | 80.0 |
| · General Internal Medicine | 538 | 53.5 | 1.9 | 10.0 | 55.0 | 99.0 |
| · Cardiovascular Diseases | 104 | 8.9 | 2.0 | 0.0 | 0.0 | 5.0 |
| · Other | 144 | 7.5 | 1.3 | 0.0 | 0.0 | 10.0 |
| Surgery | 897 | 4.5 | 0.5 | 0.0 | 0.0 | 0.0 |
| · General Surgery | 230 | 4.2 | 0.9 | 0.0 | 0.0 | 0.0 |
| · Otolaryngology | 77 | 4.5 | 1.2 | 0.0 | 0.0 | 0.0 |
| · Orthopedic Surgery | 190 | 3.3 | 0.8 | 0.0 | 0.0 | 0.0 |
| · Ophthalmology | 184 | 8.8 | 1.5 | 0.0 | 0.0 | 0.0 |
| · Urological Surgery | 97 | 1.7 | 0.6 | 0.0 | 0.0 | 0.0 |
| · Other | 119 | 2.9 | 1.3 | 0.0 | 0.0 | 0.0 |
| Pediatrics | 308 | 66.9 | 2.1 | 40.0 | 80.0 | 100.0 |
| Obstetrics/Gynecology | 247 | 22.3 | 1.6 | 2.0 | 15.0 | 40.0 |
| Radiology | 182 | 3.8 | 1.2 | 0.0 | 0.0 | 0.0 |
| Psychiatry | 290 | 3.9 | 0.8 | 0.0 | 0.0 | 0.0 |
| Anesthesiology | 148 | 0.0 | 0.0 | 0.0 | 0.0 | 0.0 |
| Pathology | 71 | 1.2 | 1.1 | 0.0 | 0.0 | 0.0 |
| Other Specialty | 378 | 23.4 | 1.8 | 0.0 | 0.0 | 50.0 |
| · Emergency Medicine | 136 | 31.3 | 2.9 | 0.0 | 20.0 | 50.0 |
| · Other | 242 | 19.2 | 2.3 | 0.0 | 0.0 | 20.0 |
| *Geographic Area* | | | | | | |
| New England | 246 | 31.3 | 2.7 | 0.0 | 5.0 | 75.0 |
| · Massachusetts | 115 | 32.9 | 4.2 | 0.0 | 2.0 | 75.0 |
| · Other | 131 | 29.7 | 3.5 | 0.0 | 5.0 | 67.0 |
| Middle Atlantic | 613 | 31.6 | 1.7 | 0.0 | 0.0 | 70.0 |
| · New Jersey | 108 | 38.4 | 4.4 | 0.0 | 20.0 | 80.0 |
| · New York | 255 | 27.5 | 2.5 | 0.0 | 0.0 | 50.0 |
| · Pennsylvania | 250 | 32.7 | 2.5 | 0.0 | 5.0 | 80.0 |
| East North Central | 562 | 29.0 | 1.7 | 0.0 | 0.0 | 60.0 |
| · Illinois | 174 | 29.6 | 3.1 | 0.0 | 5.0 | 70.0 |
| · Michigan | 106 | 24.2 | 3.7 | 0.0 | 0.0 | 50.0 |
| · Ohio | 130 | 31.6 | 3.6 | 0.0 | 15.0 | 65.0 |
| · Other | 152 | 29.6 | 3.2 | 0.0 | 0.0 | 60.0 |
| West North Central | 283 | 33.4 | 2.4 | 0.0 | 1.0 | 80.0 |
| South Atlantic | 699 | 29.0 | 1.5 | 0.0 | 0.0 | 50.0 |
| · Florida | 198 | 26.2 | 2.8 | 0.0 | 0.0 | 40.0 |
| · Other | 501 | 30.2 | 1.8 | 0.0 | 3.0 | 60.0 |
| East South Central | 221 | 32.2 | 2.6 | 0.0 | 5.0 | 75.0 |
| West South Central | 352 | 30.9 | 2.0 | 0.0 | 0.0 | 70.0 |
| · Texas | 232 | 31.5 | 2.6 | 0.0 | 5.0 | 66.0 |
| · Other | 120 | 29.5 | 3.3 | 0.0 | 0.0 | 70.0 |
| Mountain | 221 | 35.8 | 2.7 | 0.0 | 10.0 | 80.0 |
| Pacific | 625 | 31.9 | 1.6 | 0.0 | 0.0 | 75.0 |
| · California | 435 | 30.4 | 2.0 | 0.0 | 0.0 | 65.0 |
| · Other | 190 | 36.1 | 2.9 | 0.0 | 5.0 | 80.0 |
| *Practice Arrangement* | | | | | | |
| Self-Employed | 2137 | 28.0 | 0.8 | 0.0 | 0.0 | 55.0 |
| Employee | 1472 | 34.9 | 1.1 | 0.0 | 10.0 | 80.0 |
| Independent Contractor | 213 | 33.4 | 2.9 | 0.0 | 10.0 | 75.0 |

Source: 1995 Socioeconomic Monitoring System surveys of nonfederal patient care physicians and federal patient care physicians employed by the Department of Defense or the Department of Veterans Affairs. See the beginning of this section, the introduction, and appendices for a discussion of the survey sample, definitions, and computation procedures. Statistics are not reported if the number of responses is less than 25.

Table 134. **Percentage of Time Spent in Primary Care Activities, by Federal and Nonfederal Physicians Who Perform Primary Care Activities, 1995**

| | Number of Responses | Mean | Standard Error | 25th Percentile | Median | 75th Percentile |
|---|---|---|---|---|---|---|
| All Physicians | 1835 | 61.0 | 0.9 | 25.0 | 70.0 | 100.0 |
| *Specialty* | | | | | | |
| General/Family Practice | 510 | 81.3 | 1.3 | 75.0 | 100.0 | 100.0 |
| Internal Medicine | 533 | 59.2 | 1.7 | 25.0 | 60.0 | 100.0 |
| · General Internal Medicine | 452 | 65.3 | 1.8 | 30.0 | 75.0 | 100.0 |
| · Cardiovascular Diseases | 31 | 30.4 | 4.9 | 10.0 | 25.0 | 50.0 |
| · Other | 50 | 21.1 | 2.5 | 5.0 | 20.0 | 30.0 |
| Surgery | 125 | 30.7 | 2.4 | 10.0 | 20.0 | 50.0 |
| · General Surgery | 29 | 26.1 | 4.8 | 5.0 | 20.0 | 50.0 |
| · Otolaryngology | 15 | . | . | . | . | . |
| · Orthopedic Surgery | 21 | . | . | . | . | . |
| · Ophthalmology | 39 | 45.0 | 4.3 | 20.0 | 40.0 | 70.0 |
| · Urological Surgery | 11 | . | . | . | . | . |
| · Other | 10 | . | . | . | . | . |
| Pediatrics | 263 | 77.7 | 1.7 | 60.0 | 90.0 | 100.0 |
| Obstetrics/Gynecology | 193 | 29.1 | 1.7 | 10.0 | 25.0 | 50.0 |
| Radiology | 8 | . | . | . | . | . |
| Psychiatry | 41 | 26.5 | 4.2 | 5.0 | 20.0 | 40.0 |
| Anesthesiology | 1 | . | . | . | . | . |
| Pathology | 2 | . | . | . | . | . |
| Other Specialty | 159 | 52.4 | 2.8 | 20.0 | 50.0 | 80.0 |
| · Emergency Medicine | 90 | 46.9 | 3.3 | 20.0 | 40.0 | 70.0 |
| · Other | 69 | 58.4 | 4.8 | 20.0 | 70.0 | 95.0 |
| *Geographic Area* | | | | | | |
| New England | 126 | 59.1 | 3.6 | 20.0 | 70.0 | 100.0 |
| · Massachusetts | 59 | 61.5 | 5.6 | 20.0 | 70.0 | 100.0 |
| · Other | 67 | 56.7 | 4.6 | 20.0 | 60.0 | 100.0 |
| Middle Atlantic | 288 | 62.8 | 2.2 | 25.0 | 70.0 | 100.0 |
| · New Jersey | 50 | 71.8 | 4.8 | 50.0 | 75.0 | 100.0 |
| · New York | 109 | 60.6 | 3.7 | 30.0 | 60.0 | 100.0 |
| · Pennsylvania | 129 | 59.9 | 3.3 | 20.0 | 75.0 | 100.0 |
| East North Central | 274 | 56.7 | 2.3 | 20.0 | 60.0 | 100.0 |
| · Illinois | 88 | 58.0 | 4.0 | 20.0 | 65.0 | 95.0 |
| · Michigan | 46 | 51.5 | 6.2 | 10.0 | 50.0 | 100.0 |
| · Ohio | 66 | 57.0 | 4.9 | 20.0 | 50.0 | 100.0 |
| · Other | 74 | 58.3 | 4.4 | 25.0 | 60.0 | 100.0 |
| West North Central | 136 | 66.4 | 2.9 | 30.0 | 80.0 | 100.0 |
| South Atlantic | 319 | 58.9 | 2.2 | 20.0 | 60.0 | 100.0 |
| · Florida | 82 | 58.2 | 4.5 | 25.0 | 50.0 | 100.0 |
| · Other | 237 | 59.1 | 2.5 | 20.0 | 60.0 | 100.0 |
| East South Central | 118 | 58.4 | 3.5 | 20.0 | 60.0 | 100.0 |
| West South Central | 165 | 62.1 | 2.6 | 30.0 | 70.0 | 96.0 |
| · Texas | 112 | 60.9 | 3.3 | 30.0 | 60.0 | 100.0 |
| · Other | 53 | 65.2 | 4.2 | 30.0 | 75.0 | 95.0 |
| Mountain | 123 | 63.1 | 3.1 | 30.0 | 75.0 | 100.0 |
| Pacific | 286 | 63.8 | 2.2 | 30.0 | 75.0 | 100.0 |
| · California | 193 | 62.0 | 2.7 | 30.0 | 65.0 | 100.0 |
| · Other | 93 | 68.6 | 3.4 | 35.0 | 80.0 | 100.0 |
| *Practice Arrangement* | | | | | | |
| Self-Employed | 962 | 59.3 | 1.2 | 25.0 | 60.0 | 100.0 |
| Employee | 774 | 63.1 | 1.4 | 25.0 | 75.0 | 100.0 |
| Independent Contractor | 99 | 60.3 | 4.2 | 25.0 | 65.0 | 100.0 |

Source: 1995 Socioeconomic Monitoring System surveys of nonfederal patient care physicians and federal patient care physicians employed by the Department of Defense or the Department of Veterans Affairs. See the beginning of this section, the introduction, and appendices for a discussion of the survey sample, definitions, and computation procedures. Statistics are not reported if the number of responses is less than 25.

**Table 135. Average Days of Wait for an Appointment by New Patients, for Federal and Nonfederal Physicians (excluding Physicians in Radiology, Psychiatry, Anesthesiology, and Pathology), 1995**

| | Number of Responses | Mean | Standard Error | 25th Percentile | Median | 75th Percentile |
|---|---|---|---|---|---|---|
| All Physicians | 2945 | 19.8 | 0.3 | 10.0 | 15.0 | 30.0 |
| *Specialty* | | | | | | |
| General/Family Practice | 505 | 20.3 | 0.6 | 10.0 | 15.0 | 30.0 |
| Internal Medicine | 779 | 19.6 | 0.7 | 10.0 | 15.0 | 30.0 |
| · General Internal Medicine | 534 | 20.0 | 1.0 | 10.0 | 15.0 | 30.0 |
| · Cardiovascular Diseases | 103 | 17.8 | 1.2 | 10.0 | 15.0 | 20.0 |
| · Other | 142 | 19.2 | 1.2 | 10.0 | 15.0 | 30.0 |
| Surgery | 880 | 21.3 | 0.6 | 10.0 | 15.0 | 30.0 |
| · General Surgery | 220 | 20.6 | 1.0 | 10.0 | 15.0 | 30.0 |
| · Otolaryngology | 75 | 19.3 | 1.6 | 15.0 | 15.0 | 20.0 |
| · Orthopedic Surgery | 184 | 23.9 | 1.3 | 15.0 | 15.0 | 30.0 |
| · Ophthalmology | 186 | 21.3 | 1.2 | 10.0 | 15.0 | 30.0 |
| · Urological Surgery | 96 | 19.8 | 1.2 | 10.0 | 15.0 | 30.0 |
| · Other | 119 | 21.5 | 2.1 | 10.0 | 15.0 | 30.0 |
| Pediatrics | 304 | 18.3 | 0.7 | 10.0 | 15.0 | 30.0 |
| Obstetrics/Gynecology | 241 | 20.0 | 1.0 | 10.0 | 15.0 | 30.0 |
| Other Specialty | 236 | 16.6 | 0.9 | 10.0 | 15.0 | 20.0 |
| · Emergency Medicine | 0 | . | . | . | . | . |
| · Other | 236 | 16.6 | 0.9 | 10.0 | 15.0 | 20.0 |
| *Geographic Area* | | | | | | |
| New England | 185 | 15.8 | 0.9 | 10.0 | 15.0 | 20.0 |
| · Massachusetts | 84 | 14.7 | 1.0 | 10.0 | 15.0 | 20.0 |
| · Other | 101 | 16.8 | 1.3 | 10.0 | 15.0 | 20.0 |
| Middle Atlantic | 461 | 19.8 | 0.8 | 10.0 | 15.0 | 30.0 |
| · New Jersey | 87 | 17.6 | 1.2 | 15.0 | 15.0 | 30.0 |
| · New York | 180 | 22.7 | 1.7 | 10.0 | 15.0 | 30.0 |
| · Pennsylvania | 194 | 18.0 | 1.0 | 10.0 | 15.0 | 20.0 |
| East North Central | 432 | 19.7 | 0.8 | 10.0 | 15.0 | 25.0 |
| · Illinois | 145 | 20.8 | 1.5 | 10.0 | 15.0 | 25.0 |
| · Michigan | 81 | 21.0 | 1.9 | 10.0 | 15.0 | 30.0 |
| · Ohio | 97 | 16.9 | 1.1 | 10.0 | 15.0 | 20.0 |
| · Other | 109 | 19.8 | 1.3 | 10.0 | 15.0 | 30.0 |
| West North Central | 217 | 20.2 | 1.1 | 10.0 | 15.0 | 30.0 |
| South Atlantic | 545 | 19.9 | 0.6 | 10.0 | 15.0 | 30.0 |
| · Florida | 157 | 21.1 | 1.3 | 15.0 | 15.0 | 30.0 |
| · Other | 388 | 19.3 | 0.7 | 10.0 | 15.0 | 30.0 |
| East South Central | 179 | 25.7 | 1.5 | 15.0 | 20.0 | 30.0 |
| West South Central | 277 | 23.7 | 1.4 | 15.0 | 20.0 | 30.0 |
| · Texas | 184 | 22.4 | 1.3 | 15.0 | 15.0 | 30.0 |
| · Other | 93 | 26.7 | 3.1 | 15.0 | 20.0 | 30.0 |
| Mountain | 171 | 18.7 | 1.2 | 10.0 | 15.0 | 20.0 |
| Pacific | 478 | 17.7 | 0.7 | 10.0 | 15.0 | 20.0 |
| · California | 330 | 18.4 | 0.9 | 10.0 | 15.0 | 30.0 |
| · Other | 148 | 15.7 | 0.8 | 10.0 | 15.0 | 20.0 |
| *Practice Arrangement* | | | | | | |
| Self-Employed | 1757 | 19.4 | 0.3 | 10.0 | 15.0 | 30.0 |
| Employee | 1091 | 20.4 | 0.6 | 10.0 | 15.0 | 30.0 |
| Independent Contractor | 97 | 21.0 | 2.2 | 15.0 | 15.0 | 30.0 |

Source: 1995 Socioeconomic Monitoring System surveys of nonfederal patient care physicians and federal patient care physicians employed by the Department of Defense or the Department of Veterans Affairs. See the beginning of this section, the introduction, and appendices for a discussion of the survey sample, definitions, and computation procedures. Statistics are not reported if the number of responses is less than 25.

Table 136. **Average Minutes Waiting by Patients upon Arriving for a Scheduled Appointment, for Federal and Nonfederal Physicians (excluding Physicians in Radiology, Psychiatry, Anesthesiology, and Pathology), 1995**

| | Number of Responses | Mean | Standard Error | 25th Percentile | Median | 75th Percentile |
|---|---|---|---|---|---|---|
| All Physicians | 2882 | 9.6 | 0.3 | 1.0 | 4.0 | 12.0 |
| *Specialty* | | | | | | |
| General/Family Practice | 476 | 6.4 | 0.6 | 0.0 | 2.0 | 7.0 |
| Internal Medicine | 751 | 11.0 | 0.7 | 2.0 | 5.0 | 14.0 |
| · General Internal Medicine | 509 | 12.1 | 0.9 | 2.0 | 7.0 | 14.0 |
| · Cardiovascular Diseases | 102 | 9.3 | 1.5 | 2.0 | 5.0 | 10.0 |
| · Other | 140 | 8.1 | 0.9 | 2.0 | 5.0 | 10.0 |
| Surgery | 886 | 8.7 | 0.4 | 2.0 | 5.0 | 10.0 |
| · General Surgery | 225 | 4.6 | 0.5 | 1.0 | 2.0 | 7.0 |
| · Otolaryngology | 77 | 8.0 | 1.4 | 1.0 | 4.0 | 10.0 |
| · Orthopedic Surgery | 188 | 10.0 | 1.0 | 2.0 | 5.0 | 14.0 |
| · Ophthalmology | 184 | 14.2 | 1.4 | 2.0 | 7.0 | 15.0 |
| · Urological Surgery | 96 | 8.7 | 0.9 | 2.0 | 7.0 | 14.0 |
| · Other | 116 | 7.9 | 0.9 | 2.0 | 5.0 | 10.0 |
| Pediatrics | 295 | 7.2 | 0.7 | 0.0 | 2.0 | 8.0 |
| Obstetrics/Gynecology | 240 | 15.4 | 1.4 | 2.0 | 7.0 | 18.0 |
| Other Specialty | 234 | 9.6 | 0.8 | 1.0 | 5.0 | 14.0 |
| · Emergency Medicine | 0 | · | · | · | · | · |
| · Other | 234 | 9.6 | 0.8 | 1.0 | 5.0 | 14.0 |
| *Geographic Area* | | | | | | |
| New England | 177 | 11.6 | 1.2 | 2.0 | 7.0 | 14.0 |
| · Massachusetts | 81 | 10.9 | 1.9 | 1.0 | 5.0 | 14.0 |
| · Other | 96 | 12.2 | 1.5 | 2.0 | 8.0 | 14.0 |
| Middle Atlantic | 455 | 10.1 | 0.8 | 1.0 | 5.0 | 14.0 |
| · New Jersey | 87 | 5.5 | 1.1 | 1.0 | 3.0 | 7.0 |
| · New York | 179 | 11.7 | 1.4 | 2.0 | 7.0 | 14.0 |
| · Pennsylvania | 189 | 11.2 | 1.1 | 2.0 | 7.0 | 14.0 |
| East North Central | 422 | 11.6 | 0.9 | 2.0 | 5.0 | 14.0 |
| · Illinois | 143 | 8.9 | 1.2 | 1.0 | 3.0 | 10.0 |
| · Michigan | 77 | 16.9 | 3.0 | 3.0 | 7.0 | 17.0 |
| · Ohio | 94 | 10.7 | 1.4 | 3.0 | 7.0 | 14.0 |
| · Other | 108 | 12.4 | 1.8 | 3.0 | 5.0 | 14.0 |
| West North Central | 211 | 11.1 | 1.2 | 1.0 | 5.0 | 14.0 |
| South Atlantic | 541 | 8.8 | 0.6 | 1.0 | 3.0 | 10.0 |
| · Florida | 155 | 7.9 | 1.0 | 1.0 | 3.0 | 8.0 |
| · Other | 386 | 9.1 | 0.8 | 1.0 | 3.0 | 14.0 |
| East South Central | 175 | 7.7 | 1.0 | 1.0 | 3.0 | 7.0 |
| West South Central | 273 | 8.9 | 0.8 | 2.0 | 5.0 | 10.0 |
| · Texas | 183 | 9.0 | 0.9 | 2.0 | 5.0 | 10.0 |
| · Other | 90 | 8.6 | 1.5 | 1.0 | 4.0 | 8.0 |
| Mountain | 165 | 8.9 | 0.9 | 1.0 | 4.0 | 10.0 |
| Pacific | 463 | 8.1 | 0.7 | 1.0 | 3.0 | 10.0 |
| · California | 322 | 8.1 | 0.8 | 1.0 | 3.0 | 10.0 |
| · Other | 141 | 8.1 | 1.0 | 1.0 | 4.0 | 10.0 |
| *Practice Arrangement* | | | | | | |
| Self-Employed | 1725 | 8.9 | 0.3 | 1.0 | 4.0 | 10.0 |
| Employee | 1065 | 11.0 | 0.5 | 1.0 | 5.0 | 14.0 |
| Independent Contractor | 92 | 6.2 | 0.9 | 0.0 | 3.0 | 10.0 |

Source: 1995 Socioeconomic Monitoring System surveys of nonfederal patient care physicians and federal patient care physicians employed by the Department of Defense or the Department of Veterans Affairs. See the beginning of this section, the introduction, and appendices for a discussion of the survey sample, definitions, and computation procedures. Statistics are not reported if the number of responses is less than 25.

# Appendices

The Design and Methodology of the AMA Socioeconomic Monitoring System

Weighting and Computation Methodology

Definitions of Physician Classification and Characteristics

Appendix A
# The Design and Methodology of the AMA Socioeconomic Monitoring System

## Methodology for the Survey of Nonfederal Physicians

The annual core survey of the Socioeconomic Monitoring System (SMS) covers a broad range of economic and practice characteristics. The average core survey interview lasts 28 minutes and obtains data from approximately 4,000 physicians. The survey is generally fielded from March through July. The timing of the beginning of the core survey is designed to coincide with the income tax return filing deadline in order to improve reliability of information that can be obtained on physician earnings and practice expenses for the previous year.

All results reported in this volume are from the 1995 survey. The sample size is the primary determinant of the level of disaggregation at which results can be reported.

## Sample Design

The SMS surveys are designed to provide representative information on the population of all nonfederal physicians who spend the greatest proportion of their time in patient care activities. This includes both office and hospital-based physicians, but excludes residents. Samples for SMS surveys are selected from the AMA Physician Masterfile. The Masterfile contains current and historical information on every doctor of medicine in the United States, including both members and nonmembers of the AMA. Graduates of United States medical schools who are temporarily practicing overseas, and graduates of foreign medical schools who live in the United States are also included on the file.

Data included on the Masterfile are obtained from primary sources, including many organizations and institutions. The only information obtained directly from individual physicians concerns current professional activities and preferred mailing addresses. These data are obtained on a quadrennial basis from the entire United States physician population

and on a monthly basis from those physicians with changes in address or professional status. These changes may be signaled by input from professional organizations, AMA mailings, or by physician correspondence.

In addition to limiting the SMS sample to nonfederal patient care physicians who have completed their residency programs and are practicing in the United States, the following exclusions are made:

* doctors of osteopathy;
* graduates of foreign medical schools who are only temporarily licensed to practice in the United States;
* inactive physicians;
* physicians who were sampled in SMS surveys during the last five years (except for the reinterview portion of the sample).
* physicians listed as 'do not contact' on the Masterfile;
* physicians not practicing in the U.S.; and
* physicians who have no license.

Further exclusions are made after sample selection. These include:

* physicians who spend fewer than 20 hours per week in patient care activities or are federal physicians as determined from screening questions at the beginning of each interview; and
* those who cannot be located by telephone after exhaustive tracking efforts are made.

The sample design utilized for SMS is a random sampling from the listing of eligible physicians on the AMA Physician Masterfile.

The specialty information used from the Masterfile reflects physician self-designated practice specialty. Every effort is made to assure that each specialty group and region is represented in the sample in proportion to its representation in the physician population.

In order to provide reliable estimates of short-term changes in certain indicators, SMS samples include a panel component. The panel consists of a portion of the sample interviewed in a previous SMS survey. Approximately 35 percent of the completed interviews are conducted as reinterviews with physicians who had been initially interviewed in a similar survey in the previous year. The SMS program uses annual reinterviews of this type in order to monitor annual changes in various characteristics.

## Questionnaire Content

The SMS questionnaire consists of three distinct sections:

- screening questions to verify the physician's self-designated practice specialty and eligibility for the survey;

- a main questionnaire to collect information on practice characteristics, hours worked, volume of services, fees for selected procedures, income and expenses; and

- special topics questions to provide information on key socioeconomic issues.

The screening and main questionnaire portions of the survey remain basically unchanged from year to year in order to provide the basis for estimating levels and changes in economic characteristics of medical practice.

Questions for the main questionnaire were originally developed from a review of past surveys and through consultation with physicians, sources within the AMA and Mathematica Policy Research, Inc., an independent consulting firm that assisted in the development of the SMS program. Efforts are made to maintain consistency of questions with those from earlier AMA surveys from which trend information has been established over a period of years. However, modifications are made where it is deemed that the desired information would be more accurate if questions were changed.

In addition, questions in the SMS surveys are designed so that physicians are asked only questions that are generally relevant to their specialty. Special topics questions are formulated and reviewed by members of AMA staff representing a broad range of activity areas. All questions that have not been previously used in SMS surveys are pretested prior to the survey fielding to evaluate the wording and ordering of questions and to determine the ability of respondents to provide the desired information.

## Field Procedures

The SMS data collection plan is designed to provide reliable information within a tight time schedule. The survey is completed primarily by telephone. Telephone administration significantly reduces the time required to produce survey results and increases the response rate. The 1995 survey was administered by RAND of Santa Monica, California, an independent consulting firm, under contract to the AMA.

Field procedures developed for SMS surveys reflect a complex effort to minimize bias from nonresponse and accommodate the busy schedules of physicians through careful advance preparation and intensive follow-up efforts to complete interviews. Two weeks prior to data collection, advance letters are sent to each physician selected to be interviewed or reinterviewed. Each letter includes a brief description of the interview, the project sponsorship, identification of the survey contractor, information that the physician will be receiving a telephone call from an interviewer on the contractor's staff, and a pledge of data confidentiality. The letter is accompanied by a question and answer brochure describing the survey, and a list of the expense items that will be requested of practice owners. Many specialty societies endorse the survey. An endorsement letter is included in the materials mailed to physicians practicing in one of these specialties.

When the SMS program was initiated, many physicians indicated that they could not provide certain types of information during a telephone interview without advance preparation. As a result, summaries were designed to provide the physician with a listing of the expense questions. These summaries are enclosed with each advance letter.

Since inadequate coverage is a potential problem for telephone surveys, the survey contractor expends considerable effort to locate sample physicians. The basic sources used in the telephone look-up include directory assistance, physician directories, state medical societies, state licensing boards, and hospitals.

Two days of study-specific training in addition to general training are provided to each interviewer before working on SMS surveys. Training includes a detailed review of each question (including instruction on pronunciation of various medical terms), practice interviews, and a review of interviewing and administrative procedures.

Interviewing is conducted via computer-assisted telephone interviewing (CATI) process. Responses to the questions are entered directly into the computer using this on-line system during the actual interview, eliminating any keypunching or separate data entry task. This reduces time schedules and maximizes quality by minimizing sources of error. In addition, this system has provided the ability to program range checks whereby a figure that is entered which exceeds the usual range, automatically instructs CATI to prompt the interviewer to verify the response. This has helped reduce the number of invalid outlying responses.

Efforts made to achieve the cooperation of physicians and maximize the response rate are vigorous because of the short field period of SMS surveys. These efforts include the following:

- Appointments for interviews are scheduled at the convenience of physicians at any time 12 hours a day from Monday through Friday.

- A toll-free number allows physicians to complete the interview at their convenience.

- Repeated callbacks (a minimum of four) to nonrespondents are made before abandoning efforts to interview the physician.

- Letters encouraging participation and addressing specific objectives are sent to physicians who initially refuse to be interviewed.

- Refusal conversion attempts are made by a select group of interviewers. A substantial number of physicians decide to grant an interview at this stage.

Each interviewer's work is monitored by the contractor's supervisory staff for both production and quality. AMA staff also monitor interviews by remote telephone hook-up to ensure that a high level of quality is maintained throughout the survey.

## Methodology for the Survey of Federal Physicians

In 1995, a survey of federal physicians was conducted for the AMA by RAND. Only patient care physicians (excluding residents and clinical fellows) who were employed by the Department of Defense or the Department of Veterans Affairs (i.e., physicians employed at VA hospitals) were surveyed. The survey was designed to obtain approximately a one percent sample of these physicians.

The survey was designed to provide representative information on the population of non-resident patient care physicians employed by the Department of Defense or Department of Veterans Affairs. The sample was selected from the AMA Physician Masterfile.

The survey instrument is summarized in the section "Selected Statistics for Federal Physicians" that appears in this volume. The questions asked of federal physicians were similar to those asked of nonfederal physicians. However, the federal survey was only eight minutes in length, on average, and did not include a special topics section and questions on fees, expenses and third-party reimbursement. These topics were not considered relevant to the federal physician's practice. The federal survey began with a set of screener questions designed to ensure that only physicians employed by the Department of Defense or the Department of Veterans Affairs were surveyed. The survey instrument was pretested prior to the survey field period.

The survey was conducted over a three week period, including weekends, from August 21 through September 8. The federal survey field procedures were similar to the SMS nonfederal survey procedures. Interviews were conducted by telephone and the computer-assisted telephone interviewing (CATI) process was used to code responses to the survey questionnaire. One week prior to data collection, advance letters were sent to each physician selected to be interviewed. In many instances, a copy of the letter was also faxed to the physicians to be interviewed. The advance letters were similar to those sent to SMS nonfederal physician interview candidates. Each letter included a brief description of the interview, the project sponsorship, identification of the survey contractor, information that the physician will be receiving a telephone call from an interviewer on the contractors staff, and a pledge of data confidentiality. A

question and answer brochure describing the
survey was also included with the advance letter.

Considerable effort was made to locate the physicians in the federal survey sample. The basic
sources used in the telephone look-up included
directory assistance, military locating services, state
medical societies, state licensing boards, and
military and VA hospitals. Interviewers familiar with
the SMS survey of nonfederal physicians were used
to conduct the federal survey. These interviewers
received an additional half-day of study specific
training before working on the federal survey.

Vigorous efforts were made to ensure a reasonable
response rate despite the short field period. Completed interviews were obtained from 119 physicians for a response rate of 55.6%. However, as in
the case of survey of nonfederal physicians, the
survey of federal physicians appeared to suffer
from survey nonresponse bias. However, the
factors found to affect nonresponse to the federal
survey were different from those affecting
nonresponse to the nonfederal survey. Weights
were developed to correct for nonresponse bias in
the federal survey. A weight was also developed
and used to tabulate the combined results from the
federal and nonfederal surveys. In addition to
correcting for nonresponse bias in both surveys,
this weight ensured that the sample ratio of federal
to nonfederal physicians was the same as the
population ratio. The weights are discussed in
Appendix B of this volume.

## Appendix B
# Weighting and Computation Methodology

### Weights for the SMS Survey of Nonfederal Physicians

SMS measures the physician characteristics accurately but with some margin for error. There are some sources of imprecision that occur in survey work that can increase the margin for error and introduce bias into the estimates. Variations in response rates across known subpopulations can significantly reduce the ability of a sample survey to describe accurately the changing experience of the population of interest. For example, high response rates from AMA members and low response rates for nonmembers could reduce SMS's ability to represent the experience of the average physician if the experiences of these groups differ.

Unit nonresponse occurs when no information at all is collected from a sample physician because the physician is unlocatable, cannot be contacted, or refuses to be interviewed. The statistics reported in this volume weight responses from the SMS survey to correct for potential bias created by unit nonresponse. The weights were derived by first dividing the AMA Physician Masterfile population (using the year-end file from the previous year) and the survey respondents into 200 cells defined by specialty (10 categories), years since M.D. (5 categories), AMA membership status (2 categories), and board certification status (2 categories). Unit response weights were constructed as the ratio of the number of physicians in the population to the number of SMS respondents in each cell. Second, an eligibility correction was employed. Nonfederal patient care physicians (excluding residents) are eligible for SMS. The eligibility correction divides the subset of the SMS population for which eligibility is known into 40 cells (according to years in practice, AMA membership, sex, and board certification) and calculates the proportion of physicians in each cell who are eligible. This defines the eligibility weight. The overall weight applied for a given respondent is the product of a unit response weight and an eligibility weight.

An additional adjustment had to be made to the data because international medical graduates (IMGs) from certain countries were underrepresented in the SMS sample. The underrepresentation was not due to survey nonresponse; rather, these IMGs were not included in the population from which the sample was drawn. As discussed in Appendix A, the AMA sample consists of an initial sample (i.e., physician surveyed for the first time) and a reinterview sample (i.e., physicians who were also surveyed in the previous year). The reinterview sample was derived from a population that included all eligible IMGs. It was the initial sample that was drawn from a population that did not include IMGs from certain countries (and therefore these IMGs were not included in the initial sample). The adjustment gave greater weight to IMGs who were in the reinterview sample but not in the initial sample. The end result was that the weighted SMS sample was proportional to an eligible population that included all IMGs.

Table B1 shows the mean weights for the SMS nonfederal survey for the different specialty, geographic, and practice arrangement classifications reported in this volume, as well as the number of respondents and response rate for each group. The weights have been normalized so that their average value is one and their sum is equal to the overall number of survey respondents. Note that groups with higher response rates tend to have lower average weights since these groups would have been overrepresented without weighting.

### Weights for the Survey of Federal Physicians

Specialty and experience were found to affect the probability that a physician would respond to the federal survey. A four category specialty breakout and a three category experience breakout were used (due to small sample size) to derive the weights used in the tabulation of the results from a survey of federal physicians. The weights were derived by first dividing the relevant AMA Physician

Table B1. **Sample Size, Response Rates, and Average Weights for the 1995 AMA Socioeconomic Monitoring System Survey of Nonfederal Physicians**

| | Sample Size | Response Rate | Average Weight |
|---|---|---|---|
| All Physicians | 4026 | 58.8% | 1.00 |
| General/Family Practice | 517 | 56.0 | 0.97 |
| Internal Medicine | 769 | 53.0 | 1.22 |
| · General Internal Medicine | 525 | 51.3 | 1.24 |
| · Cardiovascular Diseases | 102 | 53.7 | 1.10 |
| · Other | 142 | 59.9 | 1.22 |
| Surgery | 894 | 62.0 | 0.92 |
| · General Surgery | 222 | 57.1 | 1.03 |
| · Otolaryngology | 77 | 59.2 | 0.82 |
| · Orthopedic Surgery | 188 | 63.5 | 0.87 |
| · Ophthalmology | 188 | 66.0 | 0.86 |
| · Urological Surgery | 99 | 64.7 | 0.89 |
| · Other | 120 | 63.5 | 0.99 |
| Pediatrics | 310 | 59.2 | 1.01 |
| Obstetrics/Gynecology | 251 | 56.8 | 1.11 |
| Radiology | 284 | 69.1 | 0.78 |
| Psychiatry | 276 | 62.2 | 0.96 |
| Anesthesiology | 231 | 57.8 | 0.92 |
| Pathology | 121 | 72.9 | 0.79 |
| Other Specialty | 373 | 57.6 | 1.02 |
| · Emergency Medicine | 133 | 51.4 | 0.98 |
| · Other | 240 | 61.9 | 1.04 |
| | | | |
| New England | 256 | 57.7 | 1.07 |
| · Massachusetts | 119 | 54.8 | 1.15 |
| · Other | 137 | 60.4 | 1.00 |
| Middle Atlantic | 629 | 57.3 | 1.05 |
| · New Jersey | 111 | 53.9 | 1.21 |
| · New York | 251 | 49.5 | 1.12 |
| · Pennsylvania | 267 | 69.5 | 0.91 |
| East North Central | 607 | 61.4 | 1.02 |
| · Illinois | 188 | 66.7 | 1.09 |
| · Michigan | 114 | 57.0 | 1.00 |
| · Ohio | 134 | 56.1 | 1.06 |
| · Other | 171 | 63.8 | 0.93 |
| West North Central | 295 | 63.9 | 0.91 |
| South Atlantic | 723 | 58.0 | 1.02 |
| · Florida | 203 | 55.6 | 1.08 |
| · Other | 520 | 59.0 | 1.00 |
| East South Central | 236 | 58.0 | 0.93 |
| West South Central | 370 | 58.6 | 0.94 |
| · Texas | 245 | 60.2 | 0.98 |
| · Other | 125 | 55.8 | 0.86 |
| Mountain | 235 | 63.3 | 0.93 |
| Pacific | 675 | 56.3 | 1.00 |
| · California | 471 | 53.8 | 1.05 |
| · Other | 210 | 63.2 | 0.89 |
| | | | |
| Self-Employed* | 2278 | N. A. | 0.97 |
| · Solo Practice | 1017 | N. A. | 1.04 |
| · Two Physician Practice | 271 | N. A. | 0.93 |
| · Three Physician Practice | 215 | N. A. | 0.93 |
| · Four-Eight Physician Practice | 505 | N. A. | 0.88 |
| · Over Eight Physician Practice | 268 | N. A. | 0.91 |
| Employee | 1510 | N. A. | 1.04 |
| Independent Contractor | 238 | N. A. | 1.08 |

* Includes two respondents who did not indicate practice size.
N.A. - Not available.

Table B2. **Sample Size, Response Rates, and Average Weights for the 1995 AMA Socioeconomic Monitoring System Surveys of Federal and Nonfederal Physicians**

| | Sample Size | Response Rate | Average Weight |
|---|---|---|---|
| All Physicians | 4145 | 58.7% | 1.00 |
| Federal Physicians | 119 | 55.6 | 0.89 |
| Nonfederal Physicians | 4026 | 58.8 | 1.00 |
| General/Family Practice | 525 | 56.1 | 0.98 |
| Internal Medicine | 802 | 52.8 | 1.21 |
| · General Internal Medicine | 549 | 51.0 | 1.23 |
| · Cardiovascular Diseases | 106 | 54.4 | 1.09 |
| · Other | 147 | 59.8 | 1.21 |
| Surgery | 910 | 62.0 | 0.93 |
| · General Surgery | 234 | 57.8 | 1.04 |
| · Otolaryngology | 78 | 59.1 | 0.83 |
| · Orthopedic Surgery | 190 | 62.9 | 0.88 |
| · Ophthalmology | 188 | 66.0 | 0.86 |
| · Urological Surgery | 99 | 64.7 | 0.89 |
| · Other | 121 | 63.4 | 0.99 |
| Pediatrics | 316 | 59.3 | 1.01 |
| Obstetrics/Gynecology | 251 | 56.5 | 1.11 |
| Radiology | 300 | 68.5 | 0.77 |
| Psychiatry | 292 | 62.1 | 0.95 |
| Anesthesiology | 234 | 57.5 | 0.92 |
| Pathology | 130 | 73.0 | 0.78 |
| Other Specialty | 385 | 57.4 | 1.02 |
| · Emergency Medicine | 136 | 51.3 | 1.00 |
| · Other | 249 | 61.3 | 1.04 |
| | | | |
| New England | 264 | 57.6 | 1.07 |
| · Massachusetts | 123 | 55.2 | 1.14 |
| · Other | 141 | 60.0 | 1.00 |
| Middle Atlantic | 657 | 57.8 | 1.04 |
| · New Jersey | 116 | 54.0 | 1.23 |
| · New York | 267 | 50.6 | 1.10 |
| · Pennsylvania | 274 | 69.5 | 0.91 |
| East North Central | 618 | 60.8 | 1.03 |
| · Illinois | 193 | 66.3 | 1.09 |
| · Michigan | 117 | 57.4 | 1.00 |
| · Ohio | 136 | 54.6 | 1.07 |
| · Other | 172 | 62.3 | 0.93 |
| West North Central | 300 | 63.7 | 0.91 |
| South Atlantic | 753 | 57.9 | 1.02 |
| · Florida | 214 | 56.2 | 1.08 |
| · Other | 539 | 58.6 | 1.00 |
| East South Central | 242 | 58.3 | 0.93 |
| West South Central | 379 | 58.3 | 0.94 |
| · Texas | 252 | 59.7 | 0.99 |
| · Other | 127 | 55.7 | 0.86 |
| Mountain | 241 | 62.9 | 0.93 |
| Pacific | 691 | 56.3 | 1.00 |
| · California | 481 | 53.7 | 1.04 |
| · Other | 210 | 62.9 | 0.90 |
| | | | |
| Employee | 1629 | N. A. | 1.03 |

N.A.– Not available.

Masterfile population and the survey respondents into 12 cells defined by specialty (4 categories) and years since M.D. (3 categories). Federal patient care physicians (excluding residents) employed by the Department of Veterans Affairs (VA) or Department of Defense comprised the relevant population of physicians. Unit response weights were constructed as the ratio of the number of these physicians in the population to the number of respondents in each cell. Second, the eligibility correction used for the nonfederal survey was employed. The eligibility correction divides the subset of the physician population for which eligibility is known into 40 cells (according to years in practice, AMA membership, sex, and board certification) and calculates the proportion of physicians in each cell who are eligible (i.e., patient care physicians employed by the VA or Department of Defense). This defines the eligibility weight. The overall weight applied for a given respondent is the product of a unit response weight and an eligibility weight.

## Combining the Results from the Federal and Nonfederal Surveys

Figures 40-43 and Tables 114-136 present the combined results from the federal and nonfederal surveys. For these figures and tables only, the weights for the federal survey and the weights for the nonfederal survey were adjusted in order to ensure that the sample ratio of federal to nonfederal physicians was the same as the population ratio. The new weights were than normalized so that the mean of the new weight was equal to one. Table B2 shows the weights for the combined federal and nonfederal surveys. As shown in Table B2, the average weight applied to federal physicians was 0.89 and the average weight applied to nonfederal physicians was 1.00 (the average weight was actually 1.003).

## Formula for Calculating the Weighted Means and Standard Errors

$$\overline{X}_w = \frac{\Sigma_i w_i X_i}{n}$$

where $w_i$ is the weight and $x_i$ is the characteristic value for physician i, n is the number of physicians in the group and it is assumed that the weights are normalized to sum to the number of sample physicians.

The formula for the standard error of the weighted mean is:

$$\sigma \overline{X}_w = \sqrt{\frac{\Sigma_i w_i (X_i - \overline{X}_w)^2}{n(n-1)}}$$

The 25th percentile, median, and 75 percentile values reported in this volume are based on weighted sample distributions where the weights are used as estimates of the relative frequency of each sample value in the physician population.

## Appendix C
# Definitions of Physician Classifications and Characteristics

### Definitions of Physician Classifications

Statistics for each characteristic in this volume are reported for all physicians and for physicians by specialty, geographic area, and practice arrangement. The level of disaggregation reflected in the specialty, geographic, and practice arrangement classifications reflects an effort to provide the most detailed information possible while maintaining sufficient sample sizes to ensure that reasonably accurate inferences can be drawn from the results.

#### Specialty

The specialty of each physician is determined from the AMA Physician Masterfile and verified at the beginning of each SMS survey. In particular,

physicians are asked whether the specialty recorded on the Masterfile is that from which they derived most of their income in the last year, and, if not, what is that specialty. Information in this volume is provided at two levels of specialty detail as reflected in the first two columns of Table C1. The last column of Table C1 shows the more detailed specialty definitions used on the Masterfile which map into each group for which results are reported.

#### Geographic Area

The Masterfile is used to identify the state in which each SMS sample physician is located at the time of the survey. Results are reported by Census Division and for selected individual and groups of states.

Table C1. **Specialty Classification**

| Major Specialty Classification | Detailed Specialty Classification | AMA Physician Masterfile Classification[a] |
|---|---|---|
| General/Family Practice | – | General Practice, Family Practice |
| Internal Medicine | General Internal Medicine<br>Cardiovascular Disease<br>Other | Internal Medicine<br>Cardiovascular Diseases<br>Allergy, Allergy and Immunology, Diabetes, Diagnostic Laboratory Immunology, Endocrinology, Gastroenterology, Geriatrics, Hematology, Immunology, Infectious Diseases, Nephrology, Nutrition, Medical Oncology, Pulmonary Disease, Rheumatology |
| Surgery | General Surgery<br>Otolaryngology<br>Orthopedic Surgery<br>Ophthalmology<br>Urological Surgery<br>Other | General Surgery<br>Otolaryngology<br>Orthopedic Surgery<br>Ophthalmology<br>Urological Surgery<br>Neurosurgery, Plastic Surgery, Colon and Rectal Surgery, Thoracic Surgery |
| Pediatrics | – | Pediatrics, Pediatric Allergy, Pediatric Cardiology |
| Obstetrics/Gynecology | – | Obstetrics and Gynecology |
| Radiology | – | Radiology, Diagnostic Radiology, Radiation Oncology |
| Psychiatry | – | Psychiatry, Child Psychiatry |
| Anesthesiology | – | Anesthesiology |
| Pathology | – | Forensic Pathology, Pathology |
| Other Specialty | Emergency Medicine<br>Other | Emergency Medicine<br>Aerospace Medicine, Neurology, Nuclear Medicine, Occupational Medicine, Physical Medicine and Rehabilitation, General Preventive Medicine, Public Health, Dermatology, Other Specialty, Unspecified |

a. Based on the AMA Physician Masterfile 39 specialty code classification, except under the general/family practice and internal medicine major specialties for which the specialties listed reflect the Masterfile 85 self-designated practice specialty codes.

These two levels of geographic detail are shown in the first two columns of Table C2 with the states included in each group shown in the last column of the same table.

### Practice Arrangements

The SMS surveys include questions that ascertain each physician's employment status and the number of physicians in his or her practice. The practice arrangement classification used in this volume reports information in three employment status categories and among self-employed physicians further breaks out results by the number of physicians in the practice. A further discussion of the definition of physician employment status categories, as well as the SMS survey questions used to classify each physician by practice arrangement, is given at the beginning of the section on "Nonfederal Physicians and Nonphysician Employees in Medical Practices."

## Definitions of Physician Characteristics

Definitions of each characteristic for which SMS survey results are reported are provided at the beginning of the section in which the results appear. The introduction to each section of tables also provides summaries of the questions used in the surveys to collect information on these characteristics. In some instances, the questions are paraphrased in the summary for the sake of brevity, but in a manner that does not omit any significant details.

Table C2. **Geographic Classification**

| Census Division | Geographic Detail | States |
|---|---|---|
| New England | Massachusetts<br>Other | Massachusetts<br>Connecticut, Maine, New Hampshire, Rhode Island, Vermont |
| Middle Atlantic | New Jersey<br>New York<br>Pennsylvania | New Jersey<br>New York<br>Pennsylvania |
| East North Central | Illinois<br>Michigan<br>Ohio<br>Other | Illinois<br>Michigan<br>Ohio<br>Indiana, Wisconsin |
| West North Central | – | Iowa, Kansas, Minnesota, Missouri, Nebraska, North Dakota, South Dakota |
| South Atlantic | Florida<br>Other | Florida<br>Delaware, District of Columbia, Georgia, Maryland, North Carolina, South Carolina, Virginia, West Virginia |
| East South Central | – | Alabama, Kentucky, Mississippi, Tennessee |
| West South Central | Texas<br>Other | Texas<br>Arkansas, Louisiana, Oklahoma |
| Mountain | – | Arizona, Colorado, Idaho, Montana, Nevada, New Mexico, Utah, Wyoming |
| Pacific | California<br>Other | California<br>Alaska, Hawaii, Oregon, Washington |